SEL C
THE BRITI _LES

B.S.B.I. HANDBOOK No. 1
Edition 3

revised and enlarged to include all genera of Cyperaceae by
CLIVE JERMY & DAVID SIMPSON
incorporating an account of hybrids by
MICHAEL FOLEY & MICHAEL PORTER

Illustrated by
SHEILA BOWNAS, GRETEL DALBY
MARGARET TEBBS, ROBIN WALLS and JOANNA WEBB
with additional drawings by
VALERIE JERMY & COLIN SMITH

Revised map data collated and edited by
DAVID PEARMAN
and maps prepared at the B.R.C. by
HENRY ARNOLD and CHRIS PRESTON

Edited by
PHILIP H. OSWALD

Botanical Society of the British Isles
London
2007

Based on
Handbook No. 1, Edition 2, 1982
SEDGES OF THE BRITISH ISLES
by
A.C. Jermy, A.O. Chater & R.W. David

Author information:

A.C. Jermy
Scientific Associate, The Natural History Museum, London

D.A. Simpson
Assistant Keeper, Herbarium, Royal Botanic Gardens, Kew

M.J.Y. Foley
Research Fellow, University of Lancaster

M.S. Porter
formerly Head of Sixth Form, Cockermouth School

Published by the Botanical Society of the British Isles
c/o The Natural History Museum
Cromwell Road, London SW7 5BD

Typeset by Clive Jermy (text) and Ian Vaughan (graphics)

Printed by J & P Davison, 3 James Place, Treforest, Pontypridd,
Mid Glamorgan CF37 1SQ

Dedicated
to the memory of

Tom Tutin and Dick David
whose knowledge and inspiration contributed so much
to earlier editions of this handbook.

PREFACE

In 1964 I proposed to the B.S.B.I. that they consider publishing a field book on more difficult plant groups to help members identify these taxa. The essence of the book was that it should contain descriptions of plants with adjacent line drawings. The then Treasurer, Jack Gardiner, was behind the idea and assured the Publications Committee that he could find the money. I was asked to draft samples of what I had in mind, and I selected sedges (*Carex*), a section of which I had studied with Professor T.G. Tutin at Leicester University, as the obvious subject. The Committee approved the idea if Tom Tutin would accept joint authorship. This he willingly did, and I, then at the Natural History Museum, began to draft the text and find artists. The result, '*British Sedges*, a B.S.B.I. Special Publication', was published in 1968, later to become the first of a series of *B.S.B.I. Handbooks*.

During the 1970s I was fortunate to meet Arthur Chater, another botanist interested in sedges, who was then working with Tutin preparing the accounts (including that of *Carex*) for *Flora Europaea*. He became and remains a very good friend and counsellor. Another such person was Dick David, then at the Cambridge University Press, and soon to retire and take up his 'hobby', tackling many problems of taxonomy and distribution in the sedges of Britain and Ireland (see the bibliography at the end of this book). They were both good field companions and from them I learnt much. Soon, feeling that the Sedge Handbook could be improved, I put the idea of a second edition to Arthur and Dick and was very pleased when they agreed to become joint authors. The second edition was published in 1982 under the new title of *Sedges of the British Isles*. This edition filled in gaps that had become apparent and had a new feature – the addition of Biological Records Centre distribution maps, for which Dick checked the field distribution of the rare species and worked closely with the B.R.C. on the map production.

Around 1996, the Publications Committee suggested that a new, third, edition be undertaken, increasing the coverage to include all the genera in Cyperaceae and some 50 hybrids (mostly *Carex*) and capitalising on the map data being assembled for what was then called 'Atlas 2000'. Of the three authors of Edition 2, Dick David had sadly died in 1993 (and this book is dedicated to his memory) and Arthur Chater asked not to be an author this time owing to his other commitments (especially to a Flora of Cardiganshire). Although they are not mentioned on the title page, I want to emphasise that their contribution to this edition through their input to Edition 2, as well as Arthur's continued interest in the project, has been invaluable.

I agreed to the Committee's proposal to revise the book and also that it be expanded to include all species of Cyperaceae found in the British Isles (provided that David Simpson, the Cyperaceae expert at Kew, would take on the bulk of this task) and that we include descriptions of all confirmed sedge hybrids. (In *Carex* alone some 44 have been confirmed.) I was pleased when Michael Foley and Mike Porter, two experienced sedge botanists working in Lancaster and Cumbria, agreed to take on that task, which would involve both fieldwork and considerable herbarium and literature research. This is the first time that hybrid sedges of the British Isles have been described in detail. The Society's Vice-county Recorders, co-ordinated by David Pearman (Chairman of the Records Committee), added yet further new records to those in the *New Atlas* (Preston *et al.* 2002) and new maps were prepared by the B.R.C. It was my responsibility, with appreciable help from Mike Porter and Michael Foley, to revise the accounts of *Carex* and expand the introductory chapters. The end result was then subjected to the professional scrutiny of Philip Oswald, the Handbooks Editor, to make the whole book ready for the printer and the ultimate user.

I have written this brief outline (which is expanded in the authors' acknowledgements following) to emphasise that the preparation of this book (like all B.S.B.I. Handbooks) is indeed a Society activity. I wish to put on record my own appreciation of this joint effort, notwithstanding that it is I, together with the other authors, who must take responsibility for the final result.

A. Clive Jermy, Herefordshire, 2007.

ACKNOWLEDGEMENTS

In putting together a handbook of this nature, especially when it is a revision of a former edition, one realises the level of knowledge that exists in B.S.B.I. members and other botanists and which emerges during field meetings, at workshops and on field courses. A.C.J. is grateful to the 'students' who attended his courses at Kindrogan over the years 1973–2001, whose desire (and persistence) to learn stimulated much critical analysis. He also remembers fondly the field knowledge and teaching skills of the late Brian Brooks, the centre's Warden in those early years. This wider collective knowledge will have been unwittingly incorporated into our texts, albeit without specific acknowledgement but with sincere thanks. In some specific cases we have quoted a source in the form of a personal communication (pers. comm.), but if we have misinterpreted anything we take full responsibility for any mistakes.

One new facet of this edition is the description and appropriate illustration of hybrids, and M.J.Y.F. and M.S.P., who prepared these pages, are grateful to those who sent material or who guided them to hybrid populations. For the illustrations they worked in close collaboration with Robin Walls, who, in addition to his draughtsman's skills, contributed critical analysis from his own knowledge of the plants in the field. M.J.Y.F. is most grateful to the authorities at Lancaster University for the provision of facilities and especially for enabling work on *Carex* hybrids to be carried out.

D.A.S. thanks colleagues at Kew for their support, especially Jill Marsden and Martin Xanthos for assisting with the digital scanning of artwork and Phillip Cribb and Tom Cope for their overall interest in the project.

A.C.J. wishes to thank successive Keepers of Botany at the Natural History Museum for facilities afforded him, in retirement, as a Scientific Associate. He thanks also Tim Rich, Head of Vascular Plants at the National Museum of Wales, for providing facilities for him to work on loans transferred there in the latter part of this exercise and George Hutchinson for administering those loans and for help in many other ways. He would also like to thank Martin Sanford for technical help with typesetting, Alison Paul for help with text scanning, Valerie Jermy for revising artwork used in Editions 1 and 2, and Ian Vaughan for scanning and editing on screen these and other new drawings for the present book. Gwynn Ellis kindly converted our final digital files to PDF for printing.

As in most recent handbooks, maps have been included to show the distribution in the British Isles of the taxa discussed, including most hybrids.

As our completion date moved beyond 2000 it was obvious that new records were accruing in the Society's databases held by Vice-county Recorders. The considerable task of gathering and collating these new records was undertaken by David Pearman and we thank him and all our Recorders for checking and submitting them to the Biological Records Centre. In this context, we also thank Alan Showler, who spent many hours at the Natural History Museum preparing 'pink cards' of the newly determined hybrid records, and the staff of the B.R.C., especially Henry Arnold, Chris Preston and Val Burton, for preparing and amending the maps for publication here. We thank David Pearman also for checking our comments on distribution and the latest level of threat for rare and scarce species.

We are very grateful to Curators of the following herbaria who sent to the Natural History Museum potential hybrid material for determination: **ABD, BM, DBN, E, GL, GLU, K, LANC, LIV, MAN, NMW, OXF, RNG, SLBI, TCD** and **TRIN**. We thank especially Roy Vickery, Curator of Vascular Plants at the N.H.M., for handling the administration of these loans and, when necessary, arranging for their extension for further study. Peta Hayes and, latterly, Mark Spencer helped our work there in many ways.

The following have read and commented on taxa about which they have specialist knowledge: Nigel Blackstock (*Carex flava/viridula* group); Michael Braithwaite and George Swan (*Trichophorum cespitosum* agg.); Jacques Cayouette and Mary Dean (*Carex nigra* group), and we are grateful to the latter for allowing us to use unpublished data included in her doctoral thesis; Muthama Muasya (*Isolepis*); Radomír Řepka (*Carex muricata* agg.), Jeremy Roberts (*Eleocharis*); Colin Smith (*Carex vulpina* agg.) and also for commenting on leaf anatomy and preparing and drawing transverse sections of all the *Carex* leaves; George Swan (for much help with *Eleocharis palustris/mamillata* group). Ruud van der Meiden and Ingrid de Kort sent comparative material of *Carex trinervis* from the Netherlands. Robin Walls read much of the text of the book and commented on and clarified aspects of the ecology of species and their habitats, including preparing the Principal Components Analysis for British and Irish sedges and allowing us to use these unpublished data in Chapter 4. Dick Brummitt, Katherine Challis, Charlie Jarvis and Clive Stace gave advice on the nomenclature of the new names that we have accepted. Clive Stace also commented on Chapter 5 (on hybrids).

We should like to acknowledge the help of more recent correspondents here; if we have inadvertently missed someone who should have been listed we apologise. We are very grateful to Tony O'Mahony, who gave us the benefit of his detailed knowledge of Irish sedges. In addition, the following have helped in various ways, especially in drawing our attention to potential corrections to Edition 2, sending material for critical examination and sharing their knowledge of sites, ecology and differences between taxa:

Phyl Abbott, Frances Abraham, Judith Allinson, Paul Ashton, Gillian Beckett, Peter Benoit, Caroline Brady, John Breeds, Con Breen, Elaine Bullard, Stephen Bungard, Ken Butler, Rod Corner, Gigi. Crompton, Ann Daly, Bob Ellis, Stephen Evans, Kathy Fallowfield, Carl Farmer, Mike Fay, Ralph Forbes, Martin George, Ian Green, Jean Green, Eric Greenwood, Ron Groom, Paul Hackney, Geoffrey Halliday, John Harron, John Hawksford, Bob Hodgson, Matthew Jebb, Mark and Clare Kitchen, Alex Lockton, David Marden, Douglas McKean, Caroline Mhic Daeid, Rose Murphy, Wendy Nelson, Robert Northridge, John Poland, Chris Preston, Richard Pryce, Graham Rix, Jeremy Roberts, Francis Rose†, Gordon Rothero, Fred Rumsey, Alan Showler, Alan Stirling†, Stephanie Thompson, Charles Turner, Sarah Whild, Michael Wilcox, Steve Woodward and Jean Wynn-Jones.

Arthur Chater, as a co-author with Dick David and A.C.J. of Edition 2, should have appeared as an author here, but it was his choice not to be deeply involved (perhaps wisely!). As a result much of his knowledge has been reprinted with only this blanket recognition. He nevertheless read the entire text, checked the illustrations, made valuable comments and was throughout a source of wise counsel and support.

Philip Oswald, as Handbooks Editor, is the Society's link with authors of handbooks, sometimes simultaneously processing two or three books through to publication and shouldering the burden when authors extend deadlines. It is he who does that final reading, checking, correcting and, in our case, greatly improving authors' contributions, thereby maintaining the standard that he and the previous Editor have set for these books. Not only is he a professional at technical editing, he is also a knowledgeable botanist who has greatly added to the value of this book. His care in checking the associations of the National Vegetation Classification was only one aspect where he improved our scripts. His persistence and patience 'to get things right' was invaluable. As with all editors, his efforts may be unnoticed by the reader, but they are definitely recognised and greatly appreciated by the undersigned.

Finally, thanks are also due to Julia Porter and Valerie Jermy for reading parts of the text and making helpful suggestions. We thank them and Rose Simpson for their patience and understanding during the years spent in the writing of this handbook.

Clive Jermy, David Simpson, Michael Foley and Mike Porter, 2007.

CONTENTS

1 INTRODUCTION

Carex is one of a number of groups of plants that present problems to the non-specialist and was therefore chosen as the subject for the first of this series of handbooks, Jermy & Tutin's (1968) *British Sedges* (Edition 1), with a subsequent revision, Jermy, Chater & David's (1982) *Sedges of the British Isles* (Edition 2). Besides updating the substance of the latter, we have widened the scope of the book by including all British and Irish species of the family Cyperaceae (a further 35 species) and, significantly, we have also included all confirmed hybrids in the family found in the British Isles. For the hybrids, tables are given showing diagnostic characters of parents and hybrids (44 in *Carex*, two in *Schoenoplectus* and one in *Trichophorum*). Without the possibility of carrying out DNA-based studies, attributions of hybrid parentage have been based almost entirely on the assessment of morphological characters. See the preface for the authorship of the main contributions.

We have included descriptions and figures of two extinct species, **6a** *Trichophorum alpinum* and **99** *Carex trinervis*, that may still be refound where available habitats continue to exist. The extinct *Carex davalliana* has not been treated in the same way, since we believe that its habitat around Bath has been destroyed, though we should be delighted to be proved wrong. One new species, **96** *Carex salina* Wahlenb., discovered in western Scotland in 2004, has been added. We hope that more sites for it will be found.

As in the second edition, maps are included, but they are placed adjacent to the species or hybrid to which they relate rather than gathered at the end of the descriptions. Not only have they been updated but, thanks to a major onslaught by the B.S.B.I. Records Committee and Vice-county Recorders, the maps published here have been updated even since *New Atlas of the British and Irish Flora* (Preston *et al.* 2002).

In Cyperaceae, some groups of species can be said to be 'critical', either because of an apparent lack of discontinuities between taxa, owing to hybridisation, or because vegetative spread has resulted in the production of local biotypes. Although these are distinct enough in minor characters, they embarrass taxonomists by the vastness of their numbers and their slight differentiation from other parts of the population. However, leaving aside **77–78** the *Carex flava* group, **95–102** the *Carex nigra* group and **13–14** the *Eleocharis palustris/mamillata* group, when a wide view of the taxa is taken the majority of sedge species in the British Isles are not too difficult to define. One difficulty lies, for the beginner at least, in the need to use terms

2

not directly comparable to those used for other flowering plants. A further complication in *Carex* is the occurrence of hybrids, and for these tabulated characters are now included (see above) and many are illustrated. We believe that this handbook in its various editions, particularly through its illustrations, has gone some way towards helping its users to identify and understand the group.

Our nomenclature follows that of Kent (1992) and its three supplements (Kent 1997; Kent & Stace 2000; Stace 2006), in particular in accepting **41b** *Carex muricata* L. subsp. *pairae* (F.W. Schultz) Čelak. as the correct name for what was formerly called *C. muricata* subsp. *lamprocarpa* (see Řepka & Danihelka 2005). In view of recent work on the variation of the taxon in the British Isles, we are treating *Eleocharis austriaca* Hayek as a subspecies of *Eleocharis mamillata* (H. Lindb.) H. Lindb., **14** subsp. *austriaca* (Hayek) Strandh., as originally suggested by Strandhede (1966). We realise that further work is needed on *Eleocharis* subgenus *Eleocharis*, both here and on the European mainland. We also treat the two subspecies of *Trichophorum cespitosum* as full species, **6** *Trichophorum cespitosum* (L.) Hartm. and **5** *Trichophorum germanicum* Palla and include *Eleogiton fluitans* in *Isolepis*, as **23** *I. fluitans* (L.) R. Br., as the result of work by Muasya *et al.* (2002).

In the *Carex flava* group we have dispensed with the four species recognised in Edition 2 and describe two only, **77** *C. flava* and **78** *C. viridula*, the latter with three subspecies (*cf. Flora Europaea* **5**: Chater 1980) in the belief that these taxa are difficult to separate morphologically. In keeping *C. flava* distinct (*cf.* Sell & Murrell 1996, who include all the taxa under that species) we base our decision on morphometric and molecular work by Blackstock & Ashton (2001) and Blackstock (2007), but we appreciate that continuing work by them and others in Britain and by other workers in Europe (e.g. Hedrén 2003) may eventually elucidate more discrete taxa and provide data for yet more interpretation. Like Sell & Murrell (1996), we recognise four further taxa, *C. jemtlandica* (Palmgr.) Palmgr., *C. lepidocarpa* subsp. *scotica* E.W. Davies, *C. bergrothii* Palmgr. and *C. pulchella* (Lönnr.) Lindm., though we treat these at varietal level: see the discussion in the introduction to **77–78** the *Carex flava* group on p. 387 and the descriptions on pp. 396 and 406.

Two well established names in *Carex*, *C. ovalis* Gooden. (Oval Sedge) and *C. curta* Gooden. (White Sedge) have had to be removed in favour of two earlier Linnaean names, **49** *C. leporina* L. and **54** *C. canescens* L., as a result of in-depth nomenclatural research by the Linnaean Plant Names Typification Project (see Jarvis 2007 and/or search for 'Linnaean' through http://internt.nhm.ac.uk/jdsml/mils/index.dsml).

We have kept to the original concept of the handbook series, that is for it to be as far as possible an identification manual and predominantly a field guide, and not a biological monograph on the group or family. In the introductory pages we have given an account of the general structure found in our genera of Cyperaceae, believing it will help the reader to observe those characters used in species recognition. A brief general account of sedge ecology and habitats is also provided, with a table on pp. 43–45 showing ecological groupings of species to act as a guide when one is identifying plants in the field. The descriptive accounts follow the same pattern as in Edition 2, but the results of later fieldwork and the comments of users have improved those of *Carex* species. Additionally, in the habitat paragraphs we give references to the National Vegetation Classification (NVC) of Rodwell (1991–2000) where applicable. Species that are considered threatened in *The Vascular Plant Red Data List for Great Britain* (Cheffins & Farrell 2005) have their level of threat indicated. The following status categories are used:

- **Critically Endangered**: the taxon is considered to be facing an *extremely high risk* of extinction in the wild.

- **Endangered**: the taxon is considered to be facing a *very high risk* of extinction in the wild.

- **Vulnerable**: the taxon is considered to be facing a *high risk* of extinction in the wild.

- **Near threatened**: a taxon is near threatened when it has been evaluated against the criteria but does not qualify for any of the above at the time of publication but is close to qualifying for or is likely to qualify for a threatened category in the near future.

The criteria used to make the above assessments are based on population sizes over a period of time: full details are given on pp. 17–22 of the above work. We have not given an evaluation for hybrids on the grounds that there is at present inadequate information to make an assessment.

As in Edition 2, we have mentioned, after the descriptive accounts, a number of neophytes (alien species) which have been found in the British Isles, but the list is far from complete. Aliens have become a topic of study in their own right and their inclusion would make this book unnecessarily large: we believe that they would best be presented elsewhere comprehensively, with keys and descriptions. There is one exception, **26** *Cyperus eragrostis* Lam., which has been described in full in the species accounts.

The Latin index includes synonyms which are not mentioned elsewhere in this book but have been used in earlier literature for Cyperaceae of the British Isles and might be useful when searching for early records.

2 GENERAL STRUCTURE OF CYPERACEAE

The anatomy of Cyperaceae is covered in detail by Metcalf (1971), where full references to general papers may be found. Previous to this the anatomy of British *Carices* had been studied by Crawford (1910). The following account discusses the morphology of the Cyperaceae in relation to the species accounts that follow.

Growth habit: the rhizome and shoot systems

Four kinds of growth habit have been recognised:

1 A *monopodial rhizome* system (see Figure 2.1), one in which the apical bud continues to grow horizontally while the upright shoots and flowering stems are produced from lateral buds usually at regular intervals along an often far-creeping and occasionally branched rhizome (e.g. **9–12** *Schoenoplectus* species, **17** *Eleocharis acicularis*, **43** *Carex arenaria*, **44** *C. disticha*).

2 A *sympodial rhizome* system (see Figure 2.2) in which the apical bud has finite growth in the form of an aerial shoot and lateral buds from its base produce further creeping stems that produce shoots and branches every few nodes, the general direction of growth being upwards, thus forming a tussock (e.g. **4** *Eriophorum vaginatum*, **5–6** *Trichophorum* spp., **29–30** *Schoenus* species, **35** *Carex paniculata*).

3 A *sympodial rhizome* system in which the internodes between the shoots are few and usually short, radiating from a centre; the shoots, either few or many, form a tufted or caespitose plant (e.g. **2** *Eriophorum latifolium*, **18** *Eleocharis quinqueflora*, **21–23** *Isolepis* species, **78** *Carex viridula*, **49** *C. leporina*). This group also contains species in the genus *Carex* in which the rhizomes are thick, woody and persistent for some time and may thus be called an (albeit slowly) creeping system (**46** *C. divisa*, **86** *C. montana*). They are often much branched and frequently form mats rather than tufts; the shoots are always clustered at the growing points. A further variation is seen in **80** *C. digitata* and **81** *C. ornithopoda*, where the fertile stem elongates from a lateral shoot and the main apex continues in the vegetative state.

4 A *sympodial system* in which at least some of the rhizomes are either short- or far-creeping; the shoots are in dense or loose tufts (rarely single shoots, e.g. **47** *Carex maritima*) joined by usually underground, 'pioneering' rhizomes, the number of nodes of which may be more or less constant for a given species (e.g. *c.* 13 in **100** *C. nigra*). This group also contains a few species (e.g. **45** *C. chordorrhiza*, **89** *C. limosa*) in which the lower internodes of the shoot elongate and become decumbent, often on the surface of the substratum. These species have been called 'stoloniferous', but these organs contain food reserves and are technically rhizomes, not stolons.

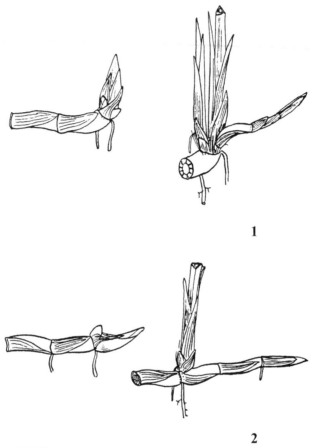

Figures 2.1–2 Rhizome types
1 Sympodial **2** Monopodial

Thus the creeping, tufted or tussock habit is diagnostic, but it can to some extent be affected by the habitat. Plants appearing to be tufted may not really be so, as Kershaw (1962) has shown for **102** *Carex bigelowii*. Here different 'pioneer' rhizomes are 'attracted' to each other or are influenced by an outside and so far unknown factor (a nutritional gradient?) so that their shoots are produced in a clump. It has been shown experimentally with **100** *C. nigra* (A.C. Jermy unpublished) that the direction of growth of the rhizomes is towards areas of higher oxygen concentration and away from anaerobic conditions, and this may be true also for several flush species at least. The importance of this is seen in those *C. nigra* populations growing in wet stagnant conditions, when the pioneer rhizomes will grow upwards to the water or peat surface and will not spread laterally. Eventually these may form a tussock or an island of peat or root mat which may well support a fen flora of its own. Such tussocks have been erroneously quoted in the ecological literature (Holdgate 1955 and others) as *C. juncella* (Fr.) Th. Fr., a Scandinavian taxon. It is imperative then to investigate the true habit of a species and not to be misled by its outward appearance.

Rhizome and root anatomy, leaf-scales and the stem

The roots of peat-loving species tend to be thick, with a small stele and copious surrounding aerenchyma; often a band of sclerenchyma lies beneath the epidermis. Root-hairs are often numerous and slender, forming a felt around the root. Secondary roots are sparse in these species. Species of dry or sandy habitats (e.g. **47** *Carex maritima*, **86** *C. montana*) have little aerenchyma and a large stele, with the result that the roots are wiry and much branched. The colour of roots from either habitat can be a useful character when identifying dried voucher or other herbarium material or when analysing peat deposits, but in stagnant (anaerobic) conditions this may be over-stained with black. In more aerobic peat, the roots may be diagnostic; for example those of **9** *Schoenoplectus lacustris* are vivid crimson-red.

The rhizomes vary in the size of the stele, the amount of aerenchyma in the outer cortex and the distribution of sclerenchyma. The epidermis is usually hard and shiny or more rarely woody (corky). There is a tendency for dry-habitat species to have more bundles or bands of thicker tissue than those of wet areas, although pioneering species such as **9** *Schoenoplectus lacustris* and **31** *Cladium mariscus* have thick, fibrous rhizomes.

Lanceolate or ovate, keeled leaf-scales arise from each node of the rhizome and may decay either completely or partially, leaving only the vascular strands as 'fibres'. They may be persistent and of a characteristic colour, but again the conditions in the substratum must be taken into consideration when deciding the colour of scales: anaerobic water can produce a false black colouration and acid water can leach out the colour; signs of the true colour can usually be seen above the water level.

The only aerial stem is that bearing a terminal inflorescence, frequently called a culm although we have maintained the use of 'stem' throughout our descriptions. In Cyperaceae it is usually a 3-sided structure and either trigonous (margins rounded) or triquetrous (margins pointed). In a few *Carex* species (e.g. **51** *C. dioica*, **106** *C. pulicaris*) it is terete and often ridged. In *Eleocharis* species it is terete or, in **17** *E. acicularis*, 4-angled. In **9–10** *Schoenoplectus lacustris* and *S. tabernaemontani* it is terete and filled with spongy cortical tissue. The illustrations of *Carex* stems show outlines and the general position of vascular bundles, but there is considerable variation within a given species and the sketches in the species descriptions cannot be compared in detail; detailed anatomical studies of large samples would be worth making. For the most part, stems are tough and often wiry; in a few species, e.g. **97** *C. aquatilis*, they are brittle and snap on bending even in the fresh state. In some species, mostly in subgenus *Vignea*, long leaf-sheaths form a stem-like shoot called in our descriptions a 'false stem'.

Leaves, leaf-sheaths and ligules

Carex leaves are, on the whole, grass-like, varying in their width and the shape of the upper part and apex. In some (e.g. **67** *C. flacca*, **100** *C. nigra*) the flat, typical leaf structure continues to the tip, the midrib channel gradually petering out. In others (e.g. **68** *C. panicea*, **76** *C. hostiana*) the tip becomes subulate and trigonous in cross-section and the midrib channel ends abruptly below this. The leaves produced early in the season, i.e. those at the base of the shoot, may be short and reduced to almost the dimensions of scales. Many *Carex* species and some of other genera (e.g. **23** *Isolepis fluitans*, **25** *Cyperus fuscus*, **27** *Blysmus compressus*) have flat leaves, or the leaves may be keeled, channelled, inrolled or folded (plicate) (see Figures 2.3–7); this is best seen in transverse section or when a cut leaf is looked at 'end-on'. A few species (e.g. **4** *Eriophorum vaginatum*, **51** *Carex dioica*) have very narrow leaves that are round or triangular in cross-section. The texture, i.e. softness or rigidity of the leaf tissue, can be diagnostic. Roughness, due usually to forward-pointing fine teeth, is confined to the margins and lower sides of the leaf-veins; these teeth may be lost with age and are best seen or felt on young leaves.

Some species show hairiness more obviously beneath the leaf than above. This may be reduced or even eliminated by wet conditions (e.g. in **55** *Carex hirta*), but hairs will always be retained around the leaf-sheath apex or ligule.

In **5–6** *Trichophorum* and **13–19** *Eleocharis* the leaf-blade is absent or much reduced to a very short setaceous tip to the leaf-sheath.

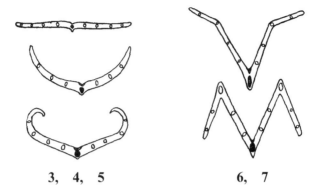

Figures 2.3–7 Leaf-section types (numbered from top to bottom)
3 Flat **4** Channelled **5** Inrolled **6** Keeled **7** Plicate

Leaf anatomy

The anatomy of Cyperaceae leaves has been studied by Metcalfe (1971). Anatomical characters are of little use in identifying most Cyperaceae, with the exception of *Carex*, which is the genus that we concentrate on in this section. The anatomy of the *Carex* leaf was studied by Crawford (1910), but a more thorough investigation of the British species of the genus has recently been made by C. Smith of Edge Hill University and is revealing a new range of taxonomic characters. On the basis of this work he has kindly prepared drawings of transverse sections of leaves of *Carex* (inserted in the species plates) to illustrate more accurately the following features that can be seen with a ×20 hand-lens. It should be noted, however, that, as with stems, there can be considerable variation in all of these features:

- the number of vascular strands (veins), although upper mature leaves should be examined;
- the tubes of aerenchyma (air-spaces);
- the nature of folding (see Figures 2.3–7).

As this handbook is predominantly a field manual, we have not elaborated further on the microscopical characters of leaves that Smith's studies show may be used to identify individual species. They include any irregularities on the leaf surface such as silica bodies that arise from the epidermal cuticle or the cell wall (as in **45** *Carex chordorrhiza* and **46** *C. divisa*). Sometimes they can be seen as a macro-feature as, for example, on the densely mamillate (at ×100) hyaline inner leaf-sheath face of **43** *C. arenaria*. This feature is often visible to the naked eye as a velvety sheen, such as that observed also on the mamillate utricle walls of **95–102** the *C. nigra* group (T. O'Mahony pers. comm.). Another useful character is the transverse septa (forming air-spaces in the leaf termed aerenchyma-blocks) often best seen against the light in the leaf-sheath or in the leaf itself just above the ligule.

Studies of *Carex* have shown that the size of the epidermal cells may be useful: those of species in wet habitats are usually smaller (e.g. **98** *C. acuta*, *c.* 15 µm wide) than those of drier habitats (e.g. **55** *C. hirta*, *c.* 37 µm). More useful are the patterns of the silica bodies, often described as papillae (e.g. in **67** *C. flacca*, **68** *C. panicea* and **100** *C. nigra*). They can be either on one or both of the leaf-surfaces and are frequently best seen around the stomata. (They show up under a lens as white dots but should not be confused with stomata; see below.) A number of workers have shown that leaf anatomy, especially epidermal patterns, can be useful in separating related species and in detecting hybrids (e.g. in **95–102** the *C. nigra* complex: see Hjelmqvist & Nyholm 1947; Faulkner 1970, 1972) and in showing taxonomic relationships (e.g. in **60–62** section *Vesicariae*: see Shepherd 1976). Anatomical studies have also shown that in section the vascular bundles of the leaves of **38** *C. vulpina* are in the centre of the lamina, whereas in **39** *C. otrubae* they are offset abaxially (Porley 1999; Smith & Ashton 2006).

Stomata

The distribution of stomata on the leaf surfaces can be a very useful identification character in *Carex* (see Chater 1998). For most of our species stomata are found in rows between the veins on the under, or abaxial, side of the leaf. (In the species descriptions the term hypostomous is used.) The stomata are arranged in rows and can usually be seen as minute white dots with the aid of a ×20 or even a ×10 lens. In **95–102** the *C. nigra* group, distribution of stomata is often linked to the distribution of epidermal papillae (see above). It is especially useful as a field character on fresh specimens: the stomata become slightly less easy to see in dried material. If a microscope is available, it is a good idea to confirm what you are looking at with a selection of specimens, either by stripping off bits of epidermis or, more easily, by making an impression of the leaf surface with clear nail varnish and placing this 'peel' on a microscope slide. Generally speaking, the leaf-surface with the most stomata becomes concave on drying, so that for example in **100** *C. nigra*, in which the stomata are mostly confined to the upper (adaxial) surface (for which we use the term epistomous), the leaf-margins roll up and inwards on drying, while in **98** *C. acuta*, which has the stomata confined to the lower surface, the leaf margins are revolute (i.e. roll beneath) on drying.

The character is especially valuable for distinguishing **60** *Carex rostrata* from **61** *C. vesicaria* and from their hybrid, vegetative **56** *C. lasiocarpa* from *C. rostrata*, **102** *C. bigelowii* from **100** *C. nigra*, and **98** *C. acuta* from **97** *C. aquatilis* and *C. nigra*. In hybrids, the distribution of stomata appears to combine that of the two parents, so that, for example, **101** × **100** *C.* × *turfosa* (*C. elata* × *C. nigra*) has stomata ± abundant on both surfaces (Chater 1998).

Smith & Ashton (2006) have suggested that stomatal shape may be of use to differentiate between the closely related species **38** *Carex vulpina* and **39** *C. otrubae*, but more work is needed.

The leaf-sheath

The lower part of the leaf that is tubular around the shoot or stem is an important diagnostic part of the plant and must always be observed. The colour, texture and characteristics on decay are important and the previous remarks about rhizome scales are relevant here, especially in relation to the effect of the habitat. The most important part of the leaf-sheath is the thin, colourless (usually hyaline) inner face, i.e. that frontal part resulting from the fused leaf-margins. The texture of this is important, e.g. the presence of cross-puckering (as in **38** *Carex vulpina*) or of brown dots or glands (as in **37** *C. diandra*). The apex of this inner face may be concave, straight or with a tongue-like protuberance (lingulate) (see Figures 2.8–10), but this can change with age (e.g. in **72** *C. binervis*).

Being easily broken on older specimens, the sheath's inner face can become V-shaped, and it is best to check younger sheaths for this character. The way in which the sheath splits can be characteristic of a species. Simple tearing (through leaf movement) is the commonest way, with the torn hyaline portion soon decaying (as in **60** *C. rostrata*) or persisting as a pale brown papery tissue (as in **98** *C. acuta*). The other method of splitting produces a ladder-like pattern (i.e. the sheath becomes fibrillose); cautious tearing will produce this pattern in those species that exhibit it (e.g. **101** *C. elata*).

Vegetative characters as seen under ×100 magnification, e.g. the papillae present on the apex of the hyaline inner leaf-sheath face in **100** *C. nigra*, may represent a unique character peculiar to that species, at least within an aggregate group (T. O'Mahony pers. comm.), but such micromorphological characters have not been elaborated in this book.

11

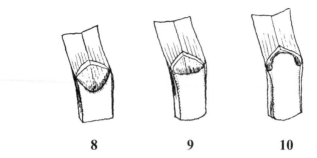

8　　　　　9　　　　　10

Figures 2.8–10　Types of apex of inner face of leaf-sheath in *Carex*
8 Concave **9** Straight **10** Lingulate

In *Carex* and a few species in other genera of this family (e.g.
1 *Eleocharis angustifolium*, **3** *E. gracile*, **7** *Scirpus sylvaticus*, **29** *Schoenus nigricans*, **30** *S. ferrugineus* and **34** *Kobresia simpliciuscula*) a ligule may be found between the leaf-sheath and the blade of the leaf as in grasses. In Cyperaceae, however, it differs in being fused for most of its length to the upper surface of the blade, and its shape is best seen if the leaf is pulled back and flattened (see Figures 2.11–14). On the whole the ligule shape reflects the shape of the stem or shoot; in those species where the sterile shoot forms a false stem, the ligule increases in length towards the apex of the shoot.

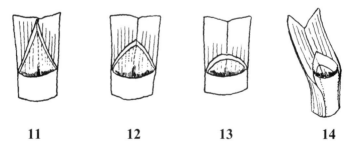

11　　　　　　12　　　　　　13　　　　　　14

Figures 2.11–14　Types of ligules
11 Acute **12** Obtuse **13** Rounded **14** Tubular

Ligule measurements in the text indicate the length of the fused portion from where it joins the inner face of the sheath to its apex. In *Carex* often the upper edge of this fused portion may be free to the extent of *c*. 1 mm, but in other species with a ligule a free portion may be almost non-existent. The free portion is usually hyaline but may in some species be brown or purplish. With a ×20 lens the upper edge may be seen to be papillate (as in **72** *Carex binervis*) or smooth (as in **71** *C. laevigata*) (T. O'Mahony pers. comm.) or with a fringe of short hairs (as in **87** *C. pilulifera*). The free portion can fuse with the sheath's inner face, forming a narrow tubular ring (see Figure 2.14).

The inflorescence

The inflorescence in Cyperaceae can be difficult to interpret owing to its highly reduced nature, making observations of the ultimate branching and position of flowers difficult to determine. Moreover, the inflorescence in *Carex* and *Kobresia* is even more complex and further modified, so we deal with these genera separately.

Cyperaceae (excluding **Carex** and **Kobresia***)*

Inflorescence structure (see Figures 2.15–21) may be of one of six types – (1) branched, with the branches arising from two or more points along the inflorescence axis and each branch subtended by an involucral bract (e.g. **31** *Cladium mariscus*, **32** *Rhynchospora alba*); (2) branched, with the primary branches arising from a single terminal point on the flowering stem (e.g. **1** *Eriophorum angustifolium*, **9** *Schoenoplectus lacustris*), the structure being subtended by one to several involucral bracts; (3) umbel-like, a specialisation of type 2, where the inflorescence forms a structure resembling an umbel subtended by involucral bracts (e.g. **24** *Cyperus longus*); (4) capitate, where spikelets are crowded into a single terminal head, which is subtended by involucral bracts (e.g. **29** *Schoenus nigricans*, **30** *S. ferrugineus*); (5) spicate, where several spikelets are sessile and crowded along the apical part of the flowering stem, making a shortly elongated structure subtended at the base by involucral bracts (e.g. **27** *Blysmus compressus*, **28** *B. rufus*); and (6) a single spikelet terminating the flowering stem (*Eleocharis*, *Trichophorum*).

Involucral bracts may be leaf-like (as in *Bolboschoenus*, *Cyperus* [Figure 2.17] and *Scirpus*) or glume-like (as in *Eleocharis* [Figure 2.20] and *Trichophorum*). The longest bract – the lowermost in an inflorescence – may be markedly longer than and distinct from the other bracts. In some taxa (e.g. **12** *Schoenoplectus pungens* [Figure 2.21]) the longest bract is erect and appears to be a continuation of the flowering stem, making the inflorescence appear lateral, although it is in fact terminal. Where the inflorescence is terminal, there may well be two or more involucral bracts at the base of the inflorescence.

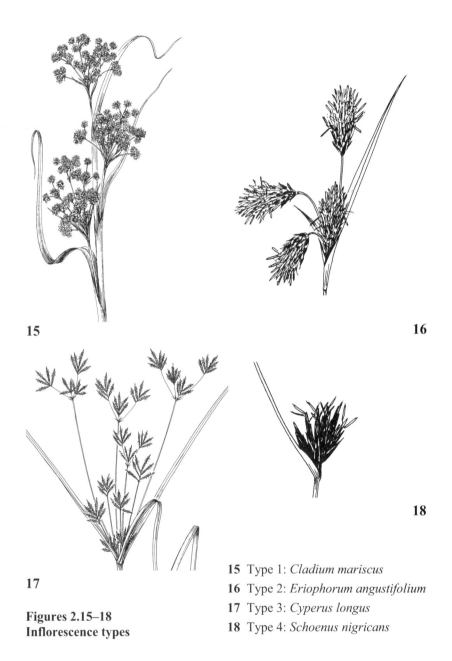

15

16

18

17

**Figures 2.15–18
Inflorescence types**

15 Type 1: *Cladium mariscus*
16 Type 2: *Eriophorum angustifolium*
17 Type 3: *Cyperus longus*
18 Type 4: *Schoenus nigricans*

19

20

21

**Figures 2.19–21
Inflorescence types (cont.)**

19 Type 5: *Blysmus compressus*

20 Type 6: *Eleocharis uniglumis*

21 *Schoenoplectus pungens*, showing the long erect bract

Spikelets (see Figures 2.22–23) are the ultimate units in an inflorescence. There may be from one (as in *Eleocharis*) to many (as in *Cyperus*) per inflorescence and, when there is more than one, they may be clustered into globose to elongate spikes. They may be rounded (terete) in cross-section (as in *Bolboschoenus* and *Scirpus*) to flattened (as in *Cyperus*) and comprise an axis that supports, and is hidden by, one to many scale-like glumes crowded along the axis. The coloration of the whole spikelet may be distinctive, for example yellowish-brown to reddish-brown in **27** *Blysmus compressus* but dark brown to blackish in **29** *Schoenus nigricans*.

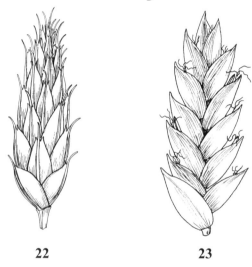

22   **23**

Figures 2. 22–23 Spikelets and glumes
22 *Bolboschoenus maritimus*: terete spikelet with spirally arranged glumes
23 *Cyperus eragrostis*: flattened spikelet with alternately arranged glumes

Glumes (see Figures 2.22–23) are rather scale-like in appearance, papery to leathery in texture and spirally (as in *Bolboschoenus* and *Isolepis*) or alternately (as in *Cyperus*) arranged along the spikelet axis. In cross-section they are more or less flat (e.g. **8** *Bolboschoenus maritimus*) to boat-shaped (*Cyperus*). They are often minute and in most genera they are more or less equal in size from the apex to the base of the spikelet, although in *Rhynchospora* the upper glumes can be markedly longer than the lower ones. They may be coloured with various shades of green to brown or reddish-brown and sometimes have a contrastingly coloured midrib or keel (as in

Isolepis, where the glume margins are brown to dark brown and the midrib is green). In **32** *Rhynchospora alba* they are whitish. The first glume on each spikelet is known as a prophyll and may be 2-keeled. The prophyll is a characteristic feature of monocotyledon inflorescences.

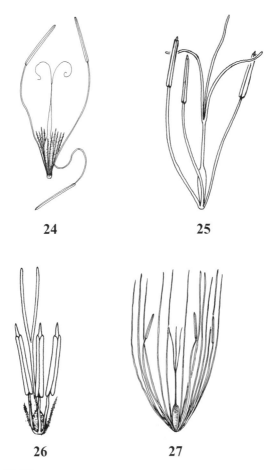

Figures 2.24–27 Flowers
24 *Rhynchospora alba*: perianth bristles 9, stamens 3, stigmas 2
25 *Cyperus longus*: perianth bristles 0, stamens 3, stigmas 3
26 *Schoenoplectus triqueter*: perianth bristles 4, stamens 3, stigmas 3
27 *Eriophorum gracile*: perianth bristles 11, stamens 3, stigmas 3

The flowers are very small and usually hidden by the glume. Each flower comprises 1–3 stamens, 1–3 stigmas, a single style and an ovary. A much-reduced perianth is present in several genera (*Blysmus, Bolboschoenus, Eleocharis, Eriophorum, Rhynchospora, Schoenoplectus* and *Scirpus*).

The perianth (see Figures 2.24 and 26–27) comprises several bristles that have either antrorse (upward-pointing) or retrorse (downward-pointing) hairs on them. They usually remain attached to the mature fruit and can be much shorter to up twice as long as it is; they probably aid dispersal by clinging to animals or birds (Goetghebeur 1998). In *Eriophorum* this is taken a stage further: the bristles are more numerous and develop into long, cotton-like structures, giving the inflorescence its characteristic, fluffy, cottongrass appearance. Similar development takes place in **6a** *Trichophorum alpinum* but not to the same extent. In both cases the elongation of the bristles probably aids in wind-dispersal of the fruit.

Stamens and stigmas (see Figures 2.24–27) are often the only parts of the flower visible, as they become exserted beyond the subtending glume (see Figures 2.18 and 20). The anthers are basifixed and in a few taxa (e.g. **11** *Schoenopectus triqueter*: see Figure 2.26) have a prominent apical connective tip. Care is needed when counting stamens, particularly in more mature material, as they easily fall away giving the false impression of fewer stamens. The number of stigma branches usually corresponds to whether the ovary has two or three sides: thus a 2-sided ovary has two stigma branches and a 3-sided ovary has three stigmas branches. Care is also needed when counting stigma branches, since on a 3-sided ovary one of the stigma branches can easily break off. If possible the number of stigma branches should be checked on a number of flowers and corroborated with the shape of the fruit, if maturing fruit is available.

The fruit (see Figures 2.28–30) is either a 2-sided (biconvex) or a 3-sided nut (also referred to as a nutlet or achene). The margins of the 3-sided type may be more or less rounded (trigonous) or sharp (triquetrous). The nut is minute and contains a single seed. As indicated above, the perianth bristles, if present, usually remain attached at maturity; sometimes the filaments remain attached as well (see, for example, p. 103). The nut surface may be smooth to minutely papillose, reticulate or sometimes trabeculate (as in **17** *Eleocharis acicularis*). It varies in colour from pale brown to blackish. In some taxa (notably *Eleocharis*) the base of the style remains attached to the nut and forms a distinct conical or pyramid-shaped structure on the nut apex.

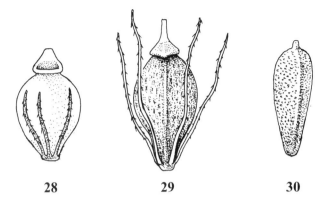

28   **29**   **30**

Figures 28–30 Fruits
28 *Eleocharis uniglumis*: 2-sided, with style-base
29 *Eleocharis multicaulis*: 3-sided, with style-base
30 *Cyperus longus*: 3-sided, without style-base

Carex *and* Kobresia

Recent thinking (e.g. Dahlgren *et al.* 1985; Bruhl 1995) is that each flower unit in *Carex* and *Kobresia* (flower plus subtending glume) is homologous to the spikelets seen in other Cyperaceae, so that, through evolution, the spikelet has lost flowers and has been reduced to the one flower that we see today. This is supported by the presence of a vestigial spikelet axis in **103** *Carex microglochin* (see Figure 2.42) and other caricoid taxa such as the southern hemisphere genus *Uncinia*. Chapter 3 (p. 19) mentions recent molecular studies indicating a close link between Cariceae, Dulichieae and Scirpeae, suggesting that the flowers of *Carex* and *Kobresia* are best interpreted as representing a reduction in the number of flowers in a spikelet.

The inflorescence structure in European *Carex* is basically a spike or a panicle; the flowers are unisexual but both kinds are borne on the same inflorescence, except in one species, *C. dioica,* which is truly dioecious as the name implies. In subgenus *Carex,* two arrangements of the unisexual flowers are found; the most common is that in which the terminal and upper spikes are entirely male and the lower are all female or occasionally the upper female spikes have male flowers at the top (see diagrammatic representation in Figure 2.31). A variation on this theme is found in **103–106** the

19

C. pulicaris group (subgenus *Psyllophora*), where the inflorescence is a single spike with male flowers at the top and female at the base (see Figure 2.32). The other arrangement is seen in the British Isles only in section *Atratae* (**92–94** *C. atrata, C. buxbaumii* and *C. norvegica*), and here the terminal spike has female flowers at the top and male at the base; the lower spikes may repeat this pattern or more likely be entirely female (see Figure 2.33): see D.L. Smith (1966) and Smith & Faulkner (1976) for an account of their development. In *Kobresia* there are two or three terminal spikes each with from one to six male flowers above the female flowers and subtended by the same bract.

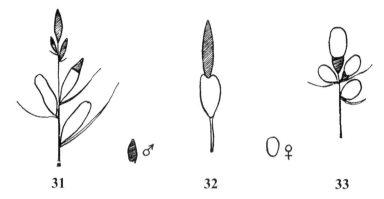

31   **32**   **33**

Figures 2.31–33 Inflorescence types in *Carex* subgenus *Carex*
31 Usual state, with male at top (shaded) and female below (unshaded)
32 State found in subgenus *Psyllophora*
33 State found in section *Atratae*

In subgenus *Carex* all spikes except the terminal one are subtended by a bract, which may be like a large glume (not green) or may be the exaggerated green midrib of the glume which is otherwise reduced (then called setaceous). On at least most of the lower spikes, however, the green midrib is exaggerated still further to form a leaf-like bract that varies in length according to the species and its position along the axis of the inflorescence. Such bracts may be connate in the lower part and thus ensheath the axis (peduncle) of the spike. That this leafy bract is homologous to the glume subtending the female flower is shown by the presence in **95–102** the *C. nigra* group of black auricles, remnants of black glume tissue, at the base of the bract; in other species with lighter glumes this is not so evident. The second and more important pointer to this is the very presence of a utricle (albeit sterile and called a cladoprophyll) at the base of the spike axis. Thus it appears that the lateral spike axis in subgenus *Carex* is an elongation of the utricle axis of the more advanced (or reduced) types like **103** *C. microglochin* or **104** *C. pauciflora*; in fact the bristle or rachilla of the former species is the beginning of that elongation (see Figure 2.42).

The length of the stem over which the spikes are produced, i.e. the length of the inflorescence, varies according to species. In most species this is short in relation to the stem length and the spikes are clustered or contiguous; in some species, however, the internodes between the spikes elongate producing a distant or even remote spike. Occasionally if the apex of the stem is damaged, e.g. grazed, a lower node will produce a remote spike out of character for the species; the bract subtending this spike will be leaf-like and abnormally long, often overtopping the whole inflorescence.

In subgenus *Vignea* the inflorescence is often more compound (e.g. a panicle) and the spikes (or spikelets as the secondary spikes are often called) are small in comparison with those of many species of subgenus *Carex* (see diagrammatic representations in Figures 2.34–37). The arrangement of the male and female flowers is basically the same as in subgenus *Carex*. The bracts are also similar but on the whole tend to be glumaceous or setaceous; some secondary spikes lack bracts altogether.

Male flowers in *Carex* and *Kobresia* consist simply of three stamens arising from a low receptacle and subtended on the abaxial side by a glume (see Figure 2.38). As the basifixed anthers mature the filaments elongate and the stamens hang free from the sheathing glume. Eventually the empty anther falls but the white filament remains, thus indicating the position of the male flowers in fruiting specimens. The lower florets of terminal male spikelets may be sterile and have correspondingly larger glumes. The shape of the glume is important but may be affected by the accidental breaking of tissue, giving a false impression of a toothed apex. Colour is usually specific, but in some species (e.g. **100** *C. nigra*) different clones may show a wide range of colour that is not correlated with other characters.

Female flowers in *Carex* consist essentially of a bottle-shaped, i.e. closed, perigynium (referred to in this book as the utricle) containing a single ovary and subtended by a glume (see Figure 2.40). The colour, shape and size of the glume are all-important in the identification of a species but, as with the male glume, laceration or curling can give a false impression of the apex. Phylogenetically the utricle is the result of fusion of the lowest glume (prophyll) along its margins (Dahlgren *et al.* 1985); as a result the utricle exhibits two lateral dominant vascular strands ('nerves'). The prominence of other nerves to form ribs can be important taxonomically but, on drying, the tissue between the nerves shrinks and accentuates the ribbing. The shape (ranging from obovoid to ovoid to ellipsoid and usually not changing after fertilisation), size, colour and texture are important taxonomic characters. In some species (e.g. **67** *C. flacca*, **100** *C. nigra*) a black pigment is produced in utricles exposed to bright sunlight, and plants showing this have wrongly been given variety or form names. The utricle is usually more elongated at the base of the spikelet and observations should always be made on utricles in a median position. Female flowers in *Kobresia* differ from those of *Carex* in having an open, spathe-like prophyll (see Figure 2.39).

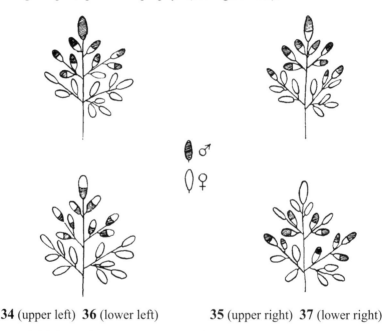

34 (upper left) **36** (lower left)   **35** (upper right) **37** (lower right)

Figures 2.34–37 Inflorescence types in *Carex* subgenus *Vignea*
34 Terminal spike male, lower spikes female with upper ones male at the top
35 An elaboration of the last where most of the spikes are male at the top and female below but with a few of the lowest spikes all female
36 Terminal and upper spikes female at the top and male below, lower spikes all female
37 Terminal and often upper spikes all female, intermediate spikes male at the top and female below, lower spikes all female again (A variation of this theme is where a few spikes at the very base are male.)

22

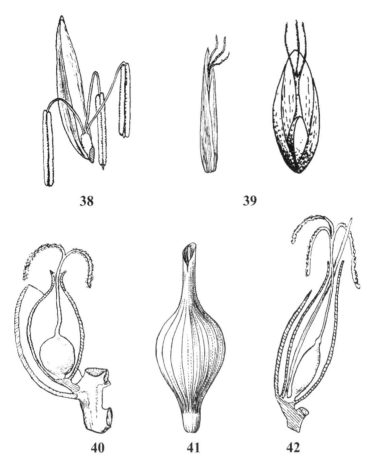

Figures 2.38–42 *Kobresia* and *Carex* flowers
38 Typical male flower (adaxial view)
39 Female flowers of *Kobresia* in bud and at a later stage, showing nut
40 Female flower of *Carex nigra* (in longitudinal section)
41 Utricle of *Carex depauperata*
42 Female flower of *Carex microglochin* (in longitudinal section), showing secondary axis (bristle or rachilla)

The utricle wall may be hairy or papillose or have unicellular spines, especially on the shoulder. An examination of wall epidermis patterns with a scanning electron microscope (or even a ×50 microscope) reveals useful taxonomic characters and has been used to show sectional relationships in subgenus *Vignea* by Toivonen & Timonen (1976). Microscopic differences in the epidermal cells of the utricle may also be used to distinguish **38** *C. vulpina* from **39** *C. otrubae*: *C. vulpina* has the epidermal cells of the utricle thick-walled and more or less square, while those of *C. otrubae* are thin-walled and oblong (Samuelsson 1922). The apex of the bottle-like utricle is drawn out into a beak (rostrum) – the neck of the bottle – which varies in length according to the species and which may be serrate along its lateral edges or smooth; in a few species (e.g. **91** *C. magellanica)* the beak may be absent altogether. The orifice through which the style protrudes may be split, bifid, notched, truncate or obliquely truncate (see Figures 2.43–47).

The utricles of several species (e.g. **40–42** the *C. muricata* group) are often inhabited by a number of species of gall midges (Cecidomyiidae), becoming, when this is the case, abnormally swollen and shiny. *Wachtliella caricis* (Loew) is a common midge, attacking other species besides **41b** *C. muricata* subsp. *pairae*, e.g. **39** *C. otrubae*, **43** *C. arenaria*, **58** *C. riparia* and **79** *C. pallescens* amongst others. In some species of section *Mitratae* (e.g. **83** *C. caryophyllea*) and of section *Acrocystis* (e.g. **86** *C. montana* and **87** *C. pilulifera*) the lower part of the young utricle is whitish and swollen, comprising an elaiosome that contains oil bodies attractive to ants; it shrinks as the seed matures. See p. 39 for the potential for seed distribution.

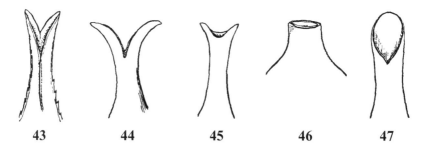

| 43 | 44 | 45 | 46 | 47 |

Figures 2.43–47 Beak apex types
43 Split **44** Bifid **45** Notched **46** Truncate **47** Obliquely truncate

Within the utricle is the ovary, which either has two stigmas and is a flat circular disc, maturing into an ellipsoid biconvex nut, or has three stigmas and is usually cylindric, maturing into a trigonous, ellipsoid or obovoid nut. In subgenus *Carex* both kinds occur in different species (but see p. 60), while in subgenus *Vignea*, as represented in the British Isles, only the ovary with

24

two stigmas is known. Hybrids between species having three and two stigmas respectively (e.g. **57** × **98** *C.* × *subgracilis*) may be found to have the two forms in the same inflorescence. The style is straight or occasionally curved at the base within the utricle. This difference has been used as a diagnostic character (e.g. in **73** *C. distans*) but is rarely constant. In some species the style is swollen at the point of attachment to the ovary. The style persists in fruit and in some species (e.g. **104** *C. pauciflora*) it may protrude some distance, when it could possibly be confused with the rachilla (bristle) in **103** *C. microglochin*. The stigmas are papillose and fall soon after fertilisation.

The fruit is a biconvex or trigonous nut, which in some species (e.g. **86** *C. montana)* is on a stalk but is usually sessile in the base of the utricle. In some species it fills the utricle at maturity; in others it does not, giving rise to what is called an inflated utricle (as in **60** *C. rostrata*). The nut is usually brown but may be yellowish (**73** *C. distans*) or purple (**68** *C. panicea*); its colour may be used to distinguish species (e.g. **72** *C. binervis* and *C. distans*).

Breeding biology

So far as is known most species of Cyperaceae are outbreeding; there is no record of apomixis although vivipary is found in *Trichophorum* and some species of *Eleocharis*. Most are wind-pollinated, but pollen-eating beetles could effect pollination in those species with bisexual flowers and those true sedges with spikes containing both male and female florets (*Carex* subgenus *Vignea*). Protogyny is quite common in subgenus *Vignea*, with most spikes opening simultaneously and their stigmas exserted and mature before any stamens are exserted and dehisced (T. O'Mahony pers. comm.). In the other subgenera, as well as in other Cyperaceae, protandry is more common and early and rapid dehiscence of anthers prevents self-fertilisation. However, those species with several male spikelets (e.g. **58** *Carex riparia*) may still be shedding pollen when the first stigmas are receptive lower down the plant.

At least in **95–102** the *Carex nigra* group, ripe pollen kept at 40% humidity for two days can fertilise female flowers lower down the same inflorescence. Certainly in the experimental garden a ramet can be pollinated from inflorescences on ramets of the same clone; this must happen in nature too. The stigmas remain receptive usually for 24 hours only; often the whole spikelet is receptive at the same time. The male spikelet on the other hand usually takes one to several days to discharge its pollen, most often in bands of 12 or so florets at a time. Little is known about the time involved in fertilisation or even for the formation of a pollen-tube; *Carex* pollen is difficult to germinate on artificial media.

Chromosome studies

Chromosome studies on British and European *Carex* in the past 25 years have been few. Earlier, Davies (1956) discussed the origin of chromosome numbers and gave counts for many British and Irish species. More recently Faulkner (1972) reported his work on section *Acutae* and gave a good review of the cytology of *Carex* generally. One significant point emerged from his work, namely that, on cytological grounds, Scottish **95** *C. recta* appears to be an interspecific hybrid between **97** *C. aquatilis* and the hitherto non-British *C. paleacea*. Studies on hybrids within section *Acutae* suggest that there is considerable homology between chromosomes of the different species. Work in North America on this group has shown that these partially fertile hybrids play a significant role in the evolution of the group (see Cayouette & Morisset 1985, 1986a, 1986b; Cayouette & Catling 1992; Standley 1990).

Chromosome numbers of Cyperaceae exhibit both a polyploid series (i.e. multiples of the base number) and (especially in *Carex*) an aneuploid series, where the differences may be only two or three chromosomes. In *Carex* the highest number recorded for the British Isles is that of **55** *C. hirta* (2n = 112) and the lowest that of **68** *C. panicea* and **69** *C. vaginata* (2n = 32). Other genera exhibit a wider range, e.g. **20** *Scirpoides holoschoenus* with 2n = 164 but some species of *Eleocharis* as low as 2n = 16.

3 NOTES ON THE CLASSIFICATION OF THE GENERA AND SPECIES OF CYPERACEAE
The arrangement used in this book

Classification of Cyperaceae

Cyperaceae comprise 109 genera and about 5500 species. The current classification is based on a combination of molecular and morphological evidence. A general synopsis as it relates to the sedges of the British Isles is shown here; the genera listed are only those described in this handbook.

Family: CYPERACEAE

Subfamily: Cyperoideae

Tribe:	Scirpeae	*Tribe*:	Dulichieae
Genera:	1 *Eriophorum*	*Genus*:	10 *Blysmus*
	2 *Trichophorum*	*Tribe*:	Schoeneae
	3 *Scirpus*	*Genera*:	11 *Schoenus*
	4 *Bolboschoenus*		12 *Cladium*
	5 *Schoenoplectus*	*Tribe*:	Rhynchosporeae
Tribe:	Eleocharideae	*Genus*:	13 *Rhynchospora*
Genus:	6 *Eleocharis*	*Tribe:*	Cariceae
Tribe:	Cypereae	*Genera*:	14 *Kobresia*
Genera:	7 *Scirpoides*		15 *Carex*
	8 *Isolepis*		
	9 *Cyperus*		

Subfamily classification of Cyperaceae is now stable, with two subfamilies being recognised, namely Mapanioideae and Cyperoideae (Simpson *et al.* 2003, 2007; Muasya *et al.* in press). This compares with the three or four subfamilies that were recognised previously (e.g. Sell & Murrell 1997). All British and Irish taxa are in Cyperoideae. At the tribal level the situation is less certain. The most recent tribal and generic classification is that of Goetghebeur (1998), which is based on morphological data. This proposed a number of differences from traditionally accepted tribal placement of British and Irish taxa. Across the whole family, tribal groupings proposed by Goetghebeur are by and large supported by molecular studies (e.g. Simpson *et al.* 2007; Muasya *et al.* in press). An exception is Rhynchosporeae, which was placed in Schoeneae by Goetghebeur. It is recognised here as a tribe in its own right, supported by molecular work (Simpson *et al.* 2007; Muasya *et al.* in press). At the generic level *Eleogiton* is subsumed into *Isolepis* (Muasya & Simpson 2002).

The Scirpeae are characterised by plants with bisexual flowers that, in all the British and Irish representatives, have perianth bristles. The latter become massively developed in Eriophorum. The flowers are aggregated into spikelets, of which there may be several to many per inflorescence; inflorescences may be capitate to paniculate. The tribe has a worldwide distribution.

The Eleocharideae are distinguished by plants that have all their leaves reduced to basal sheaths and an inflorescence comprising a single spikelet with bisexual flowers. The involucral bracts are similar to the glumes and perianth bristles are present. The nut often has a persistent style-base. The tribe has a worldwide distribution, being particularly diverse in tropical America.

The Cypereae characteristically have two or more leafy or rarely glume-like involucral bracts subtending a capitate to branched and umbel-like inflorescence. The spikelets are often flattened and distichous. The flowers have no perianth bristles and there is no style-base on the nut. The tribe occurs worldwide in temperate to tropical regions and shows the greatest diversity in eastern and southern Africa.

The Dulichieae have flattened spikelets in which the lowest glume is fertile. The spikelets are arranged into spike-like inflorescences. The flowers are bisexual and perianth segments are present. The tribe is found in temperate to subtropical regions in the northern hemisphere.

The Schoeneae are a diverse group with capitate to paniculate inflorescences, bisexual flowers and perianth bristles. Individual flowers within a spikelet are often ensheathed by wings at the base of the glume above. The tribe occurs mostly in the tropics and temperate southern hemisphere (especially in tropical Asia, Australia and New Zealand).

The Rhynchosporeae are characterised by plants with capitate to paniculate inflorescences, spikelets with the lowest one to several glumes sterile, and the upper glumes alternately fertile and sterile and sometimes unisexual. Perianth bristles are usually present and the style-base is usually well developed. The tribe occurs in temperate to tropical regions worldwide, but is particularly diverse in South America.

The Cariceae are characterised by having unisexual flowers that lack a perianth and by the pistillate (i.e. female) flowers being ensheathed by the inner glume or prophyll. The distinctions and generic limits between *Schoenoxiphium* and *Uncinia* need not be discussed here. *Kobresia*, on the other hand, will be more familiar: *K. simpliciuscula* (Wahlenb.) Mack. is found in Britain and *K. myosuroides* (Vill.) Fiori & Paol. in Europe; it differs from *Carex* in having open, spathe-like prophylls and from 1 to 6 male flowers on the same axis as the female flower and subtended by the same bract. *Carex*, contrastingly, has a closed, connate (bottle-like) prophyll (called the utricle in this book), which has only one female flower within it and no male flowers arising on the same axis.

Molecular studies have indicated a close relationship between the tribes Cariceae, Dulichieae and Scirpeae, suggesting that the differences between *Carex* and other Cyperaceae are not as great as once thought. However, in the present work we have maintained Goetghebeur's placements of these tribes.

Subgenera and species grouping in British and Irish *Carex*

The genus *Carex* contains over 1800 species throughout the world, although the majority are North Temperate; in Europe alone there are 180 (Chater 1980). Kükenthal (1909), in his monograph on the genus in Engler's *Das Pflanzenreich* series, recognised four subgenera – *Primocarex* Kük., *Vignea* (P. Beauv. ex T. Lestib.) Peterm., *Indocarex* (Baill.) Kük. and *Eucarex*. Kreczetowicz (1936) queried the primitiveness of the species in subgenus *Primocarex* and instead placed them mainly into subgenus *Carex* with a few in subgenus *Vignea*. Kern & Reichgelt (1954), in their work on the Dutch *Carices*, likewise dispensed with *Primocarex*, as did others, e.g. Koyama (1962). On the other hand Saville & Calder (1953), basing their argument on evidence from relationships between smut fungi and their *Carex* hosts, proposed a further subgenus, *Kuekenthalia* (in honour of Georg Kükenthal) and in it included the predominantly wetland and aquatic species with well-developed, inflated utricles which have developed a seed-dispersal mechanism. They also included in it some species, e.g. *C. pulicaris* and *C. pauciflora*, included by Kükenthal in subgenus *Primocarex* and by Kern in *Vignea*. Egorova (1999) has five subgenera – *Vigneastrum* (Tuckerm.) Kük. (all eastern Asian species which do not concern us), the three used here and also a fifth, *Kreczetoviczia* T.V. Egorova, in which she includes section *Phacocystis*, the *C. nigra* group. We see this latter group as being distinct, the species having a number of chromosomes (and thereby many genes) in common, hence the considerable hybridisation within the group; but hybrids are also formed outside the group (e.g. *C.* × *subgracilis*), so we have not taken that view and retain the species within subgenus *Carex*.

The classification adopted in the second edition of this handbook (Jermy *et al.* 1982) was based on Kükenthal and the arrangement of sections and species followed that of Chater (1980) in *Flora Europaea* Volume 5; apart from one nomenclatural change (subgenus *Psyllophora* (Degl.) Peterm. being an earlier name for *Primocarex* Kük.) we have retained that arrangement here. It is a compromise in that the subgenus rank has been invoked as a convenient heading under which certain anomalous species can be placed, although the group may not have any phylogenetic significance. On the other hand, from comparative studies of inflorescence development Smith & Faulkner (1976) concluded that the species within it, although possibly polyphyletic in origin, are highly advanced.

A synopsis of this classification is given here to enable readers to see similarities in related species and thereby gain some appreciation of the logic behind the arrangement of the book that we hope will help in mastering the genus as a whole. The major division in this classification is into three subgenera. subgenus *Vignea* is characterised most obviously by all the spikes being similar in appearance and by having always only two stigmas, as in *C. ovalis* or *C. paniculata*. The sections here are characterised chiefly by the distribution of male and female flowers within the spikes. *C. dioica* is the only dioecious species and has a solitary single-sex spike. Unfortunately, in the British Isles the sections of this subgenus never contain more than three species, so they are not as helpful as they are on a European scale.

In subgenus *Carex*, however, several sections are larger and are useful for the beginner to learn to recognise. This subgenus is especially characterised by having the terminal one or more (all male) spikes very different in appearance from the lateral (female) ones, as in *C. pendula* and *C. nigra*. Most of the species have three stigmas: apart from the *C. nigra* group (section *Phacocystis*; see below), the only other ones with two stigmas are *C. saxatilis* (section *Vesicariae*) and, very rarely, *C. acutiformis* (section *Paludosae*). Species with hairy utricles fall into four sections: *C. hirta* and *C. lasiocarpa* (section *Carex*) are the only two of these species with a prominent bifid beak on the utricle; of the rest, *C. digitata*, *C. ornithopoda* and *C. humilis* (section *Digitatae*) are the only ones with long, narrow female spikes; *C. caryophyllea* (our only species in section *Mitratae*) has ovoid spikes and the lowest bract sheathing, while *C. filiformis*, *C. ericetorum*, *C. montana* and *C. pilulifera* (section *Acrocystis*) also have ovoid spikes but the lowest bract not sheathing.

The larger part of subgenus *Carex* has glabrous utricles (although some are papillate). Of these, two common and closely related sections can cause especial confusion: the section containing *C. distans, C. punctata, C. binervis* and *C. extensa* (section *Spirostachyae*) can be distinguished from that containing *C. hostiana* and the *C. flava* group (section *Ceratocystis*) chiefly by the usually mucronate female glumes and speckled utricles; the latter section has obtuse to subacute female glumes and unspeckled utricles. *C. atrata* and its two allies, *C. buxbaumii* and *C. norvegica* (section *Atratae*) look at first sight as though they should belong to subgenus *Vignea* as the spikes all look the same, but the presence of three stigmas makes it clear that their correct position is as a section of subgenus *Carex*.

The last and most distinctive group (section *Phacocystis*) contains *C. nigra* and its allies. All have only two stigmas, biconvex utricles and nuts which are usually green contrasting with the black or purplish-black glumes. Egorova (1999) includes *C. recta* and *C. salina* within section *Temnemis*, with *C. paleacea*, on very slender differences (female glumes apiculate or awned and lower spikelets pedunculate). Since the distinction is so slight and because several species in that group hybridise freely with section *Phacocystis*, we prefer to include all in section *Phacocystis*.

The third subgenus, *Psyllophora* (*Primocarex*), contains the few species with a solitary bisexual spike.

Classification and arrangement of the species described

Eriophorum L.

    1 *E. angustifolium* Honck.

    2 *E. latifolium* Hoppe

    3 *E. gracile* W.D.J. Koch ex Roth

    4 *E. vaginatum* L.

Trichophorum Pers.

    5 *T. germanicum* Palla

    6 *T. cespitosum* (L.) Hartm.

       6a *T. alpinum* (L.) Pers.

Scirpus L.

    7 *S. sylvaticus* L.

Bolboschoenus (Asch.) Palla

    8 *B. maritimus* (L.) Palla

Schoenoplectus (Rchb.) Palla

  9 *S. lacustris* (L.) Palla

  10 *S. tabernaemontani* (C.C. Gmel.) Palla

  11 *S. triqueter* (L.) Palla

  12 *S. pungens* (Vahl) Palla

Eleocharis R. Br.

  Subgenus *ELEOCHARIS*

  Section *Eleocharis*

    13 *E. palustris* (L.) Roem. & Schult.

      13a subsp. *palustris*

      13b subsp. *vulgaris* Walters

    14 *E. mamillata* (H. Lindb.) H. Lindb. subsp. *austriaca* (Hayek) Strandh.

    15 *E. uniglumis* (Link) Schult.

  Section *Leiocarpae* C.B. Clarke

    16 *E. multicaulis* (Sm.) Desv.

  Subgenus *SCIRPIDIUM* (Nees) Kukkonen

  Section *Scirpidium* (Nees) Benth.

    17 *E. acicularis* (L.) Roem. & Schult.

  Subgenus *ZINSERLINGIA* T.V. Egorova

  Section *Pauciflorae* Beauverd

    18 *E. quinqueflora* (Hartm.) O. Schwarz

  Section *Parvulae* T.V. Egorova

    19 *E. parvula* (Roem. & Schult.) Link ex Bluff, Nees & Schauer

Scirpoides Ség.

  20 *S. holoschoenus* (L.) Soják

Isolepis R. Br. (incl. *Eleogiton* Link)

  Subgenus *ISOLEPIS*

  Section *Isolepis*

    21 *I. setacea* (L.) R. Br.

  Section *Cernuae* (C.B. Clarke) Muasya

    22 *I. cernua* (Vahl) Roem. & Schult.

Subgenus *FLUITANTES* (C.B. Clarke) Muasya
>   **23** *I. fluitans* (L.) R. Br.

Cyperus L.
Subgenus *CYPERUS*
Section *Rotundi* C.B. Clarke
>   **24** *C. longus* L.

Section *Fusci* Kunth
>   **25** *C. fuscus* L.

Section *Luzuloidei* Kunth
>   **26** *C. eragrostis* Lam.

Blysmus Panz. ex Schult.
>   **27** *B. compressus* (L.) Panz. ex Link
>   **28** *B. rufus* (Huds.) Link

Schoenus L.
>   **29** *S. nigricans* L.
>   **30** *S. ferrugineus* L.

Cladium P. Browne
>   **31** *C. mariscus* (L.) Pohl

Rhynchospora Vahl
Subgenus *DIPLOSTYLEAE* Benth. & Hook. f.
Section *Albae* C.B. Clarke
>   **32** *R. alba* (L.) Vahl

Section *Fuscae* C.B. Clarke
>   **33** *R. fusca* (L.) W.T. Aiton

Kobresia Willd.
Subgenus *KOBRESIA*
Section *Kobresia* Kunth
>   **34** *K. simpliciuscula* (Wahlenb.) Mack.

Carex L.
Subgenus *VIGNEA* (P. Beauv. ex T. Lestib.) Kük.
Section *Heleoglochin* Dumort.

35 *C. paniculata* L.

36 *C. appropinquata* Schumach.

37 *C. diandra* Schrank

Section *Vulpinae* (J. Carey) H. Christ

  38 *C. vulpina* L.

  39 *C. otrubae* Podp.

Section *Phaestoglochin* Dumort.

  40 *C. spicata* Huds.

  41 *C. muricata* L.

    41a subsp. *muricata*

    41b subsp. *pairae* (F.W. Schultz) Čelak.

  42 *C. divulsa* Stokes

    42a subsp. *divulsa*

    42b subsp. *leersii* (Kneuck.) W. Koch

Section *Ammoglochin* Dumort.

  43 *C. arenaria* L.

  44 *C. disticha* Huds.

Section *Divisae* H. Christ ex Kük.

  45 *C. chordorrhiza* L. f.

  46 *C. divisa* Huds.

Section *Foetidae* (L.H. Bailey) Kük.

  47 *C. maritima* Gunnerus

Section *Remotae* (Asch.) C.B. Clarke

  48 *C. remota* L.

Section *Ovales* (Kunth) H. Christ

  49 *C. leporina* L.

Section *Stellulatae* (Kunth) H. Christ

  50 *C. echinata* Murray

Section *Physoglochin* Dumort.

  51 *C. dioica* L.

Section *Elongatae* (Kunth) Kük.

  52 *C. elongata* L.

Section *Canescentes* (Fr.) H. Christ

    53 *C. lachenalii* Schkuhr

    54 *C. canescens* L.

Subgenus *CAREX*

Section *Carex*

    55 *C. hirta* L.

    56 *C. lasiocarpa* Ehrh.

Section *Paludosae* (Fr.) H. Christ

    57 *C. acutiformis* Ehrh.

    58 *C. riparia* Curtis

Section *Pseudocypereae* (L.H. Bailey) Kük.

    59 *C. pseudocyperus* L.

Section *Vesicariae* (O. Lang) H. Christ

    60 *C. rostrata* Stokes

    61 *C. vesicaria* L.

    62 *C. saxatilis* L.

Section *Rhynchocystis* Dumort.

    63 *C. pendula* Huds.

Section *Strigosae* (Fr.) H. Christ

    64 *C. sylvatica* Huds.

    65 *C. capillaris* L.

    66 *C. strigosa* Huds.

Section *Glaucae* (Asch.) H. Christ

    67 *C. flacca* Schreb.

Section *Paniceae* (O. Lang) H. Christ

    68 *C. panicea* L.

    69 *C. vaginata* Tausch

Section *Rhomboidales* Kük.

    70 *C. depauperata* Curtis ex With.

Section *Elatae* Kük.

    71 *C. laevigata* Sm.

Section *Spirostachyae* (Drejer) L.H. Bailey

72 *C. binervis* Sm.

73 *C. distans* L.

74 *C. punctata* Gaudin

75 *C. extensa* Gooden.

Section *Ceratocystis* Dumort.

76 *C. hostiana* DC.

77 *C. flava* L.

78 *C. viridula* Michx.

    78a subsp. *brachyrrhyncha* (Čelak.) B. Schmid

    78b subsp. *oedocarpa* (Andersson) B. Schmid

    78c subsp. *viridula*

Section *Porocystis* Dumort.

79 *C. pallescens* L.

Section *Digitatae* (Fr.) H. Christ

80 *C. digitata* L.

81 *C. ornithopoda* Willd.

82 *C. humilis* Leyss.

Section *Mitratae* Kük.

83 *C. caryophyllea* Latourr.

Section *Acrocystis* Dumort.

84 *C. filiformis* L.

85 *C. ericetorum* Pollich

86 *C. montana* L.

87 *C. pilulifera* L.

Section *Aulocystis* Dumort.

88 *C. atrofusca* Schkuhr

Section *Limosae* (O. Lang) H. Christ

89 *C. limosa* L.

90 *C. rariflora* (Wahlenb.) Sm.

91 *C. magellanica* Lam. subsp. *irrigua* (Wahlenb.) Hiitonen

Section *Atratae* H. Christ

    92 *C. atrata* L.

    93 *C. buxbaumii* Wahlenb.

    94 *C. norvegica* Retz.

Section *Phacocystis* Dumort.

    95 *C. recta* Boott

    96 *C. salina* Wahlenb.

    97 *C. aquatilis* Wahlenb.

    98 *C. acuta* L.

    99 *C. trinervis* Degl.

    100 *C. nigra* (L.) Reichard

    101 *C. elata* All.

    102 *C. bigelowii* Torr. ex Schwein.

Subgenus *PSYLLOPHORA* (Degl.) Peterm.

Section *Leucoglochin* Dumort.

    103 *C. microglochin* Wahlenb.

    104 *C. pauciflora* Lightf.

Section *Petraeae* (O. Lang) Kük.

    105 *C. rupestris* All.

Section *Unciniiformes* Kük.

    106 *C. pulicaris* L.

4 ECOLOGY OF CYPERACEAE

Introduction and earlier studies

The majority of species of Cyperaceae are, by reason of their habit and mode of vegetative growth, important if not dominant in a wide variety of plant communities. It is therefore not surprising that information on their habitats is to be found in reports and papers resulting from wider surveys at regional, county or, more often, site level. The last may be linked with management plans prepared by staff of, or commissioned by, government conservation agencies – Natural England (NE), Countryside Council for Wales (CCW), Scottish Natural Heritage (SNH), Environment Agency (EA), in Northern Ireland the Department of Agriculture (NI) and, in the Republic of Ireland, the National Parks and Wildlife Service of the Department of the Environment, Heritage and Local Government. Similar information may be found from surveys by local authorities (especially those involved in Biological Action Plans) and non-government organisations (e.g. Plantlife, Royal Society for the Protection of Birds and Wildlife Trusts). Sources of such reports may be found on the websites of these organisations.

More academic research on ecology pertinent to our sedges may be found in journals such as *Journal of Ecology*, *Transactions of the Edinburgh Botanical Society* (now *Edinburgh Journal of Botany*) and *Irish Naturalists' Journal*. Notes on many of our sedge species may be found scattered through the Botanical Exchange Clubs' reports and *Proceedings of the Botanical Society of the British Isles* (see Simpson 1960, especially pp. 10–11) and in *Watsonia*, *BSBI News* and the Botanical Society's regional bulletins as well as in the increasing number of newsletters and bulletins published by county botanical groups. When working in, or simply enjoying, the botany of a particular area it is always sensible to refer to the relevant County Flora, where it exists. Many describe the vegetation and geology of the area, often in some detail, and so give a useful ecological background for any naturalist. One Flora that made a point of stressing the ecology of the vascular plants of a confined area is *An Ecological Flora of the Shropshire Region* (Sinker *et al.* 1985, 1991). Another very significant book is *Aquatic plants in Britain and Ireland* by Preston & Croft (1997), which discusses the ecology not only of swamp species but also of those of the wetter mires. For relevant Biological Flora accounts in *Journal of Ecology* see below. More general, but very interesting, information may be found also in articles in *British Wildlife*. Other specific papers are mentioned in individual taxon accounts in Chapter 7 and in 'References and selected bibliography' at the end of the book.

Seed dispersal, germination and autecological studies

Seed dispersal

In the genus *Carex* the utricle is often inflated at maturity, thus containing air that increases buoyancy (e.g. **60** *C. rostrata* and **61** *C. vesicaria*), with flotation and water dispersal an obvious consequence. In two riparian species (**59** *C. pseudocyperus* and **101** *C. elata*), which can only be effectively established in a very narrow band along the side of a slow-flowing stream or dyke, the utricles are dropped singly at maturity and so decrease the competition that would occur if the whole spikelet fell into the water. According to Wiinstedt (1945) the papillose nature of the utricle wall in **67** *C. flacca* enhances buoyancy. See also Leck & Schutz (2005).

The carrying of utricles by ants and other foraging insects can disperse terrestrial species only short distances. In some species, for example **83** *C. caryophyllea* and those of section *Acrocystis* (e.g. **86** *C. montana* and **87** *C. pilulifera*), the cell walls of the lower part of the young utricles have papillae-like organelles called elaiosomes that are rich in oils (see p. 24). These utricles are grazed by ants, which often collect whole fruits and remove them to their nests, thus aiding dispersal. See Kjellsson (1985) on the role of ants in effecting seed dispersal in **87** *C. pilulifera* in Denmark and, for wider aspects of ant/sedge relationships, Sernander (1906).

In other genera of Cyperaceae that we find in our area, those in drier habitats have a nut that is naked and small, so seed dispersal is most likely by invertebrates or by wind.

Germination

Most species of Cyperaceae require an after-ripening period of 3–12 months; low-temperature treatment does not substantially reduce this. Artificial abrasion of the testa increases the percentage germination, but complete removal of the utricle wall (in *C. nigra* at least) produces a lower percentage, which suggests some substance there affecting imbibition rate. In *C. flacca* a colourless mucilage is exuded from the nut before the testa breaks, but this has not been observed in the germination of aquatic species (Taylor 1956). Light certainly hastens germination: *C. nigra* sown under soil in pots took six months to sprout, whereas when sown on damp filter-paper in the light it germinated within 14 days.

Autecological studies

Autecological studies of dominant sedge species will undoubtedly show some species to be good ecological indicators, especially in relation to pH, calcium, phosphate, the carbon/nitrogen ratio and potentially toxic ions such as manganese, iron and aluminium. Moving water of flushes gives aeration, necessary for good rhizome growth in some species, and a constant supply of nutrients. The delicately balanced, but slightly different, ecological requirements of closely related species can be useful in identification. Moreover, a detailed analysis of these requirements can show the species, once identified, to be good ecological pointers. Such differences within species groups can prevent competition for available space. The effect of aluminium in relation to calcium has been demonstrated in **78a** and **78b** *Carex viridula* subspp. *oedocarpa* and *brachyrrhyncha* by Clymo (1962). A positive correlation between soil moisture and plant size in **97** *C. aquatilis* was shown by Shaver *et al.* (1979). The Biological Flora accounts of the biology and ecology of individual species published in *Journal of Ecology* include a number of Cyperaceae – **1** *Eriophorum angustifolium* (Phillips 1954b), **4** *E. vaginatum* (Wein 1973), **13–19** *Eleocharis* (Walters 1949), **29** *Schoenus nigricans* (Sparling 1968), **31** *Cladium mariscus* (Conway 1942), **40–42** *Carex spicata*, *C. muricata* and *C. divulsa* (David & Kelcey 1985), **43** *C. arenaria* (Noble 1982) and **67** *C. flacca* (Taylor 1956).

Habitat characteristics of sedge-dominated vegetation

In 1975 a comprehensive programme was set up to analyse and describe British vegetation types. The result was finally published in five data-packed volumes edited by John Rodwell, *British Plant Communities – Woodlands and scrub* and *Mires and heaths* in 1991, *Grasslands and montane communities* in 1992, *Aquatic communities, swamps and tall-herb fens* in 1995 and *Maritime communities and vegetation of open habitats* in 2000. In all 286 communities were defined in the following categories:

Woodlands and scrub: **W1–25**;
Mires: **M1–38**;
Heaths: **H1–22**;
Mesotrophic grasslands: **MG1–13**;
Calcicolous grasslands: **CG1–14**;
Calcifugous grasslands and montane communities: **U1–21**;
Aquatic communities: **A1–24**;
Swamps and tall-herb fens: **S1–28**;
Salt-marsh communities: **SM1–28**;
Shingle, strandline and sand-dune communities: **SD1–19**;
Maritime cliff communities: **MC1–12**;
Vegetation of open habitats: **OV1–42**.

Peatlands of which species of Cyperaceae are a major constituent may be classified either according to their differing physical characteristics (topographical, hydrological and chemical) or by their present composition of vegetation (i.e. species) or by a combination of the two. Nomenclature of peatlands in Britain and Ireland (blanket bogs, fens, mires, swamps, valley bogs etc.) became somewhat confused in the 1970s owing to loose usage, and we use here the definitions proposed by Ratcliffe (1977) for *A Nature Conservation Review* as being more meaningful in terms of *Carex* ecology. A number of major accounts describe sedge-dominated vegetation on this basis (Birse & Robertson 1967, 1973, 1976; McVean & Ratcliffe 1962; Ratcliffe 1964a, 1964b; Spence 1964; Wheeler 1978, 1980a, 1980b, 1980c).

For any reader who wants to obtain a good picture of upland vegetation in Britain that includes the majority of sedges of the British Isles, *An illustrated guide to British upland vegetation* (Averis *et al.* 2004) gives an excellent and very readable account of the mires, upland grasslands, screes and plateau communities, putting the majority of our sedges into an ecological context.

Sedges are commonly associated with permanent water, lakes, rivers, streams and drainage channels (see Table 4.1). Some species are characteristic of peatlands and similar wet habitats, notably the various kinds of mires including flushes, bogs and marshes as well as heathland and wet meadows, especially in the western areas of our islands that are strongly affected by the oceanic climate. Also significant is altitudinal variation (shown in the climate maps published by Wheeler & Mayes 1997). Some interesting maps showing climatic parameters (e.g. January and July mean temperature, annual rainfall and the number of wet days) have been published in *Atlas of bryophytes of Britain and Ireland* (Hill *et al.* 1991) and indices of climatic severity and oceanicity by Ratcliffe (1968). On the other hand, a number of species are associated with drier sites – dry heaths, sand-dunes, cliffs, screes and grasslands of various kinds (see Table 4.1).

For all mire habitats the quality of the water (i.e. chemical content available to the plants growing there) is the most significant ecological factor. The terms *oligotrophic* (base-poor and generally acidic) or *dystrophic* (where the soil water has very low concentrations of dissolved nutrients of any kind) and *eutrophic* (rich in base cations – positively charged ions – and neutral or alkaline in reaction) are used to amplify the ecological notes; *mesotrophic* is an intermediate condition. *Eutrophic* conditions are imposed upon oligotrophic mires in lowland coastal situations by deposition of additional cations from salt-laden winds and sea-spray, containing potassium and magnesium in particular (Holden 1961; Jermy *et al.* 1978). Artificial enrichment by over-fertilisation in arable agricultural areas can also produce eutrophic conditions in the same water catchments and there it is the anions (e.g. the nitrates and phosphates) that are more important than the bases.

In the ecological notes in the taxon accounts, we have used, where appropriate, the following terminology (after Ratcliffe 1977) for wet peatlands, in all of which *Carex* and other sedge genera are frequent:

A *Ombrogenous mires* (in which the water component originates through rainfall)

i *Blanket mires* (blanket bogs) – continuous acidic areas of peat-forming vegetation over flat or sloping ground with impeded drainage, *Sphagnum*-dominated and mainly upland. Dystrophic waters are a common feature of blanket mires in Scotland but are extremely rare in England and Wales, where the number of sites of Special Areas for Conservation quality is correspondingly small. The preponderance of sites in Scotland reflects the uneven distribution of this habitat type in the U.K. A small number of dystrophic pools occurs in the lowlands of England; those associated with mires in the West Midlands have been seen as having particular value for nature conservation because of the rarity of the habitat type in this part of the U.K. (For further discussion see the Joint Nature Conservation Committee website: http://www.jncc.gov.uk/ProtectedSites/SACselection/)

ii *Raised mires* (raised bogs) – usually deep peat (up to 10 m), often formed in initially more eutrophic conditions; *Sphagnum* is a dominant component.

B *Topogenous mires* (formed by run-off from higher ground, resulting in a permanently high water-table)

i *Open water transition* (reed-swamp) and *flood-plain mires* (fens) – usually mesotrophic or eutrophic mires in eastern and southern Britain in which oligotrophic nuclei may develop locally and accommodate species tolerant of acidic conditions and/or intolerant of bases. Flood-plain mires on the siliceous rocks of northern and western Britain are usually more oligotrophic. Open water mires grade or develop into flood-plain mires and both contain communities that are changing over time to form a climax type of vegetation, usually woodland.

ii *Basin mires* – developed in enclosed waterlogged depressions and frequent in areas of glacial deposition, in which groundwater plays a significant part in the overall mire water budget. These mires are similar to raised mires in their oligotrophic *Sphagnum* communities but 'brown' (hypnoid) mosses are more frequent and **56** *Carex lasiocarpa* is an indicator of mesotrophic conditions.

iii *Valley mires* (valley bogs) – occurring in small, shallow valleys or channels in which there is lateral water movement. They often show a range of base content and correlated vegetation mosaic and are frequently very similar to ombrogenous raised mires and soligenous mires.

C *Soligenous mires* (flushes and spring communities)

These are associated with surface water seepage of varying chemical content on slopes of all kinds. Characteristically these often base-rich areas develop communities richer in species than the surrounding and often base-poor ombrogenous mires. They are frequently grazed, especially in upland areas, and the resulting community is low in stature. Different sedge species are indicators of differing content of base cations, but this is not fully understood and there is scope for study in the requirements of soligenous mire Cyperaceae.

Sedges likely to be found in selected habitats are listed in Table 4.1 and the relationships between Cyperaceae associated with soligenous mires (generally termed flushes) and the differing amounts of alkaline base salts in the ground-water flowing through those soils are tentatively shown in Table 4.2 on p. 46.

Table 4.1 Sedges likely to be found in the major habitats

Rare and local species indicated by *.

Sea-spray zone, brackish ditches, estuarine flats
Blysmus rufus; *Carex* distans, divisa, extensa, *maritima, nigra, otrubae, punctata, *recta, salina, viridula* subsp. *viridula*; *Cyperus* longus; *Eleocharis parvula*.

Stream/dyke and pond/lake edges, ditches
Carex acuta, acutiformis, aquatilis, elata, *elongata, otrubae, paniculata, pseudocyperus, riparia, vesicaria, *vulpina*; *Cladium* mariscus; *Cyperus* *fuscus, longus; *Eleocharis* acicularis, mamillata subsp. *austriaca, palustris; *Isolepis* fluitans; *Schoenoplectus* lacustris, tabernaemontani, *triqueter.

Base-rich mires (usually on deep organic soil)
Carex acutiformis, appropinquata, *buxbaumii, diandra, disticha, elata, *flava, lasiocarpa, nigra, paniculata, riparia, vesicaria, viridula subsp. *brachyrrhyncha, viridula* subsp. *viridula*; *Cladium* mariscus;

Eleocharis quinqueflora; ***Eriophorum*** *latifolium*; ***Schoenus*** *nigricans*; ***Trichophorum*** **cespitosum, germanicum.*

Base-poor mires (including valley mires on deep organic soil)
Carex *canescens, *chordorrhiza, dioica, echinata, elata, hostiana, lasiocarpa, limosa, nigra, panicea, paniculata, pulicaris, rostrata, vesicaria, viridula* subsp. *oedocarpa, viridula* subsp. *viridula*; ***Eriophorum*** *angustifolium, *gracile, vaginatum.*

Base-rich flushes (soligenous mires on shallow organic soils on steep slopes)
Carex *dioica, flacca, hostiana, nigra, pulicaris, *rupestris, viridula* subsp. *brachyrrhyncha*; ***Eleocharis*** *multicaulis, quinqueflora*; ***Eriophorum*** *latifolium*; ***Schoenus*** *ferrugineus, nigricans*; ***Trichophorum*** **cespitosum.*

Base-poor mires (including valley mires on deep organic soil)
Carex *canescens, *chordorrhiza, dioica, echinata, elata, hostiana, lasiocarpa, limosa, nigra, panicea, paniculata, pulicaris, viridula* subsp. *oedocarpa.*

Base-poor flushes (shallow organic soils on steep slopes)
Carex *canescens, dioica, echinata, hostiana, *lachenalii, panicea, *rariflora, rostrata, saxatilis*; ***Eleocharis*** *multicaulis, uniglumis*; ***Eriophorum*** *angustifolium*; ***Trichophorum*** *germanicum.*

Oligotrophic (i.e. *Sphagnum*) ombrogenous mires (blanket peat)
Carex *canescens, echinata, limosa, magellanica, nigra, pauciflora, pulicaris, rostrata*; ***Eriophorum*** *angustifolium*; ***Schoenus*** *nigricans*; ***Trichophorum*** *germanicum.*

Wet corries and ledges above 600 m altitude
Carex *atrata, *atrofusca, bigelowii, binervis, flacca, *lachenalii, *microglochin, nigra, *norvegica, panicea, pulicaris, *rupestris, saxatilis, vaginata*; ***Trichophorum*** *germanicum.*

Mountain acid grassland
Carex *bigelowii, binervis, hirta, nigra, leporina, pilulifera*; ***Trichophorum*** *germanicum.*

Chalk/limestone grassland
Carex *capillaris, caryophyllea, ericetorum, *filiformis, flacca, *humilis, *montana,*ornithopoda.*

Dry limestone woodland/scrub
Carex *depauperata, *digitata, *filiformis, muricata* subsp. *muricata, sylvatica.*

Sand-dunes/slacks, heaths and damp acid grassland
Carex arenaria, binervis, flacca, hirta, nigra, leporina, panicea, pilulifera, viridula* subsp. *viridula*; *Eleocharis* uniglumis*; *Eriophorum* angustifolium*; *Isolepis* setacea.*

Roadsides, hedgerows, rough pasture/scrub, trackways
Carex divulsa, hirta, leporina, muricata* subsp. *pairae, otrubae, pilulifera, spicata, sylvatica, *tomentosa*; *Isolepis* cernua, setacea.*

Lowland wet or clay woodland
Carex *elongata, laevigata, nigra, paniculata, pendula, remota, strigosa, sylvatica, vesicaria*; *Scirpus* sylvaticus.*

Multidimensional concept of habitat

Habitat or niche is a multidimensional concept that can be analysed in various ways by computer. Principal Components Analysis (P.C.A.) is such a technique that arranges values (in this case ecological) in a multidimensional space along the axis that best describes the variation. Having done so, it can then extract a second axis to describe the remaining variation and continue to extract axes until the residual variance is insignificant or random. The result is that points with similar characteristics are grouped on a graphical two-dimensional representation (see Figure 4.2).

Robin Walls (pers. comm.) has used a Principal Components Analysis to highlight similarity in the edaphic preferences of the sedge species found in the British Isles and has allowed us to use these unpublished data described below and shown in Table 4.3 and Figures 4.1 and 4.2.

In his studies on central European ecology, Ellenberg (1988) introduced scores to rank species along an environmental gradient. More recently five of these ecological parameters have been reviewed and extended to cover all species in the British Isles (Hill *et al.* 1999). These scores provide numerical values to characterise a species' preference for open site or light intensity (**L**), wetness (**F**), pH or base status (**R**), nutrient status (**N**) and salinity (**S**).

In the graphs on pp. 48–49 (Figure 4.2) the Ellenberg species scores have been plotted on the first two axes derived by the P.C.A. The most significant component (plotted horizontally) is primarily a combination of increasing pH or base status (**R**) and nutrient status (**N**). The second axis (plotted vertically)

45

Table 4.2   The relationships between sedges of flushes and the chemical content of the ground-water
   * high altitudes only   † mainly coastal flushes

Base-poor or low water movement	Species
↑	*Carex canescens*
	Carex echinata
	Eriophorum angustifolium
	Carex panicea
	Rhynchospora alba
	Rhynchospora fusca
	Eleocharis multicaulis
	Trichophorum germanicum
	Carex rostrata
	Carex viridula subsp. *oedocarpa*
	Carex nigra
	Eleocharis quinqueflora
	Carex hostiana
	Carex pulicaris
	Carex lasiocarpa
	Carex vaginata*
	Carex flacca
	Carex dioica
	Carex paniculata
	Schoenus nigricans
	Eriophorum latifolium
	Schoenus ferrugineus
	Carex saxatilis*
	Carex viridula subsp. *viridula*†
	Carex viridula subsp. *brachyrrhyncha*
↓	*Blysmus rufus*†

Base-rich or high water movement

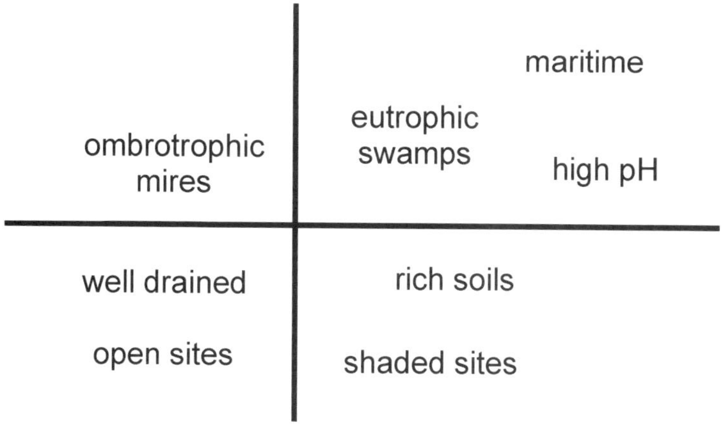

	maritime
ombrotrophic mires	eutrophic swamps high pH
well drained	rich soils
open sites	shaded sites

Figure 4.1   How the ecological parameters are arranged in the P.C.A. graph in Figure 4.2 (after R.M. Walls unpublished)

describes increasing wetness (**F**). Salinity tolerance (**S**) increases towards the top right and shade requirement towards the bottom right (with lower values for **L**). Thus plants preferring a eutrophic swamp with a high pH appear in the top right-hand quadrant. Plants of better-drained, shaded sites are at the bottom of the graph, with those requiring richer soils to the right. Plants of oligotrophic mires tend to be in the top left quadrant. Species of well-drained, open grassland are in the bottom left of the graph. A summary is provided in the diagram above (Figure 4.1). The Ellenberg values for each species are given in Table 4.3 on pp. 50–53.

One has to remember that the graph does not encompass the whole story and that some sedges plotted close together would never grow in the same place; other factors such as climate and altitude explain these apparent anomalies.

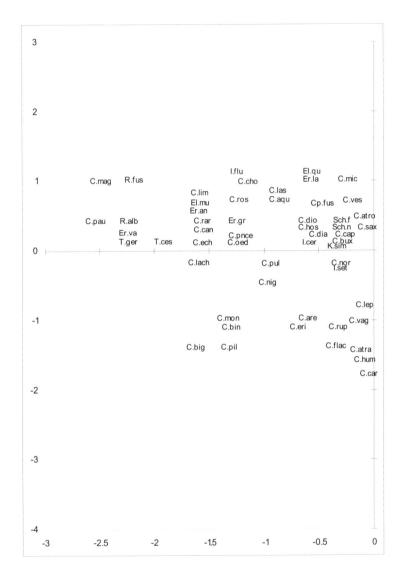

Figure 4.2 Sedge species clustered according to various ecological parameters and Ellenberg values (after R.M. Walls unpublished)

See Table 4.3 (pp. 50–53) for key to species names and Ellenberg values.

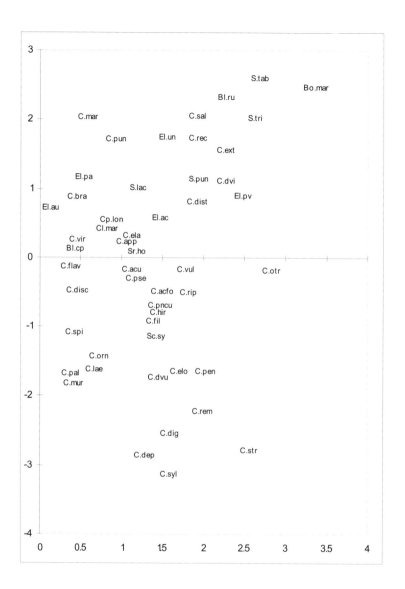

49

Table 4.3 Key to species abbreviations used in Figure 4.2 (pp. 48–49)
Numbers prefixing taxon names are those used in this book. Ellenberg
values (Hill *et al.* 1999) are given for (**L**) open site or light intensity;
(**F**) wetness; (**R**) pH or base status; (**N**) nutrient status; and (**S**) salinity.
Data for **6** *Trichophorum cespitosum* and **96** *Carex salina* are estimated
by R.M. Walls. **6a** *Trichophorum alpinum*, **26** *Cyperus eragrostis* and
99 *Carex trinervis* are excluded from both Figure 4.2 and this table.

Code	Sp. no.	Species	L	F	R	N	S
Bl.cp	**27**	*Blysmus compressus*	8	8	8	3	0
Bl.ru	**28**	*Blysmus rufus*	8	8	7	4	5
Bo.mar	**8**	*Bolboschoenus maritimus*	8	10	8	7	4
C.acfo	**57**	*Carex acutiformis*	7	8	7	6	0
C.acu	**98**	*Carex acuta*	7	9	7	5	0
C.app	**36**	*Carex appropinquata*	7	10	8	4	0
C.aqu	**97**	*Carex aquatilis*	8	10	4	3	0
C.are	**43**	*Carex arenaria*	8	3	5	2	1
C.atra	**92**	*Carex atrata*	7	5	6	3	0
C.atro	**88**	*Carex atrofusca*	8	9	7	3	0
C.big	**102**	*Carex bigelowii*	7	5	2	2	0
C.bin	**72**	*Carex binervis*	7	6	3	2	0
C.bra	**78b**	*Carex viridula* subsp. *brachyrrhyncha*	8	9	8	2	1
C.bux	**93**	*Carex buxbaumii*	8	8	7	2	0
C.can	**54**	*Carex canescens*	8	9	3	2	0
C.cap	**65**	*Carex capillaris*	9	6	8	2	0
C.car	**83**	*Carex caryophyllea*	7	4	7	2	0
C.cho	**45**	*Carex chordorrhiza*	9	9	4	3	0
C.dep	**70**	*Carex depauperata*	5	4	7	4	0
C.dia	**37**	*Carex diandra*	8	9	5	3	0
C.dig	**80**	*Carex digitata*	5	5	8	4	0
C.dio	**51**	*Carex dioica*	8	9	6	2	0

C.disc	44	*Carex disticha*	7	8	6	4	0
C.dist	73	*Carex distans*	8	6	7	5	3
C.dvi	46	*Carex divisa*	8	7	7	6	3
C.dvu	42	*Carex divulsa*	7	4	7	6	0
C.ech	50	*Carex echinata*	8	8	3	2	0
C.ela	101	*Carex elata*	7	10	7	5	0
C.elon	52	*Carex elongata*	5	8	6	6	0
C.eri	85	*Carex ericetorum*	8	4	7	1	0
C.ext	75	*Carex extensa*	8	7	7	5	4
C.fil	84	*Carex filiformis*	7	7	8	5	0
C.flac	67	*Carex flacca*	7	5	6	2	0
C.flav	77	*Carex flava*	7	9	8	2	0
C.hir	55	*Carex hirta*	7	7	7	6	0
C.hos	76	*Carex hostiana*	8	9	6	2	0
C.hum	82	*Carex humilis*	8	3	8	2	0
C.lach	53	*Carex lachenalii*	8	7	4	1	0
C.lae	71	*Carex laevigata*	5	8	5	4	0
C.las	56	*Carex lasiocarpa*	8	10	6	3	0
C.lep	49	*Carex leporina*	7	7	5	4	0
C.lim	89	*Carex limosa*	8	10	4	1	0
C.mag	91	*Carex magellanica* subsp. *irrigua*	9	9	2	1	0
C.mar	47	*Carex maritima*	9	8	7	2	3
C.mic	103	*Carex microglochin*	9	9	8	2	0
C.mon	86	*Carex montana*	7	6	4	1	0
C.mur	41	*Carex muricata*	7	4	6	4	0
C.nig	100	*Carex nigra*	7	8	4	2	0
C.nor	94	*Carex norvegica*	8	7	7	2	0
C.oed	78a	*Carex viridula* subsp. *oedocarpa*	8	8	4	2	0
C.orn	81	*Carex ornithopoda*	8	3	9	3	0

Code	Sp. no.	Species	L	F	R	N	S
C.otr	39	*Carex otrubae*	6	8	7	7	2
C.pal	79	*Carex pallescens*	6	6	5	4	0
C.pau	104	*Carex pauciflora*	8	9	1	1	0
C.pen	63	*Carex pendula*	5	8	7	6	0
C.pil	87	*Carex pilulifera*	7	5	3	2	0
C.pnce	68	*Carex panicea*	8	8	4	2	0
C.pncu	35	*Carex paniculata*	6	9	6	6	0
C.pse	59	*Carex pseudocyperus*	7	9	6	6	0
C.pul	106	*Carex pulicaris*	8	7	5	2	0
C.pun	74	*Carex punctata*	9	7	7	3	3
C.rar	90	*Carex rariflora*	8	9	3	2	0
C.rec	95	*Carex recta*	8	9	7	5	3
C.rem	48	*Carex remota*	4	8	6	6	0
C.rip	58	*Carex riparia*	7	8	7	7	0
C.ros	60	*Carex rostrata*	8	10	4	2	0
C.rup	105	*Carex rupestris*	8	4	7	2	0
C.sal	96	*Carex salina*	8	10	7	5	3
C.sax	62	*Carex saxatilis*	8	9	7	3	0
C.spi	40	*Carex spicata*	7	6	6	4	0
C.str	66	*Carex strigosa*	3	8	7	6	0
C.syl	64	*Carex sylvatica*	4	5	6	5	0
C.vag	69	*Carex vaginata*	7	6	6	3	0
C.ves	61	*Carex vesicaria*	8	10	5	4	0
C.vir	78c	*Carex viridula* subsp. *viridula*	8	7	7	3	1
C.vul	38	*Carex vulpina*	7	9	8	6	0
Cl.mar	31	*Cladium mariscus*	8	9	8	4	0
Cp.fus	25	*Cyperus fuscus*	9	8	5	4	0
Cp.lon	24	*Cyperus longus*	8	9	7	5	0

El.ac	17	*Eleocharis acicularis*	7	10	7	5	1
El.au	14	*Eleocharis mamillata* subsp. *austriaca*	8	10	5	5	0
El.mu	16	*Eleocharis multicaulis*	8	10	4	1	0
El.pa	13	*Eleocharis palustris*	8	10	6	4	1
El.pv	19	*Eleocharis parvula*	6	10	7	5	3
El.qu	18	*Eleocharis quinqueflora*	9	9	7	2	0
El.un	15	*Eleocharis uniglumis*	8	9	7	4	3
Er.an	1	*Eriophorum angustifolium*	8	9	4	1	0
Er.gr	3	*Eriophorum gracile*	8	9	4	2	0
Er.la	2	*Eriophorum latifolium*	9	9	7	2	0
Er.va	4	*Eriophorum vaginatum*	8	8	2	1	0
I.cer	22	*Isolepis cernua*	8	8	5	3	0
I.flu	23	*Isolepis fluitans*	8	11	4	2	0
I.set	21	*Isolepis setacea*	7	9	5	3	0
K.sim	34	*Kobresia simpliciuscula*	8	8	8	1	0
R.alb	32	*Rhynchospora alba*	8	9	2	1	0
R.fus	33	*Rhynchospora fusca*	9	9	3	1	0
S.lac	9	*Schoenoplectus lacustris*	8	11	7	6	0
S.pun	12	*Schoenoplectus pungens*	8	10	7	7	1
S.tab	10	*Schoenoplectus tabernaemontani*	9	10	8	7	3
S.tri	11	*Schoenoplectus triqueter*	8	10	7	7	3
Sc.sy	7	*Scirpus sylvaticus*	6	8	6	6	0
Sch.f	30	*Schoenus ferrugineus*	8	9	7	2	0
Sch.n	29	*Schoenus nigricans*	8	8	7	2	0
Sr.ho	20	*Scirpoides holoschoenus*	8	8	7	6	0
T.ces	6	*Trichophorum cespitosum*	8	8	3	1	0
T.ger	5	*Trichophorum germanicum*	8	8	2	1	0

5 HYBRIDISATION IN CYPERACEAE

Introduction

Sedges, like almost all plants and animals, produce offspring which are the product of a random mix of parental genes. Such offspring will display a range of phenotypes (physical appearances) that are the result of their genetic inheritance. The degree to which they resemble, differ from or are intermediate between their parents in their morphology is defined by certain factors – dominant or recessive alleles (forms of a gene which determine a physical character) in the parents, the laws of inheritance (i.e. random assortment of chromosomes and recombination between chromosomes) and the plant's environment. That a phenotype which is intermediate between the parents occurs on occasions is of help to taxonomists in identifying hybrids.

Hybrids in *Carex*

To our knowledge, no organised attempt has yet been made to describe in detail the morphology of all known British and Irish *Carex* hybrids. Kükenthal (1909), in his classic work on the genus which covered a number of our *Carex* hybrids, stressed that in many cases hybrids occur in two 'super' forms in which they are closer morphologically to one or other parent. An example of this is the hybrid **60** *C. rostrata* × **61** *C. vesicaria*, which was described by Kükenthal as having two separate forms – *super-rostrata* and *super-vesicaria* (both of these having earlier been given varietal rank by Kneucker). This approach was also largely followed by Pearsall (1934) with regard to some of our *Carex* hybrids, while latterly Corner (2002) has emphasised the same point when considering the various forms produced by introgression between **102** *C. bigelowii* and **100** *C. nigra*.

During the active period of the Botanical Exchange Club various other authors (e.g. Druce, Nelmes and Pearsall) published notes and records of putative *Carex* hybrids new to Britain or Ireland, or indeed, new to science. These, where relevant, are mentioned in the text. To date the most useful account of hybrid sedges is that by Wallace (1975), currently being revised and updated by Foley & Porter. Wallace's approach was to outline briefly the taxonomy, ecology and distribution of British *Carex* hybrids and to supply where possible other details such as valid binomials, chromosome numbers and any experimental work undertaken. Faulkner's work on the cytology and artificial synthesis of hybrids of section *Phacocytis* (Faulkner 1972, 1973) showed the evolutionary significance of hybridisation in this critical group, an aspect taken further by other researchers (e.g. Cayouette, Standley and others in North America and Dean in Britain: see bibliography and **95–102** *Carex nigra* group introduction). Detailed fieldwork in Ireland and subsequent study by Tony O'Mahony (1989, 2004 and pers. comm.) have improved our understanding of several hybrids. Use of isoenzyme techniques is helping to identify hybrids in **77–78** the *C. flava–viridula* complex (Blackstock & Ashton 2001; Blackstock 2007).

Sterility in *Carex* hybrids

Carex hybrids sometimes attract attention in the field by reason of their 'jizz'. On the one hand, they may appear different from other sedges around them in size, habit and/or colour (particularly of the inflorescence); on the other, they may show some of the principal characters of two different easily recognisable species. Deciding whether a sedge is a hybrid is not always straightforward since a plant may also differ from its fellows because of extremely local differences of habitat, ecological stress or predation rather than hybridity.

In the British Isles more than 40 interspecific *Carex* hybrids are known. Many of these are completely sterile, but others, especially members of section *Phacocystis* (**95–102** *Carex nigra* group), are partially fertile. Among the former, a degree of morphological intermediacy is often apparent (e.g. in **35** × **48** *C.* × *boenninghausiana* and **39** × **48** *C.* × *pseudoaxillaris*), although there are also sterile hybrids in which the offspring appear to bear little morphological relationship to either parent (e.g. **50** × **51** *C.* × *gaudiniana*) and others where the hybrid is much closer to one parent than to the other (see above). Within the *nigra* group, as a result of back-crossing to one or other parent, partially fertile hybrids can exist in a spectrum of morphological forms, making the description of a 'typical' specimen somewhat problematic.

Critical characters which may indicate sterility, and therefore hybridity, include the following:

- the existence at maturity of tightly appressed male glumes (with no evidence of exerted anthers, of dehiscence or of viable pollen);
- emptiness of the utricle;
- at a more specialised level, a significantly different chromosome number from that of the parents. (It should be borne in mind that in some species, for example **60** *C. rostrata*, **61** *C. vesicaria* and **78** *C. viridula*, there is an appreciable range in the recorded chromosome numbers.)

N.B. The above may not apply to the partially fertile *C. nigra* group hybrids.

As stated above, with the exception of the *C. nigra* group, many sedge hybrids are sterile since effective pollination does not take place and no nut is formed. This sterility is often the clearest indication that a potential hybrid has been found. In the field, empty, often malformed utricles that are soft and readily compressible may suggest hybridity, but this character, although easy to check, is not by itself wholly reliable. The utricles of certain sedges, notably **60** *C. rostrata* and **61** *C. vesicaria*, often feel empty because of their large size combined with the smallness of the nut within them (a character described as 'inflated'). In other species utricles may appear empty through immaturity, disease or the larvae of gall-midges. Likewise, pollination may have been prevented through a sudden drop in temperature or by drought or flooding of the female spikes at the crucial moment when the stigmas are receptive. Additionally, some species, particularly those in the *C. nigra* group, may have empty, infertile utricles as a result of self-incompatibility.

Perhaps a better guide to sterility, although not always practicable in the field, may be provided by examining the male spikes. Early in the season, the anthers of fertile sedges emerge from the male glumes which, having shed their pollen, then wither and fall. The filaments which bore the anthers persist until, later in the season, they too fall away. However, in a sterile *Carex* hybrid, the anthers do not emerge but stay hidden behind the male glumes and may remain thus until late into the season. If this appears to be the case, careful removal of the glume (best done under a dissecting microscope but also possible by using a hand-lens whilst bending the spike) may reveal the unemerged anthers. If anthers are present (usually tightly appressed to the axis of the spike), it is highly probable that the plant is sterile. If anthers are absent, it is likely that the plant in question is fertile, the anthers and filaments having dehisced and fallen in the normal way. Also, the male spikes of sterile plants often hold their shape (although becoming paler in colour) until late in the season, whilst those of normal fertile plants often disintegrate after the anthers have dehisced and fallen. However, it is important to remember that not all hybrids behave in this way. It should also be noted that there are other causes for pollen sterility besides hybridity, e.g. genetic abnormalities, environmental factors and disease. Moreover, sterile pollen grains are not always empty or shrunken and may not appear abnormal in any way (e.g. in **100** *C. nigra*), but they will still fail to effect pollination. The use of sterility as a criterion for hybridity should therefore be approached with some caution. Wherever possible, it should be used in conjunction with morphological characters in deciding whether a plant is a hybrid or not.

Characters useful in identifying *Carex* hybrids

Other *Carices* occurring in the presence of the putative hybrid may give the best guide to the latter's identity. However, the hybrid can outlive its parents or occasionally occur in the absence of one or both of the parents from the immediate surroundings (e.g. **76** *Carex hostiana* × **78b** *C. viridula* subsp. *oedocarpa*). If a plant is found which appears to be a hybrid, careful comparisons with the presumed parents should be made. The characters in the following checklist have been found to be the most useful for this purpose, although most hybrids differ from each parent in only a small number of these:

- distribution of stomata on upper and lower leaf-surfaces;
- leaf colour and width;
- leaf section – i.e. plicate (W-shaped) or canaliculate (U-shaped);
- length of lowest bract;
- colour of basal sheaths;
- upper stem section – terete or trigonous;
- ligule length and shape;
- male spike length and shape;
- female spike length and shape;
- male glume – length, shape and amount of hyaline (i.e. colourless papery) material present;
- female glume – length, shape and amount of hyaline material present;
- utricle – length, shape, veining, pubescence and beak length and shape.

When constructing the comparative tables in the accounts of hybrids we have listed only those characters where differences occur between the hybrid and one or both of the parents. Additionally, we have not attempted to include in our tables the various forms that a hybrid may take but have instead aimed to show the most typical form, although we have occasionally described other forms in the account where we felt this was appropriate.

It must be appreciated that this is the first attempt to effect a detailed account of British *Carex* hybrids. We hope that the publication of the following hybrid descriptions will provide a basis for further study and clarification.

Cyperaceae hybrids other than *Carex*

Trichophorum

The hybrid between **5** *T. germanicum* and **6** *T. cespitosum* is sterile but, as *T. germanicum* often fails to set seed, this character, although a good pointer, is not conclusive. Identification may be best confirmed by observation of the shape and size of the leaf-sheath opening and the anatomy of the stem. See also Swan (1999).

Schoenoplectus

The key field character distinguishing the two *Schoenoplectus* hybrids from their parents is the stem section. In both hybrids the lower part of the stem is terete, the upper triquetrous, combining the stem section of **9** *Schoenoplectus lacustris* or **10** *S. tabernaemontani* with that of **11** *S. triqueter*. In other characters the hybrids closely resemble one or other parent. Until recently, it was thought that both hybrids were sterile, but continuing fieldwork suggests that the hybrid between *S. tabernaemontani* and *S. triqueter* may be at least partially fertile. See also Lousley (1975).

Hybrid taxa not included in this handbook

Various specimens of putative hybrid sedges exist in herbaria throughout the country. We have examined many of these but, for the present, feel unable to accept the following putative hybrids. We are aware, however, that other botanists may feel differently and that future developments may prove us wrong. Also in this list are two *Carex* hybrids that we have not been able to see; we hope that these can be included in a later edition of this handbook.

35 *Carex paniculata* × **39** *C. otrubae*: None of the herbarium specimens that we have examined is fully convincing and we follow Wallace (1975) in considering all British records of this hybrid to be unsubstantiated.

35 *Carex paniculata* × **43** *C. arenaria*: A plant reportedly with this parentage was found in 2004 by P.M. Benoit. We have not seen this plant either in the field or as a herbarium specimen.

62 *Carex saxatilis* × **100** *C. nigra*: We have examined numerous field and herbarium specimens of this possible hybrid and feel that they are almost certainly forms of the highly variable *C. saxatilis*. So far we have seen no specimens which show conclusive evidence of the influence of *C. nigra*.

67 *Carex flacca* × **100** *C. nigra* (*C.* × *winkelmannii*): A plant found at Onich on Loch Linnhe was identified as this hybrid by R.W. David in 1976.

However, on seeing further material, A.O. Chater and A.C. Jermy later redetermined it as *C. nigra*.

71 *Carex laevigata* × 78b *C. viridula* subsp. *oedocarpa*: A plant said to have this parentage was found near Egryn Abbey (v.c. 48) by P.M. Benoit in 1970. We have not seen this plant either in the field or as a herbarium specimen.

71 *Carex laevigata* × 79 *C. pallescens*: A plant from Ardgour (v.c. 97) originally determined as this hybrid in 1973 by R.W. David, A.O. Chater and A.C. Jermy was later redetermined as *C. laevigata* by A.O. Chater and A.C. Jermy.

75 *Carex extensa* × 78c *C. viridula* subsp. *viridula*: An interesting specimen from v.c. H21 could possibly be this hybrid, but many of the utricles are fertile and there is no conclusive evidence of any influence from *C. viridula*. We believe it is safer to consider this an atypical form of *C. extensa*.

CAVEAT LECTOR HYBRIDARUM

Some sedge hybrids are classic examples of what may be expected, i.e. the anthers are unemergent, the utricles are flat, malformed and with undeveloped nuts, important diagnostic characters are intermediate between those of the parent species and the hybrid, whilst growing in the presence of its parents, nevertheless has a 'jizz' which distinguishes it from both of them.

Unfortunately, such hybrids form only a small percentage of the total and most, whilst fulfilling some of the above criteria, do not meet all of them. In such cases the hybrid will not exhibit intermediacy but will be morphologically closer to one or other of the parents.

In some hybrids the anthers dehisce but the utricles fail to develop or occasionally the anthers remain unemerged (and therefore undehisced) but the utricles develop fully. In other cases the anthers emerge and the utricles develop but indisputable characters still show that the plant is a hybrid. Contradictory characters such as these can give rise to considerable confusion and, in some cases, it may be impossible to give an accurate identification of such a plant.

In the field, the presence of the putative parents is a useful guide **when supported by morphological evidence suggesting a degree of intermediacy**, but in some cases one of the actual parents may be absent.

---

6 KEYS TO FERTILE SEDGE MATERIAL IN THE BRITISH ISLES

For accurate identification of Cyperaceae good fruiting material should be used wherever possible. The habit of the plant and, if it is rhizomatous, whether it is short- or long-creeping should be noted. In *Carex* the basal leaf-sheaths of the flowering stem can be diagnostic.

Care is needed when counting the number of stigmas, as these are easily broken off: several utricles should be observed on the same specimen. If the stigmas have fallen completely, the shape of the nuts may indicate their number: in *Carex* a biconvex or lens-shaped nut indicates two stigmas, a trigonous nut three; in other genera the shape of a nut with two stigmas may be more globose than biconvex and thus be difficult to distinguish from a three-sided nut with rounded corners.

In *Carex* subgenus *Vignea* checking the sex of the flowers at the inflorescence apex can be difficult when they are very young. Most species in that subgenus are protandrous and the anthers may hide the younger developing stigmas. On the other hand, later on the anthers can easily break off, leaving the filaments partially hidden within the glumes and the by then well-developed stigmas may be misleading; usually, however, the remaining bare filaments will indicate a male flower.

In other genera care must be taken not to confuse filaments with perianth bristles (which have antrorse or retrorse hairs on them: see p. 18), the number and characters of which may be needed to help in identification.

The following keys are for species and subspecies in flower or fruit and do not include hybrids. See also the guidance on pp. 76–77. Terms used in the keys are defined in the glossary and are often elaborated in Chapter 2.

1a	Individual flowers unisexual; ovary and nut partially to fully enclosed by a sac-like or bottle-like utricle	2
1b	At least some individual flowers bisexual; female flowers not enclosed by a utricle (see **Key 1**, opposite)	3
2a	Utricles ± open towards the top, leaving nut exposed	
	34 Kobresia simpliciuscula	
2b	Utricles entirely closed, with only style or stigmas extruding at apex through a beak of varying length and nut not exposed	
	Carex (see **Key 2**, p. 65)	

Key 1 to all species except *Carex* and *Kobresia*

3a   Stems hollow; leaves with coarsely and sharply serrate margins
31 Cladium mariscus

3b   Stems solid, often with soft pith; leaves without teeth or with finely toothed margins or leaves reduced to bladeless sheaths   4

4a   Inflorescence comprising 2–8 primary branches terminating in globose spikes each 2–12 mm in diameter, composed of numerous densely packed spikelets   **20 Scirpoides holoschoenus**

4b   Inflorescence not as above   5

5a   Perianth bristles present, inconspicuous in flower, becoming much longer than glumes in fruit, forming a whitish cotton-like head   6

5b   Perianth bristles present or absent, but when present inconspicuous, shorter than glumes, not forming a whitish cotton-like head   10

6a   Spikelet 1, less than 10 mm long excluding perianth bristles; perianth bristles 4–6; extinct in British Isles   **6a Trichophorum alpinum**

6b   Spikelets 1 to several, more than 10 mm long excluding perianth bristles; perianth bristles more than 6   7

7a   Spikelet 1, erect; involucral bracts absent; leaf-blade absent or much reduced on strongly inflated uppermost stem-sheath
4 Eriophorum vaginatum

7b   Spikelets several, pendulous or ± nodding in fruit; involucral bracts present; leaf-blade well developed on uppermost stem-sheath   8

8a   Stems subterete to trigonous near apex; uppermost stem-sheath ± inflated; peduncles smooth; anthers 2.5 mm or more long
1 Eriophorum angustifolium

8b   Stems sharply trigonous (triquetrous); uppermost stem-sheath close-fitting; peduncles rough, densely and minutely hairy; anthers up to 2 mm long   9

9a   Rhizomes short; stems loosely tufted; leaf-blade 3–8 mm wide; glumes 1-nerved   **2 Eriophorum latifolium**

9b   Rhizomes long-creeping; stems distant, solitary; leaf-blade 0.5–2 mm wide; glumes several-nerved   **3 Eriophorum gracile**

10a   Inflorescence of 1 terminal spikelet; lowest involucral bract glume-like, shorter than inflorescence   11

10b   Inflorescence of 2 or more spikelets; lowest involucral bract leaf-like or stem-like, usually equalling or exceeding inflorescence   20

11a Plant with branched stems; leaves with well developed blades always present; plant often floating in water   **23 Isolepis fluitans**

11b Plants with unbranched stems; leaves reduced to bladeless sheaths or uppermost 1–2 sheaths with a short blade; plants not floating but sometimes growing in or on margin of water   12

12a Uppermost 1–2 sheaths with a short blade; nuts without a persistent style-base   13

12b All sheaths without blades; nuts with a persistent style-base   14

13a Upper leaf-sheath fitting loosely round stem, with an oblique and oval opening 1.8–2.2(–3) × 1 mm; spikelets with 8–20 flowers; stem aerenchyma tissue between vascular bundles obvious in transverse section; substomatal pits very obscure, 6–7 μm deep   **5 Trichophorum germanicum**

13b Upper leaf-sheath fitting tightly round stem, with a ± transverse and circular opening typically *c.* 1 mm in diameter; spikelets with 3–5 flowers; stem lacking aerenchyma tissue (view in transverse section); substomatal pits conspicuous, 20–26 μm deep   **6 Trichophorum cespitosum**

14a Stigmas 2; nuts 2-sided (biconvex)   15

14b Stigmas 3; nuts 3-sided (trigonous)   17

15a Only lowest glume empty, ± completely surrounding base of spikelet   **15 Eleocharis uniglumis**

15b Lowest 2 glumes empty, each surrounding not more than 2/3 of base of spikelet   16

16a Glumes 2–2.5 mm wide (from middle of spikelet); perianth bristles 0–4   **13 Eleocharis palustris**

16b Glumes 1–1.5 mm wide; perianth bristles 4–6 (usually 5)   **14 Eleocharis mamillata** subsp. **austriaca**

17a Robust plants with stout rhizomes; at least some stems more than 15 cm long and 0.5 mm wide; bladeless sheaths up to 11 cm long   18

17b Slender; stems up to 15 cm long (to 50 cm in submerged, non-flowering *E. acicularis*) and 0.5 mm wide; bladeless sheaths up to 1 cm long   19

18a Glumes *c.* 10–30 per spikelet, the lowest *c.* 1/4 as long as spikelet; style-base not confluent with nut   **16 Eleocharis multicaulis**

18b Glumes up to 7 per spikelet, the lowest 1/2 or more as long as spikelet; style-base confluent with nut   **18 Eleocharis quinqueflora**

19a Rhizomes not terminating in a tuber; stems 4-angled, 0.2–0.3 mm wide; glumes up to 15 per spikelet, the lowest up to 1/2 as long as spikelet; perianth bristles 0–1(–4), up to 1/2 as long as nut; style-base not confluent with nut **17 Eleocharis acicularis**

19b Stolons often terminating in a small whitish tuber; stems terete, 0.3–0.5 mm wide; glumes up to 9 per spikelet, the lowest 1/2 or more as long as spikelet; perianth bristles usually 3, equalling or longer than nut; style-base confluent with nut **19 Eleocharis parvula**

20a Inflorescence a terminal, flattened, ± compact head of crowded, distichously arranged spikelets, often obscured by their subtending bracts 21

20b Inflorescence not as above and, if forming a head, then with spikelets not distichously arranged 22

21a Leaves flat; glumes yellowish- to reddish-brown; nuts up to 2 mm long **27 Blysmus compressus**

21b Leaves involute; glumes dark brown; nuts 3 mm or more long **28 Blysmus rufus**

22a Spikelets distinctly flattened; glumes distichously arranged 23
22b Spikelets ± rounded in section; glumes arranged spirally around axis 27

23a Stems terete to somewhat flattened above; inflorescence capitate; perianth bristles present 24

23b Stems 3-sided (trigonous to triquetrous); inflorescence umbel-like, with the umbel sometimes compact; perianth bristles absent 25

24a Leaves at least 1/2 as long as stems; lowest inflorescence bract exceeding inflorescence; inflorescence usually with 5 or more spikelets **29 Schoenus nigricans**

24b Leaves up to 1/3 as long as stems; lowest inflorescence bract shorter than to equalling inflorescence; inflorescence with up to 4 spikelets **30 Schoenus ferrugineus**

25a Annual; glumes dark purplish-brown **25 Cyperus fuscus**
25b Perennial; glumes not as above 26

26a Spikelets in elongated spikes; glumes reddish-brown **24 Cyperus longus**

26b Spikelets in dense clusters; glumes pale yellowish- to greenish-brown **26 Cyperus eragrostis**

27a Leaves 3 mm or more wide **28**
27b Leaves up to 2 mm wide or reduced to bladeless sheaths **29**

28a Inflorescence capitate or with 1–3 shortly pedunculate clusters of spikelets; spikelets 10 mm or more long **8 Bolboschoenus maritimus**
28b Inflorescence branched, somewhat umbel-like; spikelets up to 6 mm long **7 Scirpus sylvaticus**

29a Inflorescence with an obvious terminal head of spikelets; lowermost involucral bracts leaf-like **30**
29b Inflorescence with an apparently lateral head of spikelets; lowermost involucral bract ± stem-like and appearing to be an extension of the stem (pseudolateral), although, when in fruit, this may begin to shrivel and appear leaf-like **31**

30a Rhizomes short; stems tufted; lowest involucral bract not exceeding the terminal head; spikelets whitish to pale brown; perianth bristles 9–13, bearing minute retrorse hairs **32 Rhynchospora alba**
30b Rhizomes long-creeping; stems distant; lowest involucral bract usually exceeding the terminal head; spikelets dark reddish-brown; perianth bristles 5–6, bearing minute antrorse hairs **33 Rhynchospora fusca**

31a Stems very slender, up to 1 mm wide; glumes up to 2.5 mm long; nuts up to 1.3 mm long **32**
31b Stems more robust, 2 mm or more wide; glumes 2.5 mm or more long; nuts 2 mm or more long **33**

32a Nut surface shiny, with longitudinal ribs and densely set transverse bars connecting the ribs; glumes darkish green, sometimes with brown patches **21 Isolepis setacea**
32b Nut surface dull, smooth, minutely tuberculate to finely reticulate; glumes pale greenish-white to mid green, sometimes with brown patches **22 Isolepis cernua**

33a Stems terete **34**
33b Stems sharply 3-sided (triquetrous) **35**

34a Glumes with few or no papillae; apex of glumes with a substantial mucro and lateral lobes acutely pointed; stigmas usually 3; nuts 2.5–3 mm long **9 Schoenoplectus lacustris**
34b Glumes with numerous minute reddish papillae especially towards apex; apex of glumes shortly apiculate and lateral lobes ± rounded; stigmas usually 2; nuts 2–2.5 mm long **10 Schoenoplectus tabernaemontani**

35a Leaf-blade present on uppermost sheath only; apex of glumes with obtuse lobes on either side of mucro; perianth bristles 6, more than half as long as nut **11 Schoenoplectus triqueter**

35b Leaf-blade present on uppermost and at least some lower sheaths; apex of glumes with acute lobes on either side of mucro; perianth bristles 0–6, less than half as long as nut **12 Schoenoplectus pungens**

Key 2 to *Carex* species

1a Flowering stems with a single spike **Group A**: below
1b Flowering stems with 2 spikes or more 2

2a Spikes all ± similar in appearance, the terminal usually at least partly female 3
2b Spikes dissimilar in appearance, the terminal or upper usually entirely male, the lower usually entirely female, or with male flowers at top 4

3a Stigmas 2; nuts biconvex **Group B** (subgenus *Vignea*, spp. **35–54**): p. 66
3b Stigmas 3; nuts trigonous **Group C** (section *Atratae*, spp. **92–94**): p. 68

4a Stigmas 2; utricles usually plano-convex or biconvex; nuts biconvex
Group D (section *Phacocystis*, spp. **95–102**, and **62** *C. saxatilis*): p. 69
4b Stigmas 3; utricles usually trigonous or inflated; nuts trigonous 5

5a Utricles ± hairy or pilose **Group E**: p. 70
5b Utricles ± glabrous, scabrid or papillose **Group F**: p. 72

Group A
Flowering stems with a single spike

1a Stigmas 2; nuts biconvex 2
1b Stigmas 3; nuts trigonous 3

2a Plant dioecious; utricles 2.5–3.5 mm **51 dioica**
2b Plant monoecious; utricles 4–6 mm **106 pulicaris**

3a Mature utricles erecto-patent to erect; female glumes persistent; at least some leaves distinctly curled at apex **105 rupestris**
3b Mature utricles deflexed; female glumes caducous; leaves ± straight 4

4a Utricles 3.5–4.5(–6) mm, with a bristle arising from base of nut and protruding from top of beak along with style-base **103 microglochin**
4b Utricles 5–7 mm, without a bristle (although style-base may protrude)
104 pauciflora

Group B

Spikes all ± similar; stigmas 2 (subgenus *Vignea*, spp. **35–54**)

1a	All spikes with female flowers at apex	2
1b	At least one spike with male flowers at apex	7

2a Body of utricles distinctly winged for at least part of length **49 leporina**
2b Utricles unwinged, except sometimes narrowly so on beak 3

3a Lowest bract leaf-like, exceeding inflorescence **48 remota**
3b Lowest bract usually not leaf-like, shorter than inflorescence 4

4a Spikes subglobose; utricles not more than 10, usually very divaricate
at maturity **50 echinata**
4b Spikes ovoid to oblong; utricles more than 10, erect or erecto-patent 5

5a Spikes whitish, greenish or pale brown **54 canescens**
5b Spikes dark reddish-brown 6

6a Spikes (5–)8–12(–18); utricles without a slit down the back of the beak;
plant of lowland wet woods and ditches, forming substantial tussocks
52 elongata
 · 6b Spikes (2–)3–4(–5); utricles with a slit down the back of the beak; plant
of alpine wet slopes and rock-ledges, forming tufts only **53 lachenalii**

7a Plants densely caespitose, without creeping rhizomes 8
7b Plants not or laxly caespitose, with creeping rhizomes 17

8a Utricles weakly to strongly convex on adaxial side, strongly convex on
abaxial side 9
8b Utricles plane on adaxial side, weakly convex on abaxial side 11

9a Utricles broadly winged in upper half **35 paniculata**
9b Utricles not or only very narrowly winged 10

10a Usually tussock-forming; basal sheaths fibrous; lower clusters of spikes
± pedunculate **36 appropinquata**
10b Not or loosely tussock-forming; basal sheaths entire; lower spikes or
clusters of spikes sessile **37 diandra**

11a Stems more than 2 mm wide; leaves (2–)4–10 mm wide; utricles
distinctly nerved ± throughout   12

11b Stems less than 2 mm wide; leaves 2–4(–5) mm wide; utricles nerveless
except for faint nerves at the base   13

12a Ligule obtuse, much wider than long, overlapping edges of leaf; utricles
dull, minutely papillose, with ± isodiametric, thick-walled epidermal
cells (best seen on adaxial surface)   **38 vulpina**

12b Ligule acute, longer than wide, not overlapping edges of leaf; utricles,
± shiny, with oblong, thin-walled epidermal cells   **39 otrubae**

13a Utricles more than 4.5 mm, with a broadly attenuated beak;
nuts set well above the corky and thickened base (usually accentuated
as fruit dries); roots – and sometimes (but not invariably) basal sheaths,
stem-bases, ligules and glumes – purplish-tinged; ligule distinctly
longer than wide   **40 spicata**

13b Utricles less than 4.5 mm, with a narrower, less pronounced beak;
nuts arising from a base which is not corky and thickened; roots, basal
sheaths and stem-bases not purplish-tinged; ligule not or only slightly
longer than wide   14

14a Inflorescence not more than 4.5 cm long; spikes ± contiguous;
base of utricles flat or rounded with the nut set close upon it   15

14b Inflorescence usually more than 4.5 cm long, distinctly interrupted,
with intervals of 1–3 cm between the lowest two spikes; utricles
narrowed at base as well as at beak (i.e. diamond-shaped)   16

15a Flowering stems erect, rigid; glumes markedly shorter than utricles,
dark, contrasting in colour with utricles until these ripen and darken;
utricles rounded, with a broad margin or flange, narrowing abruptly
into a short beak; strongly calcicolous; flowering from May
        41a muricata subsp. **muricata**

15b Flowering stems flexuous; glumes ± as long as utricles, pale brown
or golden-brown, concolorous with unripe utricles but becoming white
and then contrasting with the brown ripe utricles; utricles ovoid,
narrowly margined, narrowing evenly into the beak; calcifugous;
flowering from June   **41b muricata** subsp. **pairae**

16a   Stems flaccid, drooping; mature leaves bronze- or grey-green, often
       as long as flowering stem; inflorescence very interrupted, up to 10 cm
       long or even more, with intervals of 2 cm or more between lowest
       spikes; utricles 3.5–4(–4.5) mm, appressed to the stem-axis, becoming
       greyish-black when fully mature   **42a divulsa** subsp. **divulsa**
16b   Stems robust, erect; mature leaves bright yellow-green, shorter than
       flowering stem; inflorescence not more than 6 cm long, with intervals
       of less than 2 cm between lowest spikes; utricles (4–)4.5–4.8 mm,
       markedly divaricate, becoming red-brown when mature
                                                    42b divulsa subsp. **leersii**

17a   Body of utricles distinctly winged for at least part of its length   18
17b   Utricles unwinged, except sometimes narrowly so on the beak   19

18a   Terminal spike entirely male; middle spikes male at top, female below
                                                                    43 arenaria
18b   Terminal or upper spikes entirely female; middle spikes entirely male
                                                                    44 disticha

19a   Stems smooth   20
19b   Stems rough at least towards the top   21

20a   Plant of very wet inland bogs; stems 15–40 cm, erect; utricles ovoid-
       ellipsoid, ± compressed   **45 chordorrhiza**
20b   Plant of coastal sands or rocks; stems 1–18 cm, often markedly curved;
       utricles ovoid or subglobose   **47 maritima**

21a   Laxly caespitose, with short-creeping, ascending rhizomes;
       beak comprising more than 1/3 of length of utricle; lowest bract shorter
       than its spike   **37 diandra**
21b   Rhizomes usually wide-creeping; beak comprising less than 1/3 of
       length of utricle; lowest bract longer than its spike and usually longer
       than the whole inflorescence   **46 divisa**

Group C
Terminal spike female at top, male at base; stigmas 3 (section *Atratae*)

1a   Lowest bract not overtopping inflorescence; plant of lowland mires and
       lake margins   **93 buxbaumii**
1b   Lowest bract overtopping inflorescence; plants of high alpine ledges
       and flushes   2

2a   Spikes in a loose, often pendulous cluster, at least the lowest with a peduncle as long as spike; utricles not papillose   **92 atrata**

2b   Spikes in a compact cluster; lower peduncles shorter than spike; utricles minutely papillose   **94 norvegica**

Group D
Stigmas 2[1]; female glumes black with pale midrib
(section *Phacocystis*, spp. **95–102**, and **62** *C. saxatilis*)

1a   Utricles ± inflated, patent   **62 saxatilis**

1b   Utricles not inflated, erect or erecto-patent   2

2a   Plants forming stout tussocks   3

2b   Plants loosely tufted and/or creeping, not forming tussocks   4

3a   Rhizomes very short, erect, forming dense tussocks; lowest bract much shorter than inflorescence; leaves with stomata confined to lower surface; basal sheaths pale yellow, splitting on inner face to form fibrillae   **101 elata**

3b   Rhizomes creeping upwards away from anaerobic water-table and thus accumulating peat and forming substantial tussocks; lowest bract ± equalling inflorescence; leaves with stomata mainly on upper surface; basal sheaths brown or black, not forming fibrillae   Tussock form[2] of **100 nigra**

4a   Leaves with stomata mainly confined to one surface only (either upper or lower); at all altitudes, in various mires and heaths   5

4b   Stomata ± common on both surfaces of the leaves[3]; maritime, near sea level, usually dominant plants of brackish mires and silty or sandy estuaries   8

5a   Lowest bract considerably exceeding inflorescence   6

5b   Lowest bract ± equalling or shorter than inflorescence   7

---

[1]   **62** *Carex saxatilis* (a plant of high-altitude mires) may occasionally have some utricles with 3 stigmas. See discussion about potential hybrids under that species.

[2] These tussocks often contain other mire species growing amongst the sedge.

[3] Stomata on both surfaces can also indicate hybrids between species with stomata on opposite surfaces. Such specimens should be reviewed in that light.

6a Leaves bright green and shiny beneath, with stomata mainly confined to upper surface; stem brittle; female glumes appressed to utricles, giving female spikes a neat, smooth appearance   **97 aquatilis**
6b Leaves dull green beneath, with stomata mainly confined to lower surface; stem not brittle; female glumes stiff, giving female spikes a prickly appearance   **98 acuta**

7a Lowest bract not stiff, ± equalling inflorescence; leaves with stomata mainly confined to upper surface; stem slender and pliable; basal sheaths brown or black   **100 nigra**
7b Lowest bract stiff, usually much shorter than inflorescence; leaves with stomata confined to lower surface; stem stout, rigid and sharply trigonous; basal sheaths shiny, reddish- or purplish-brown   **102 bigelowii**

8a Female spikes not clustered; lower female glumes of lowest spike with arista up to 5 mm; leaves not inrolled, up to 130 cm × 3–7 mm   **95 recta**
8b Female spikes clustered, the lowest, if aristate, with aristas not more than 1 mm long; leaves inrolled, up to 60(–70) cm × 2–4 mm   9

9a Lowest bract ± equalling inflorescence; female glumes longer than utricles; aristas on lowest female spike, if present, no more than 1 mm long, toothed   **96 salina**
9b Lowest bract exceeding inflorescence; female glumes shorter than utricles and without an arista, although sometimes mucronate; utricles broader and longer than glumes; extinct in British Isles   **99 trinervis**

Group E
Utricles hairy or pilose to some degree on at least part of the surface of the body-wall

1a Utricles with a prominent, bifid beak usually more than 0.5 mm   2
1b Utricles without or with a short, usually conical, entire or notched beak not more than 0.5 mm   3

2a Utricles 5–7 mm; leaves more than 3 mm wide, hairy at least on the sheaths   **55 hirta**
2b Utricles 3.5–5 mm; leaves less than 2 mm wide, glabrous   **56 lasiocarpa**

3a Plants not or only laxly caespitose, with creeping rhizomes   4
3b Plants ± densely caespitose, without creeping rhizomes   7

| 4a | Male spikes usually 2 or more; female spikes ± pendent; utricles papillose | **67 flacca** |
| 4b | Male spike solitary; female spikes not pendent; utricles strongly hairy | 5 |

| 5a | Basal sheaths red, shiny; stems usually more than 20 cm; leaves erect; lowest bract exceeding spike | **84 filiformis** |
| 5b | Basal sheaths brown; stems usually less than 20 cm; leaves ± recurved; lowest bract usually shorter than spike | 6 |

| 6a | Lowest bract with a sheath 3–5 mm; female glumes equalling utricles, acute, green or brownish, without or with a narrow scarious margin | **83 caryophyllea** |
| 6b | Lowest bract not sheathing or with a sheath less than 2 mm; female glumes usually shorter than utricles, obtuse, purplish-black, with a wide scarious and often ciliate margin | **85 ericetorum** |

| 7a | Inflorescence comprising ± all of stem; female spikes with 2–4 flowers | **82 humilis** |
| 7b | Inflorescence comprising not more than 2/3 of stem; female spikes with usually more than 4 flowers | 8 |

| 8a | Female spikes not more than 3 mm wide, lax; flowering stems lateral, leafless | 9 |
| 8b | Female spikes 4–6 mm wide, dense; flowering stems terminal, leafy at base | 10 |

| 9a | Utricles 3–4.5 mm, ± equalling the purplish glumes; female spikes separated | **80 digitata** |
| 9b | Utricles 2–3 mm, projecting well beyond the straw-coloured glumes; female spikes all arising from ± the same point | **81 ornithopoda** |

| 10a | Utricles 3–4.5 mm, pyriform; female glumes reddish-black with pale midrib; leaves soft, pale green; basal sheaths reddish-brown | **86 montana** |
| 10b | Utricles 2–3.5 mm, obovoid; female glumes red-brown with green midrib; leaves ± rigid, mid green or grey-green; basal sheaths brown | **87 pilulifera** |

Group F

Utricles glabrous, scabrid or papillose on surface of body, though sometimes ciliate or hispid-denticulate on veins or on beak

1a	At least lowest spike pendent	2
1b	Spikes not pendent	18
2a	Male spikes 2 or more	3
2b	Male spike solitary	8
3a	Utricles without a beak or with an entire or weakly notched beak less than 0.5 mm	4
3b	Utricles with a usually strongly bifid beak more than 0.5 mm	5
4a	Leaves more than 7 mm wide; lowest bract with a sheath (30–)50–100 mm	**63 pendula**
4b	Leaves less than 7 mm wide; lowest bract not sheathing or with a sheath not more than 3–10 mm	**67 flacca**
5a	Plants with creeping rhizomes and stout, erect stems, not caespitose	6
5b	Plants caespitose, without rhizomes or with very short creeping ones, usually with ± slender, slanting stems	7
6a	Female glumes exceeding utricles; leaves glaucous	**58 riparia**
6b	Female glumes shorter than utricles; leaves mid green or yellow-green	**61 vesicaria**
7a	Female spikes 3–5 mm wide	**64 sylvatica**
7b	Female spikes 6–8 mm wide	**71 laevigata**
8a	Utricles without or with a truncate or obliquely truncate beak	9
8b	Utricles with a distinct, bifid or prominently notched beak	14
9a	Densely caespitose, without creeping rhizomes	10
9b	Not or laxly caespitose, with distinct creeping rhizomes	11
10a	Leaves more than 7 mm wide; female spikes 70–160 mm	**63 pendula**
10b	Leaves less than 3 mm wide; female spikes 5–25 mm	**65 capillaris**
11a	Utricles ± nerveless, minutely papillose	**67 flacca**
11b	Utricles ± nerved, smooth	12
12a	Female spikes 3–4 mm wide, with 5–8 flowers; not below 790 m alt.	**90 rariflora**
12b	Female spikes 5–7 mm wide, with 7–20 flowers; not above 830 m alt.	13

13a Leaves 1–2 mm wide; female glumes usually less than 1.5 times as long as and slightly wider than utricles; beak 0.5 mm **89 limosa**

13b Leaves 2–4 mm wide; female glumes usually more than 1.5 times as long as and narrower than utricles; beak ± absent **91 magellanica**

14a Female spikes ovoid, of shaggy, blackish, appearance **88 atrofusca**

14b Female spikes cylindrical, green or pale brown to purplish-brown, of neat appearance 15

15a All spikes overlapping; lowest bract at least twice as long as inflorescence **59 pseudocyperus**

15b At least the lower spikes distant; lowest bract less than twice as long as (usually shorter than) inflorescence 16

16a Female spikes 3–5 mm wide; utricles with smooth beak **64 sylvatica**

16b Female spikes 5–8 mm wide; utricles with scabrid beak 17

17a Leaves 6–12 mm wide; ligule 7–15 mm **71 laevigata**

17b Leaves 3–6 mm wide; ligule 1–2 mm **72 binervis**

18a Sheaths and usually lower surface of leaves at least sparsely pubescent **79 pallescens**

18b Plants glabrous 19

19a Lowest bract not sheathing peduncle 20

19b Lowest bract with a cylindrical sheath 24

20a Utricles papillose, scabrid or finely mamillate 21

20b Utricles smooth (convex surface of epidermal cells should not be taken for low papillae) 22

21a Stem sharply angled; ligule acutely pointed (when pulled back or flattened); utricles with beak *c.* 0.5 mm, notched **57 acutiformis**

21b Stems trigonous-subterete; ligule rounded; utricles with beak 0.2 mm, truncate **67 flacca**

22a Leaves yellowish-green; utricles 6–8 mm, gradually narrowed into a broadly notched beak *c.* 2 mm long **61 vesicaria**

22b Leaves glaucous at least above; beak on utricles bifid, 1–1.5 mm long 23

23a Leaves ± abruptly attenuate to a short trigonous apex, glaucous on both sides; stomata mainly confined to lower surface; sheath aerenchyma thin, not spongy around ± triangular shoot; utricles 5–8 mm; apex tapered into beak **58 riparia**

23b Leaves tapering to a long (2–6 cm) acicular point, glaucous on upper
surface, dark green and shiny beneath; stomata mainly confined to
upper surface; sheath aerenchyma thick and spongy around a ± terete
shoot; utricles 4–6 mm, ± abruptly contracted into beak **60 rostrata**

24a Plants not or only laxly caespitose, with long creeping rhizomes, often
forming extensive populations 25
24b Plants ± densely caespitose, without rhizomes or with very short
creeping ones 29

25a Utricles papillose or scabrid **67 flacca**
25b Utricles smooth (convex surface of epidermal cells should not be
taken for low papillae) 26

26a Utricles 7–9 mm **70 depauperata**
26b Utricles less than 7 mm 27

27a Utricles with a prominent, scabrid, bifid beak **76 hostiana**
27b Utricles without a beak or with a smooth, entire or weakly
notched beak 28

28a Sheath of lowest bract not inflated, tight; leaves glaucous; utricles
abruptly contracted into a very short beak c. 0.3 mm long **68 panicea**
28b Sheath of lowest bract inflated, loose; leaves yellow- to bronze-green;
utricles gradually narrowed into a beak 0.5–1 mm long **69 vaginata**

29a Flowering stems lateral, leafless **81 ornithopoda**
29b Flowering stems terminal in middle of leaf-rosettes, usually
leafy at base 30

30a Utricles 7–9 mm **70 depauperata**
30b Utricles less than 7 mm 31

31a At least lower and middle utricles in each spike patent or deflexed 32
31b All utricles ± erect or appressed (though at 45–60° to stem axis in
73 C. distans) 37

32a Female glumes with prominent, wide, silvery scarious margin; apex
of sheath of stem leaves with a lingulate apex **76 hostiana**
32b Female glumes without prominent, scarious margin; apex of sheath of
stem leaves without a projection 33

33a Female spikes oblong to cylindrical, ± distant **74 punctata**
33b Female spikes ovoid, on some stems at least the 2 upper
± contiguous 34

34a Ripe utricles (3.5–)4.4–6.5 mm, gradually tapered into a beak 2–
2.8 mm long; leaves about as long as stems, 3–7(–10) mm wide; ligule
2–5 mm   **77 flava**
34b Ripe utricles 1.5–5.5 mm, with beak up to 2 mm long (usually less);
leaves usually shorter than stems, 0.5–5.4 mm wide; ligule *c.* 1 mm   35

35a Leaves not more than 1/2 as long as stems, 1.2–3.5(–5.4) mm wide;
utricles 3–5.5 mm, usually distinctly curved (as well as being deflexed
in lower part of spike), with beak occupying at least 1/3 of total length
78a viridula subsp. **brachyrrhyncha**
35b At least some leaves more than 1/2 as long as stems, 0.5–5 mm wide;
utricles 2–4 mm, straight or weakly curved (though often deflexed),
with beak occupying less than 1/3 of total length   36

36a Stems often curved; leaves ± flat with keeled midrib; lowest female
spike often widely separated from the others; utricles 3–4 mm,
with beak usually 1 mm or more   **78b viridula** subsp. **oedocarpa**
36b Stems straight; leaves usually ± channelled, with midrib rounded
beneath; female spikes usually all clustered at apex of stem; utricles
1.5–3(–4) mm, with beak usually less than 1 mm
78c viridula subsp. **viridula**

37a Apex of sheath of stem-leaves truncate opposite the ligule;
female spikes 2–3 mm wide, lax   **66 strigosa**
37b Apex of sheath of stem-leaves with a projection opposite the ligule;
female spikes at least 4 mm wide, dense   38

38a Leaves deeply channelled and often inrolled; lowest bract equalling
or exceeding inflorescence   **75 extensa**
38b Leaves ± flat, keeled or plicate; lowest bract shorter than inflorescence 39

39a At least some leaves on the plant more than 6 mm wide; ligule more
than 5 mm   **71 laevigata**
39b Leaves not more than 6 mm wide; ligule less than 5 mm   40

40a Female glumes with prominent, wide, silvery scarious margin;
leaf-blade abruptly contracted below linear, veinless apex   **76 hostiana**
40b Female glumes without prominent scarious margin;
leaf-blade gradually narrowed to veined apex   41

41a Basal sheaths orange-brown; female glumes dark reddish- or purplish-
brown; utricles usually purple-brown or with purple blotches **72 binervis**
41b Basal sheaths pale to dark brown, not orange; female glumes pale
brown or pale reddish-brown; utricles usually green   **73 distans**

7 DESCRIPTIONS OF SPECIES AND HYBRIDS WITH ILLUSTRATIONS AND MAPS

Arrangement

The arrangement and numbering follow those set out in Chapter 3. Descriptions, distribution and ecological data have been tailored to fit into one page so that the original design of our handbooks in which text and illustration could be seen in tandem could be maintained as far as possible. In this edition, however, we have inserted the maps close to the taxa they refer to, alternating either before or after the two pages mentioned above. Hybrid descriptions are contrasted with the two parents in a tabulated format. The position of the hybrids is determined by the number of the first-named parent, following the pages devoted to that parent as closely as possible.

Notes on the illustrations

The size of plants and plant parts illustrated has been indicated by scale-bars; that next to the drawing of the whole plant or fertile shoot is the most significant, showing the size and habit of the plant as seen in the field. We have not given a scale-bar for the ligule in *Carex* (Figure **D**) and readers should refer to the text for the size (see below).

For flower parts and nuts, bars are given where appropriate. In *Carex* a single bar has been given for glumes, utricles and nuts (Figures **F, G, H, J**) where the scale is the same, rather than clutter the plate.

The illustrations of both stem and leaf transverse sections are given to help convey the third dimension which may not be obvious from the drawing of the whole plant or shoot; we have omitted a scale-bar for these as being superfluous. They will vary, within limits, both in structure, shape and width, depending on where the section is cut, and the stem of many species will be hollow towards the base; if differences are seen between related species they should not be thought to be diagnostic unless this is stated as so in the text. In the case of the leaf sections, these are intended to give a realistic impression of the number of vascular bundles, which can sometimes be useful (e.g. in distinguishing between **67** *Carex flacca* and **68** *C. panicea*).

Ligule measurements in the text indicate the *length* of the fused portion from where it joins the inner face of the sheath to its apex. The various shapes of the apex are shown in Figures 2.11–14 on p. 12. The ligule is best measured when the leaf is pulled back and flattened. In the illustrations accompanying the species and hybrid accounts the ligule has been drawn in three dimensions, which may exaggerate the acuteness of its apex.

In the illustrations of the genera other than *Carex* the flower (Figure **C**) is shown in the state when the anthers are active, usually before the nut has been fertilised, and may bear no resemblance to the final shape of that nut.

Notes on the text

Unless otherwise stated, the following can be taken as the general state: *scales* and *leaf-sheaths* are dull; *stems* are smooth, leafy and often hollow at their base; *leaves* are glabrous; *roughness* on stems and leaves means they are serrulate on angles or margins and veins; *utricles* and *nuts* are not shiny. The *stem length* is that of the fruiting stem (culm) including the inflorescence. The *ligule shape* (and length if significant) is best observed on lower leaves on the flowering or fruiting stem, although in subgenus *Vignea* leaves on the expanded first-year sterile shoots (pseudostems) usually show typical ligules. Lengths of both leaves and their ligules are usually shorter on culms. Some lengths or breadths may not be given if they have no diagnostic value; in *Carex* the glume and utricle measurements indicate *length* and that of the latter includes the beak.

Where the size of one organ is compared with that of another, e.g. female glumes with the utricle, the glume will age and shrink more than the solid three-dimensional utricle. Furthermore the appearance of the utricle in some species of *Carex*, when seen from the side, may be different from the more obvious frontal (abaxial) view drawn in the plate. Where this view is significant (e.g. in the yellow-sedges, **78a–c** *C. viridula* subspecies), an additional illustration has been provided. See also the guidance on p. 60.

The figures given after *Fr.* are those of the months of the fruiting period.

Note on the maps

The maps show the distribution at the 10-km square level, as in-the *New Atlas* (Preston *et al.* 2002), but they also include later records submitted up to the end of 2006. Additional maps not included in the *New Atlas*, showing the distribution of hybrids, are published here for the first time, but hybrids that have only one or two known records are not mapped.

The symbols that are used on the maps are not as in the *New Atlas* (i.e. including separate ones for 1970–1986 and 1987–1999) but are as follows:
Native species and hybrids: ● 1970–2006; ○ pre-1970.
Introduced species: × 1970–2006; + pre-1970.

1 *Eriophorum angustifolium* Honck.

Common Cottongrass   *Map 1*

Rhizomes extensive, long-creeping. *Stems* 15–75 cm × 1–2 mm, rather distant, erect, smooth, nodose, subterete to trigonous near apex. *Leaves* basal and cauline; blade 2–60 cm × 2–5(–7) mm, linear, channelled, gradually narrowed to a long triquetrous apex, otherwise flat to V-shaped in cross-section, yellowish- to bluish-green; sheaths up to 27 cm long (up to 8 cm on cauline leaves), ± inflated, pale to mid brown (greenish on some cauline leaves), the uppermost with a well developed blade usually at least 1.5 times as long as sheath; ligule very short, rounded. *Inflorescence* terminal, comprising (1–)3–7 pedunculate spikelets, ± nodding in fruit; peduncles up to 8 cm long, slender, smooth; involucral bracts 1–2, leaf-like to glume-like, sheathing, the lowest ± equalling or exceeding the lowermost spikelet. *Spikelets* ovoid to ellipsoid when young, soon becoming obscured by the lengthening perianth bristles. *Glumes* 4–10 × 1.5–4 mm, spirally arranged, ovate to ovate-lanceolate or lanceolate, the upper narrower than the lower, ± obtuse, membranous, 1-nerved, reddish- to greyish-brown; margins hyaline. *Flowers* bisexual or male-sterile with abortive stamens; perianth bristles many, entire at the apex, elongating to 4–5 cm and forming a white cotton-like head; stamens 3; anthers 2.5–5 mm long; stigmas 3. *Nuts* 1–3 × 0.7–1 mm, obovoid, trigonous, dull dark brown, ± smooth.   *Fr.* 6–7.

A ubiquitous species, found in most acid communities including shallow bog-pools with *Sphagnum denticulatum*, *S. cuspidatum* etc. (**M1–3**), in bogs typically with *Carex canescens*, *C. nigra* and *C. rostrata* (**M5, M7, M9**) and *C. saxatilis* (**M12**), and in various blanket mires (**M17–21**); also found in *Trichophorum–Erica tetralix* wet heath (**M15**) and the *Eleocharis multicaulis* sub-community of *Erica vagans–Schoenus nigricans* heath (**H5**). See also the Biological Flora account (Phillips 1954b) and other studies by Phillips (1953, 1954a).

Eriophorum angustifolium is recognised by the stems that are ± terete to indistinctly trigonous, leaf-blades that are flat to V-shaped in cross-section, leaf-like inflorescence bracts, several ± nodding spikelets in fruit, smooth peduncles, and anthers 2.5–5 mm long. Vegetatively, the long (> 10 cm) trigonous tip to the leaf is unique and the leaf also ages characteristically, showing a wine-red band between the decaying tissue and the living leaf.

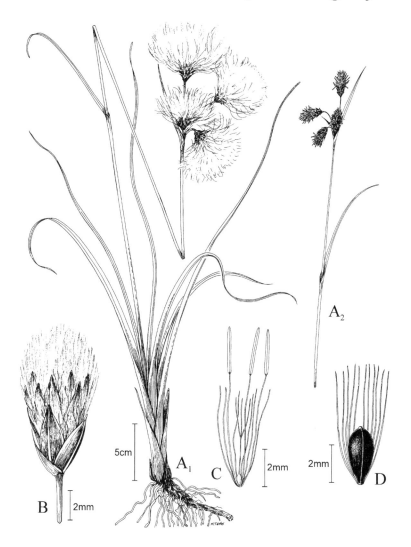

A₁ Plant habit and fruiting stem; **A₂** Young flowering stem; **B** Spikelet; **C** Floret; **D** Nut.

M1 *Eriophorum angustifolium*

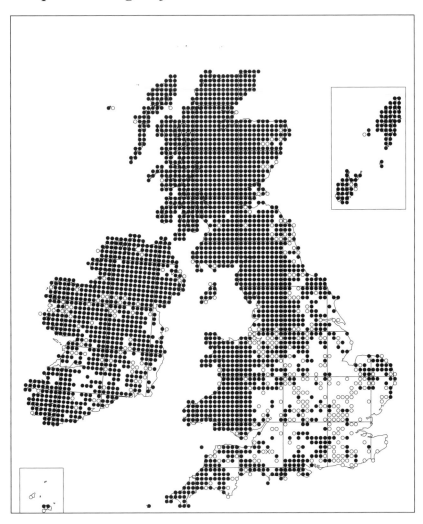

Eriophorum angustifolium is common to locally abundant throughout N and
W Britain, but is declining in the Midlands and SE owing to drainage,
ground-water extraction and cessation of grazing (Porter & Foley 2002). In
Ireland it is common throughout but will decline as peatlands are removed.

Eriophorum latifolium M2

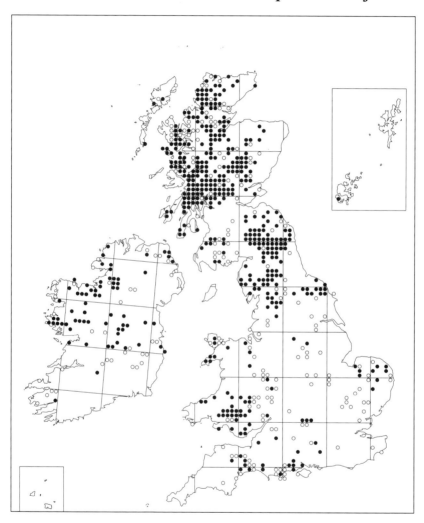

Eriophorum latifolium occurs in scattered localities throughout Britain where calcium or magnesium influences soil-water, especially on limestone in N England and mica schist areas in Scotland. Similarly distributed in Ireland.

2 *Eriophorum latifolium* Hoppe

Broad-leaved Cottongrass *Map 2*

Rhizomes short. *Stems* 20–70 cm × 1–2 mm, loosely tufted, erect, smooth, nodose, triquetrous. *Leaves* basal and cauline; blade 2–60 cm × 3–8 mm, linear, narrowed to a triquetrous apex, otherwise flat, yellowish- to bluish-green; sheaths less than 12 cm long (to 5 cm on cauline leaves), close-fitting, pale to mid brown; lower leaves with a rounded ligule with free portion 0.5 mm; uppermost cauline leaf with a well developed blade about equalling sheath and no ligule. *Inflorescence* terminal, comprising 2–12 pedunculate spikelets, ± nodding in fruit; peduncles up to 5 cm long, slender, rough with dense, minute, forward-pointing, stiff hairs (best detected when peduncle is drawn between the lips); involucral bracts 2–3, leaf-like to glume-like, sheathing, the lowest ± equalling or exceeding the lowermost spikelet. *Spikelets* ovoid to ellipsoid when young, soon becoming obscured by the lengthening perianth bristles. *Glumes* 5–6 × 1–2.1 mm, spirally arranged, ovate-lanceolate to lanceolate, the upper narrower than the lower, ± acute, membranous, 1-nerved, greyish-brown to blackish above, somewhat olivaceous below; margins narrowly hyaline. *Flowers* bisexual; perianth bristles many, minutely papillose at the apex, elongating to 2–2.5 cm and forming a neat, almost 'brilliant' white, cotton-like head; stamens 3; anthers 1.3–2 mm long; stigmas 3. *Nuts* 3–3.5 × 1–1.4 mm, obovoid, trigonous, dull reddish-brown, ± smooth. *Fr.* 6–7.

Found in calcareous, often open and stony, mires, e.g. **M10a**, in which small sedges such as *C. viridula* subspp. *oedocarpa* and *brachyrrhyncha* and *Schoenus ferrugineus* form small hummocks and where *Carex dioica*, *C. hostiana*, *Eleocharis quinqueflora* and *Schoenus nigricans* can be plentiful; also in base-rich meadows of the *Briza media–Primula farinosa* sub-community (**M10b**), growing with *Selaginella selaginoides*, *Kobresia simpliciuscula* and the moss *Ctenidium molluscum*.

Eriophorum latifolium is recognised by the loosely tufted, triquetrous stems, leaf-blades that are 3–8 mm wide, rough, minutely hairy peduncles, several spikelets ± nodding in fruit and 1-nerved glumes. The perianth bristles are also minutely papillose at their apices (best seen under binocular microscope). The species is most easily observed in flower in early June, when the head is more compact and 'cleaner' than that of **1** *E. angustifolium*, but it becomes inconspicuous when the seeds disperse from mid July onwards.

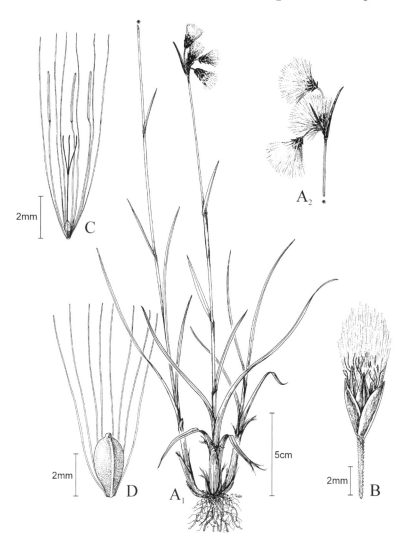

A₁ Plant habit and flowering stem; **A₂** Flowering head in seed; **B** Spikelet; **C** Floret;
D Nut.

3   *Eriophorum gracile* W.D.J. Koch ex Roth

Slender Cottongrass   *Map 3*

Rhizomes extensive, long-creeping. ***Stems*** 20–60 cm × 0.4–0.8 mm, distant, solitary, erect, smooth, nodose in lower half only, triquetrous. ***Leaves*** basal and cauline; blade 2–40 cm × 0.5–2 mm, linear, 3-angled and slightly channelled, narrowed to an obtuse apex, yellowish- to bluish-green; sheaths up to 8 cm long (to 5 cm on cauline leaves), close-fitting, pale to mid brown (greenish on some cauline leaves), the uppermost with blade rarely more than 1/2 as long as the sheath; ligule short, rounded. ***Inflorescence*** terminal, comprising 3–6 pedunculate spikelets, becoming ± pendulous in fruit; peduncles up to 3 cm long, slender, rough, densely but minutely hairy; involucral bracts 1–2, leaf-like to glume-like, sheathing, the lowermost ± equalling or shorter than the lowermost spikelet. ***Spikelets*** ovoid to ellipsoid when young, soon becoming obscured by lengthening perianth segments. ***Glumes*** 4–5 × 1.5–2.2 mm, spirally arranged, ovate to ovate-lanceolate, the upper slightly narrower than the lower, ± acute, membranous, several-nerved, yellowish-brown to greenish-brown; margins entire. ***Flowers*** bisexual; perianth bristles many, entire at the apex, elongating to 1.5–2 cm and forming a white, cotton-like head; stamens 3; anthers 1.3–2 mm long; stigmas 3. ***Nuts*** 2.5–3 × 0.5–0.7 mm, ellipsoid-cylindric, trigonous, dull yellowish-brown, ± smooth.   ***Fr.*** 7–8.

Eriophorum gracile is found in wet neutral to slightly basic mires such as those included in the *Carex dioica–Pinguicula vulgaris* community (**M10**), where it forms a variant with *Molinia caerulea*, especially where poached by grazing stock.

E. gracile is recognised by the distant, solitary, triquetrous stems, leaf-blades that are 0.5–2 mm wide, rough and minutely hairy peduncles, several somewhat nodding spikelets in fruit, several-nerved glumes and, when in flower, anthers 1.3–2 mm long; the apices of the perianth bristles are entire.

Eriophorum gracile is a **Red Data List** species in Great Britain; *Status*: **Near threatened** (Cheffings & Farrell 2005). It is also protected under the Flora (Protection) Order 1999 in the Republic of Ireland.

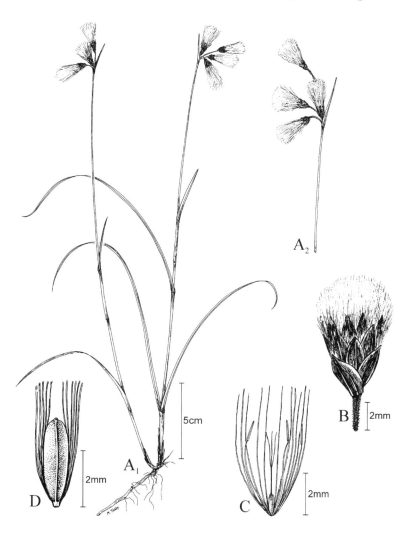

A₁ Plant habit and flowering stems; **A₂** Flowering stem in seed; **B** Spikelet; **C** Floret; **D** Nut.

M3 *Eriophorum gracile*

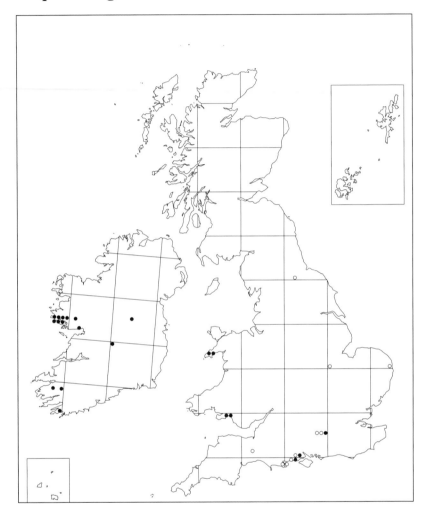

Eriophorum gracile still occurs very locally from Surrey to Caernarvonshire but has been lost from Somerset, Dorset and many sites in Hampshire. There are old records from Acle (v.c. 27), Easton Hornstocks (v.c. 32) and Croft-on-Tees (v.c. 65). In Ireland it is scarce in the centre and local in the west.

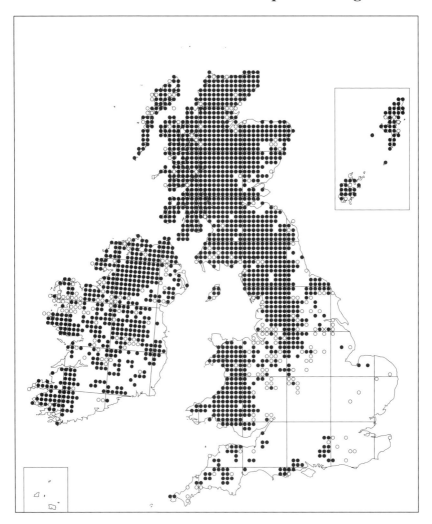

Eriophorum vaginatum is common in England north of the Mersey–Humber line and in Wales, but local south of SE Yorks/Cheshire, being lost from the valley bogs drained in lowland England. In Ireland, throughout the island but less common in the SE.

4 *Eriophorum vaginatum* L.

Hare's-tail Cottongrass   *Map 4*

Rhizomes short, forming compact tussocks. **Stems** (15–)30–60(–80) cm ×
0.8–1.5 mm, tufted, erect, smooth, nodose in lower half only, triquetrous
above, terete below. **Leaves** basal and cauline; blade 3–50 cm × 0.4–0.8 mm,
linear to ± setaceous, narrowed to an obtuse apex, ± triquetrous, yellowish- to
bluish-green; sheaths up to 12 cm long (to 6 cm on cauline leaves), close-
fitting, becoming fibrous on basal leaves, strongly inflated and pale to mid
brown on cauline leaves, the uppermost sheath without a blade or with blade
much reduced; ligule 0. **Inflorescence** a single, terminal, erect spikelet;
involucral bracts 0. **Spikelet** ovoid to ellipsoid when young, soon becoming
obscured by the lengthening perianth bristles. **Glumes** spirally arranged,
ovate-lanceolate, 6–7 × 1.5–2.2 mm, acuminate, membranous, 1-nerved,
translucent mid to dark greyish, with margins hyaline, the lower 5–15 glumes
sterile and often darker. **Flowers** bisexual or male-sterile with abortive
stamens; perianth bristles many, entire at apex, elongating to 2–2.5 cm and
forming a white, cotton-like head; stamens 3; anthers 1.5–2 mm long;
stigmas 3. **Nuts** 2–3 × 1–1.5 mm, obovoid, trigonous, dull yellowish-brown
to dark brown, ± smooth.   **Fr.** 5–6.

Found in bogs, e.g. pool communities with *Sphagnum cuspidatum/fallax*,
Calluna and *Vaccinium oxycoccos* (**M2**), frequent in deep waterlogged peat
areas where *E. vaginatum* and *Trichophorum germanicum* can be codominant
with *E. angustifolium* and *Molinia* as common species (**M17**); also in raised
and blanket mires with *Erica tetralix*, *Calluna*, *Sphagnum* spp. (including
S. papillosum, *S. capillifolium* and *S. subnitens*) and 'brown' mosses (**M18**,
M19) and on degraded plateau peat and subsequent 'slumped' peat in basins
and on lower slopes (**M20**). It can also be found in high-level heath of
Vaccinium myrtillus–Rubus chamaemorus, possibly as a relict. See also the
Biological Flora account (Wein 1973).

E. vaginatum is easily recognisable, being the only species of *Eriophorum*
in the British Isles with a single spikelet forming the inflorescence. In
addition, there are no involucral bracts and the leaf-blade is ± triquetrous in
cross-section and absent or reduced on the uppermost stem-sheath. See also
5 *Trichophorum germanicum* concerning vegetative characters.

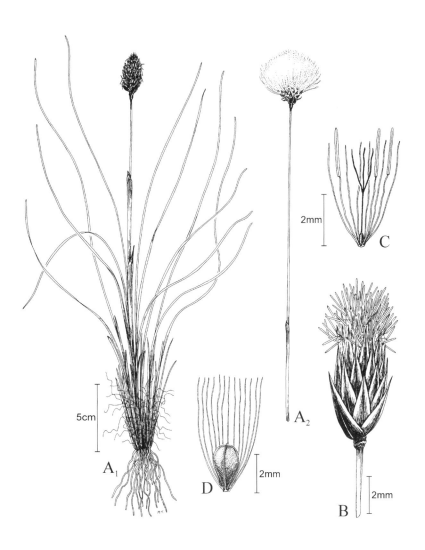

A₁ Plant habit and flowering stem; **A₂** Flowering stem in seed; **B** Spikelet; **C** Floret; **D** Nut.

5 *Trichophorum germanicum* Palla

Deergrass *Map 5*

Rhizomes short, forming substantial tufts or small tussocks. **Stems** 5–35(–60) cm × 1–1.6 mm, ± terete, smooth, but with indistinct ridges; substomatal pits very obscure, 6–7 μm deep; aerenchyma tissue between vascular bundles obvious in transverse section, showing tube-like spaces between cells. **Leaves** 5–18 cm long, mostly reduced to bladeless sheaths at base of stem; upper sheaths loose-fitting, with an oblique and oval opening 1.8–2.2(–3) × 1 mm and a short blade 5–10 mm long. **Inflorescence** a single terminal spikelet 3–8 × 1.5–3 mm, obovoid to cylindrical, pale brown to rusty brown, with 8–20 flowers; involucral bracts 2, 4–5(–7) mm long, glume-like, brown to orange-brown, with midrib pale yellow-green with an obtuse, green apical projection. **Glumes** 2.5–4 × 1.5–2 mm, linear-lanceolate, subobtuse, membranous, 3-nerved, pale brown to rusty-brown; apex subobtuse, attenuated into a subulate tip. **Flowers** bisexual, sometimes forming young plantlets within the spikelet; perianth bristles 5–6, shorter than glumes but *c.* 1.5 times as long as nut, pale to mid brownish, smooth to papillose; stamens 3; anthers 1.5–2 mm long; stigmas 3. **Nuts** 1.5–2 × 0.9–1 mm, ellipsoid to obovoid-trigonous, greyish-brown to yellowish-brown, minutely punctate. **Fr.** 6–8(–9).

T. germanicum is a characteristic, common and often dominant species of some 20 acidic peat communities, in blanket and raised mires and wet heath communities from the lowlands to 1190 m above Caenlochan, v.c. 90 (Foley & Porter 2002). Codominant or abundant in *Eriophorum vaginatum* mires (**M17–20**) and common with *Erica tetralix* (**M15–16**, especially **M16d**); also on montane heaths (**H10, H12–17, H20–22**) with *Calluna, Erica cinerea, Vaccinium myrtillus, Juniperus communis* subsp. *nana* and *Sphagnum* spp.

The simplest way to distinguish *Trichophorum* spp. from **4** *Eriophorum vaginatum* and **13–19** *Eleocharis* spp. vegetatively is by the small leaf-like appendage (a vestigial blade) on the upper, tubular sheaths. The sheaths of these other species lack this appendage and those of *E. vaginatum* are not tubular. If the leaf-blades have fallen off and the upper sheaths have split, further investigation is required: in *Trichophorum* the basal sheaths are pale brown, lanceolate to ovate-lanceolate, and thick and glossy, whereas in *E. vaginatum* they are pale reddish-brown, long and fibrous.

Trichophorum germanicum hybridises with *T. cespitosum* (**6** × **5** *T.* × *foersteri* (G.A. Swan) D.A. Simpson).

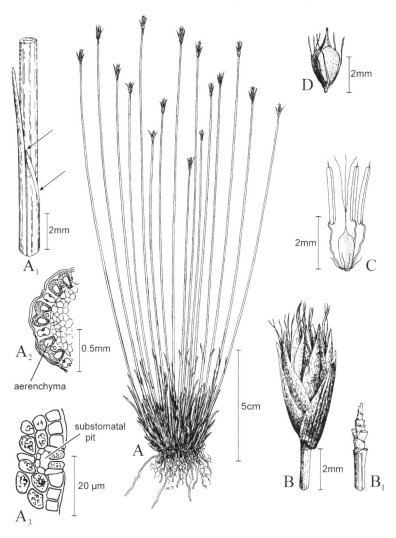

A Plant habit and flowering stems; **A₁** Upper sheath with leaf (arrows indicating length of opening); **A₂** Partial transverse section of stem, showing aerenchyma; **A₃** Enlarged portion of stem, showing substomatal pit; **B** Spikelet; **B₁** Spikelet rachis, showing glume bases; **C** Floret; **D** Nut. (**A₁**, **A₂**, **A₃**, **B₁**, **D** *drawn by R.M.W.*)

91

M5 *Trichophorum germanicum*

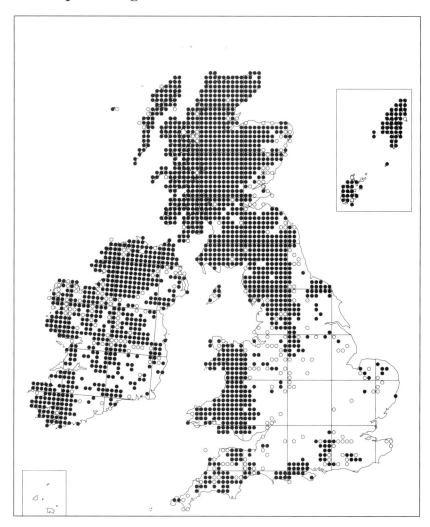

Trichophorum germanicum is common in all upland areas of Britain and in the southern lowland bogs but is mostly lost from the Midlands through drainage. In Ireland, more or less throughout but less common in the SE coastal areas. [Map compiled from records of the aggregate *T. cespitosum*.]

Trichophorum cespitosum M6

Trichophorum cespitosum was first confirmed for Britain by G.A. Swan (1999) in Northumberland in 1988, growing often with *T. germanicum* and their hybrid. In later examination of herbarium material Swan has found specimens scattered in Britain from Sutherland to the North Welsh Borders and Somerset; more recently it has been found in Shetland. In Ireland there are recent records in Fermanagh and Co. Waterford.

6   *Trichophorum cespitosum* (L.) Hartm.

Northern Deergrass   *Map 6*

Rhizomes short, forming small ± open tufts. ***Stems*** 5–25 cm × 0.5–0.8 mm, ± terete, smooth, but with distinct ridges; substomatal pits conspicuous in transverse section of stem, 20–26 μm deep; aerenchyma tissue between vascular bundles absent. ***Leaves*** as in **5** *T. germanicum*, but upper leaf-sheath fitting tightly round stem, with a ± transverse and circular opening typically *c.* 1 mm in diameter. ***Inflorescence*** smaller and more compact than in *T. germanicum*, with fewer (3–5) flowers; sometimes up to 20% of the population proliferating (in Northumberland: see Swan 1999); involucral bracts 2, 4–5(–7) mm long, glume-like, brown to orange-brown, with midrib pale yellow-green with an obtuse, green apical projection. ***Glumes*** similar in size and texture to those of *T. germanicum* but sometimes paler brown with the central nerve dominant and the marginal ones indistinct; apex subobtuse, attenuated into a subulate tip. ***Flowers*** and ***nuts*** as in *T. germanicum*.

Fr. 5–7.

The ecology of *Trichophorum cespitosum* is difficult to define owing to the small number of populations found. In Northumberland it appears to be confined to the margins of raised or valley mires where there is some water movement and base enrichment, whilst **5** *T. germanicum* tolerates a wider range of habitats (see Swan 1999). In Perthshire (v.c. 88) it can be found on limestones in open, often stony, calcareous mires with *Carex panicea*, *C. pulicaris*, *C. viridula* subsp. *oedocarpa* and occasionally *C. viridula* subsp. *brachyrrhyncha* with *Schoenus ferrugineus* and *Saxifraga aizoides* (**M11**).

The general morphology of *Trichophorum cespitosum* is similar to that described for **5** *T. germanicum*, with which it can grow. The micro-characters seen in stem section are the best way to confirm it. The species should be looked for in often open and stony, base-rich mires (as described above), which often show a mosaic with residual peat islands where *T. germanicum* will be more common; also in apparently base-poor communities, where it can be dominant (see Swan 1999). In the field it appears as a more slender-stemmed and more open tuft with a distinctive 'jizz'.

The name *Trichophorum cespitosum* has in the past generally been used for *T. germanicum*, which is treated as a subspecies of *T. cespitosum* even by Stace (1997) and Sell & Murrell (1996).

94

Trichophorum cespitosum   6
T. × foersteri (T. cespitosum × T. germanicum)   6 × 5

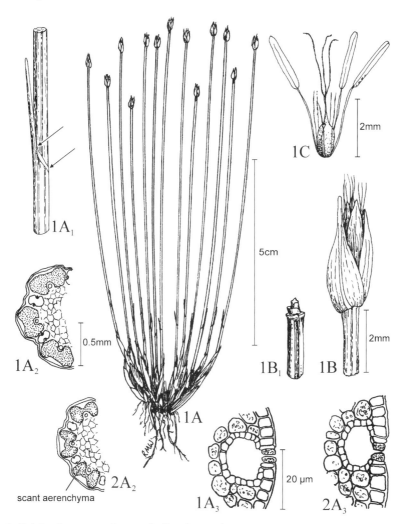

1 *Trichophorum cespitosum* 2 *T.* × *foersteri*
A Plant habit and flowering stems; **A₁** Upper sheath with leaf (arrows indicating length of opening); **A₂** Partial transverse section of stem (with no or little aerenchyma); **A₃** Enlarged portion of stem, showing substomatal pit; **B** Spikelet; **B₁** Spikelet rachis, showing glume bases; **C** Floret.

M6 × 5 *Trichophorum* × *foersteri*
(*T. cespitosum* × *T. germanicum*)

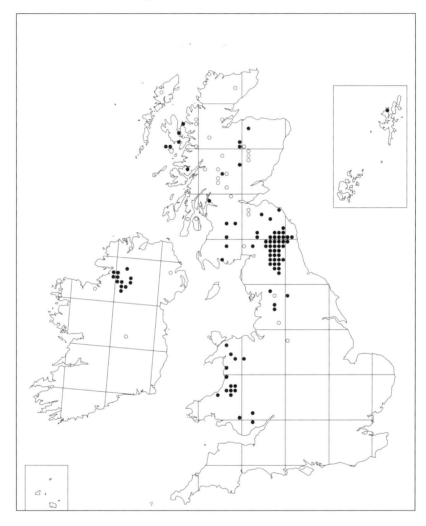

Trichophorum × *foersteri* reflects parts of the distribution of *T. germanicum* in Britain, often in sites where *T. cespitosum* has not been found. Distribution in Ireland, as elsewhere, is probably wider than the records suggest.

Trichophorum × foersteri (G.A. Swan) D.A. Simpson   **6 × 5**

Trichophorum cespitosum × *T. germanicum*   Map 6 × 5

The table is based on Swan (1999) and observations by M.E. Braithwaite and A.O. Chater (pers. comm.). Lack of seed-set is significant, but it is the bare stems without spikelets that, from early July, will draw attention to possible hybrids. If some heads remain, these will feel empty, but they usually contain unripened, but not shrivelled, nuts *c.* 1 mm long, pale greenish-brown with a style on top. *T. germanicum* can often show lack of seed-set and so *T.* × *foersteri* can be confidently identified only by stem anatomy (small amount of aerenchyma and intermediate substomatal pits; see **6** *T. cespitosum* plate).

T. × *foersteri* is associated with the wetter *T. germanicum* associations, i.e. raised, valley and blanket mires (e.g. **M15, M17, M18, M21**) with *Erica tetralix*, *Eriophorum vaginatum* and *Sphagnum papillosum*, often forming extensive populations. In the blanket mires it is more often found in the soligenous flushes at their margins, presumably requiring an element of base nutrients normally found in *T. cespitosum* communities.

T. cespitosum	*T.* × *foersteri*	*T. germanicum*
Tufts usually more open and smaller than in *T. germanicum*.	Tufts more open than in *T. germanicum*.	Densely cespitose.
Stems 0.5–0.8 mm in diameter; ridges distinct; substomatal pits conspicuous, 20–26 μm deep; aerenchyma tissue absent.	**Stems ± 1 mm in diameter; ridges indistinct; substomatal pits 8–18 μm deep; aerenchyma tissue usually absent or scant.**	Stems usually 1–1.6 mm in diameter; ridges indistinct; substomatal pits 6–7 μm deep, inconspicuous; aerenchyma tissue obvious in TS.
Upper leaf-sheath fitting tightly round stem; opening typically *c.* 1 mm, less oblique and ± circular when viewed from above.	**Upper leaf-sheath** fitting fairly tightly round stem; **opening 1–2 × 1 mm, intermediate between parents.**	Upper leaf-sheath fitting loosely round stem; opening 1.8–2.2(–3) × 1 mm, oblique and oval.
Spikelets with 3–10 flowers; anthers well developed.	**Spikelets with 6–14 flowers**; anthers rarely developed, pale.	Spikelets with 8–20 flowers; anthers well developed.
Spikelets not shed until mid July or later.	**Spikelets shed by early July, leaving stem bare.**	Spikelets not shed until mid July or later.

6a   *Trichophorum alpinum* (L.) Pers.

Cotton Deergrass   *(not mapped)*

Trichophorum alpinum was last recorded in Angus (v.c. 90) in 1813 and is considered extinct in the British flora, though it is possible that a small population still exists in that part of Scotland. It is distinguished from the above two species by having a creeping rhizome, rough trigonous stems and perianth bristles up to 25 mm long in fruit so that in June it resembles a very small *Eriophorum* (Sell & Murrell 1996).

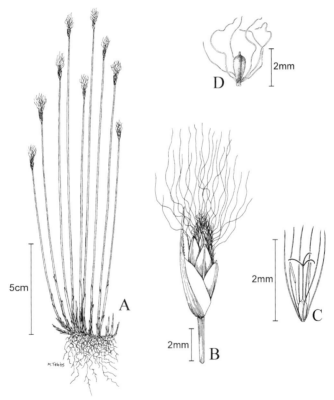

A Plant habit and fruiting stems; **B** Spikelet in seed; **C** Floret; **D** Nut.

98

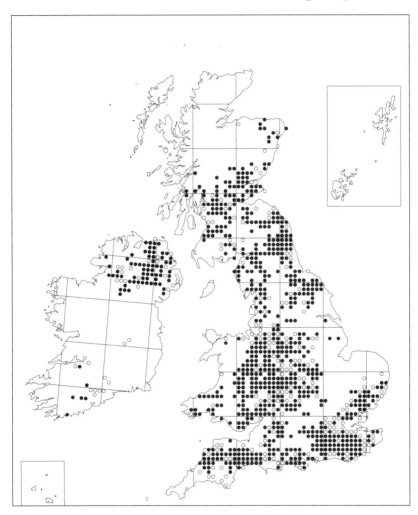

Scirpus sylvaticus is widespread throughout England and Wales with a gap in East Anglia and the East Midlands; in Scotland it is rare N of the southern foothills of the Grampians and Loch Fyne in the west. In Ireland it is frequent in the north but absent in the peaty centre and rare in the southern counties.

7   *Scirpus sylvaticus* L.

Wood Club-rush   *Map 7*

Rhizomes creeping. ***Stems*** 30–120 cm × 4–8 mm, erect, trigonous to triquetrous above, terete below. ***Leaves*** basal and up to 7 cauline, up to 40 cm × 5–20 mm, acuminate, ± flat; ligule absent; basal sheaths pale to chestnut brown; cauline sheaths greenish-brown; vegetative shoots forming a pseudostem. ***Inflorescence*** terminal, branched, somewhat umbel-like, 10–25 × 10–25 cm; primary branches 3 to 8, up to 10 cm long, unequal; secondary and tertiary branches up to 5 cm long. ***Spikelets*** in finger-like to ± globose clusters of 3–10, 2.5–6 × 2–3 mm, ovoid to oblong-ovoid, obtuse, rarely subacute, dark brown; involucral bracts 2–4, up to 50 cm long. ***Glumes*** 1.2–2.5 × 1–1.5 mm, ovate to ± orbicular, obtuse, ± mucronulate, membranous. ***Flowers*** bisexual; perianth bristles 6, shorter than glume, scaberulous above; stamens 2–3; stigmas 3. ***Nuts*** 0.7–1 4 × 0.5–0.8 mm, obovoid to subglobose, compressed-trigonous, pale brown, smooth.   ***Fr.*** 6–8.

S. sylvaticus can be found on wet silty soils in the *Phragmites australis* sub-community of valley alder woodland (**W5a**), where other trees include *Fraxinus excelsior*, *Betula pubescens* and *Salix cinerea*; the ground flora typically includes *Carex paniculata* and *C. acutiformis*, but *S. sylvaticus* may totally replace them with unusual abundance (Rodwell 1991a). Also often in more open areas, along stream and river margins and around lakes and pools which are periodically flooded. Often on gravel, sandy or clay substrates where there is an indication of free iron and high nitrogen, e.g. with *Phalaris arundinacea* in the *Bidens tripartita–Persicaria amphibia* community (**OV30**).

Vegetatively, *S. sylvaticus* can be confused superficially with **55** *Carex hirta*, which is of a similar colour and can grow in similar riparian habitats. However, the latter has a ligule and hairs at least on the inner face of the sheath. When flowering stems are present *S. sylvaticus* is very distinctive.

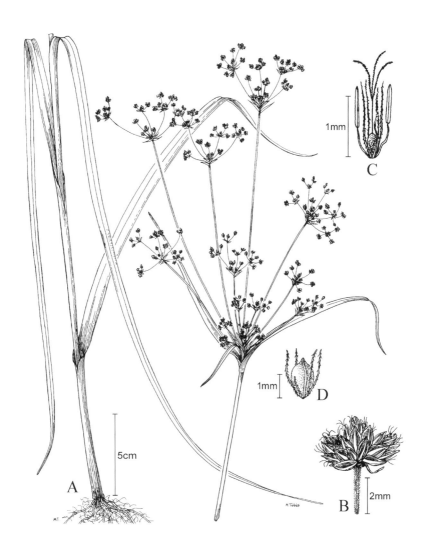

A Plant habit and flowering stem; **B** Spikelet; **C** Floret; **D** Nut.

8   *Bolboschoenus maritimus* (L.) Palla

Sea Club-rush   *Map 8*

Rhizomes wide-creeping, *c.* 2 mm wide, becoming wiry and black. *Stems* 10–100 cm × 3–4 mm, usually solitary, trigonous to triquetrous, smooth; base thickened, somewhat ribbed. *Leaves* basal and cauline, 10–40 cm × 3–6 mm, gradually narrowed to a long-acuminate apex; sheath up to 20 cm long, pale to mid brown, with inner face truncate at apex; ligule absent. *Inflorescence* terminal, 2–7 × 2–6 cm, capitate or with 1–3 clusters of spikelets; involucral bracts 2–3, the lowest 10–25 cm long, patent to reflexed. *Spikelets* 10–40 × 5–7.5 mm, ovoid to ellipsoid, terete, pale to dark brown, ± sessile or in shortly pedunculate clusters of 2–10, rarely solitary; peduncles 0.5–5 cm long. *Glumes* 5–7 × 2.5–3.2 mm, spirally arranged, ovate to elliptic, acute, membranous, pale to dark brown, often lacerate at apex, glabrous to sparsely pubescent; awn up to 1.7 mm long, somewhat recurved. *Flowers* bisexual; perianth bristles 0–6, unequal, minutely retrorsely scabrid, usually not persistent in fruit; stamens 3; anthers 3–5 mm long, with connective tip scabrid; stigmas (2–)3. *Nuts* 2.2–4 × 1.5–2.4 mm, broadly obovoid, trigonous below, plano-convex above, rarely biconvex, shiny, brown, smooth; apex rounded.   *Fr.* 7–9.

This species occurs mainly on wet, silty substrates by the coast, in both fully saline and brackish sites, being dominant in **S21** and occasional in some dune-slacks (e.g. **SD15a** and **c**) and the *Elymus repens* saltmarsh community (**SM28**). It is occasionally found further inland, particularly along the upper tidal reaches of rivers where silt is periodically deposited. It is sometimes deliberately planted around lakes and ponds.

B. maritimus is distinguished by an inflorescence that is capitate or bears 1–3 shortly pedunculate clusters of spikelets that are 10–40 mm long.

A similar species, *Bolboschoenus yagara* (Ohwi) Y.C. Yang & M. Zhan, has recently been reported from western Europe (Browning *et al.* 1997). It differs from *B. maritimus* in the following: perianth segments persistent on the mature nut; nut narrowly obovate with a tapered apex (*cf.* the rounded apex in *B. maritimus*); nut equally trigonous in cross-section. In addition, specimens in the Kew Herbarium from v.cc. 6, 17 and 21 have been determined by J. Browning as possible hybrids between *B. maritimus* and *B. yagara* and further work will be necessary to determine the precise status both of this material and of this taxon.

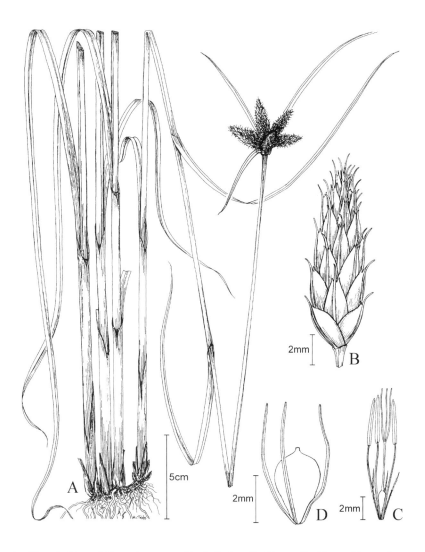

A Plant habit and flowering stem; **B** Spikelet; **C** Floret; **D** Nut, with persistent stamen filaments.

M8 *Bolboschoenus maritimus*

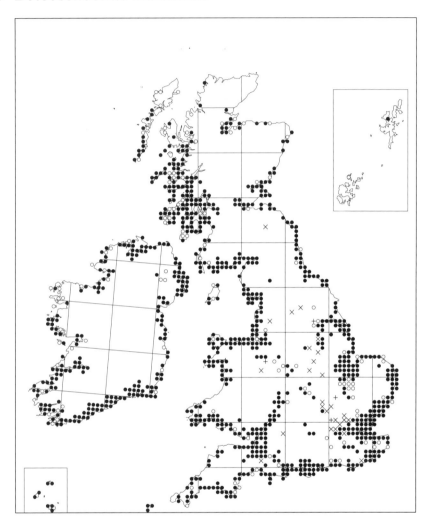

Bolboschoenus maritimus is common in maritime areas in the British Isles but absent from the extreme N of Scotland except for a site in Shetland (v.c. 112). It is also scattered inland through C and S England, where it is sometimes planted around ponds.

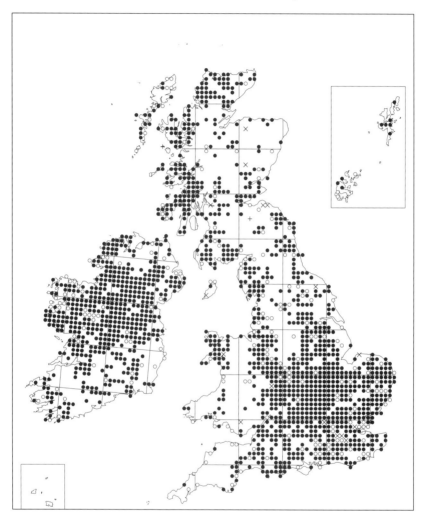

Schoenoplectus lacustris is frequent in lowland Britain and was prolific in the Norfolk Broads in 1900, but decreased considerably during the twentieth century (George 1992); less common in the SW peninsula and parts of Wales and Scotland. In Ireland it is more common in the centre and west. It is sometimes planted.

9 *Schoenoplectus lacustris* (L.) Palla

Common Club-rush   *Map 9*

Rhizomes creeping, >10 mm thick. *Stems* up to 350 cm × 5–15 mm, terete, smooth, spongy, green to blue-green, with base thickened by leaf-sheaths. *Leaves* mostly reduced to bladeless sheaths; blade sometimes formed when plants submerged, 3–100 cm (or possibly more in deep, fast-flowing rivers, e.g. R. Teifi: A.O. Chater pers. comm.) × 1.8–2.5 mm, linear-subulate; sheath up to 40 cm long, purplish-brown to mid brown, membranous and splitting early; ligule present, membranous, brown. *Inflorescence* terminal (often appearing to be lateral when young), compound, usually lax, with 3–10 flattened, scaberulous primary branches up to 10 cm long, sometimes with secondary branches up to 1.5 cm long; branches terminating in 1 to several spikelets; involucral bracts 2, subulate, with a membranous base, the lower up to 10 cm long, shorter to longer than inflorescence, erect and stem-like. *Spikelets* 6–15 × 3–5 mm, ovoid to ovoid-ellipsoid, acute to subacute, mid brown to dark reddish-brown. *Glumes* 2.5–4 × 1.5–3 mm, spirally arranged, broadly ovate, nerveless, mid brown to reddish-brown, with hyaline ciliate margins; surface with no or few papillae; apex emarginate with a substantial mucro; lateral lobes acutely pointed. *Flowers* bisexual; perianth bristles 4–6, ± equalling nut, retrorsely scabrid; stamens (2–)3, with anthers 2–2.5 mm; stigmas (2–)3. *Nuts* 2.5–3 × 1.8–2.5 mm, broadly obovoid, compressed-trigonous, grey-brown, shiny, ± smooth to minutely papillose. *Fr.* 8–9.

S. *lacustris* favours shallow lakes or slow-flowing rivers and canals as a single species community or codominant with *Phragmites*, *Sparganium erectum* and *Equisetum fluviatile* (**S8** sub-communities); in the E Norfolk Broads often a primary coloniser of open water which remains in successive communities of the sere, e.g. tall-herb fen with *Peucedanum palustre* (**S24**). Also in less eutrophic waters with *Potamogeton natans*, *Juncus bulbosus* and *Myriophyllum alterniflorum* (**A9c**). When preserved in peat deposits, roots of S. *lacustris* may be distinguished by being a deep crimson.

S. *lacustris* is distinguished from **10** S. *tabernaemontani* in being usually larger, with deep green stems usually over 150 cm tall, and having glumes without papillae (or only a few on the midrib towards its apex) and 3 stigmas.

The species hybridises with S. *triqueter* (**11** × **9** S. × *carinatus* (Sm.) Palla). Plants intermediate between spp. **9** and **10** (treated by some, e.g. Sell & Murrell 1996, as two subspp.) have been described and drawn from Cambridgeshire (Easy 1990), but no proof of hybridisation has been given.

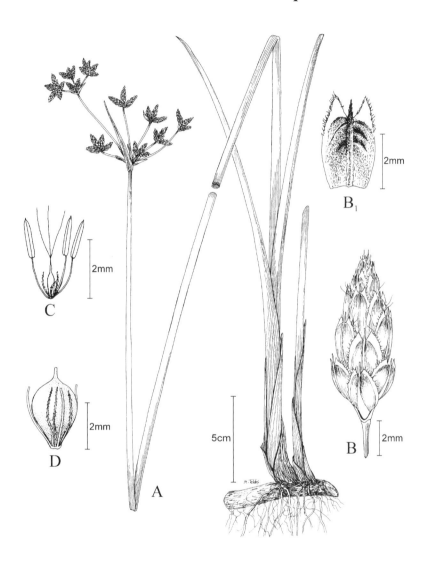

A Plant habit and flowering stem; **B** Spikelet; **B₁** Glume (*drawn by R.M.W.*);
C Floret; **D** Nut.

10 *Schoenoplectus tabernaemontani* (C.C. Gmel.) Palla

Grey Club-rush — Map 10

Rhizomes creeping, > 10 mm thick. **Stems** up to 150 cm × 3–9 mm, terete, smooth, spongy, glaucous, with base thickened by leaf-sheaths. **Leaves** mostly reduced to bladeless sheaths; blade not formed underwater (Preston & Croft 1997) but occasionally present when plant terrestrial, 3–20 cm × 0.8–1.5 mm, linear-subulate; sheath up to 18 cm long, purplish-brown to mid brown, membranous and splitting early; ligule present, membranous, brown. **Inflorescence** terminal (often appearing lateral when young), usually lax, with 3–10 flattened, scaberulous primary branches up to 5 cm long, sometimes with secondary branches up to 1.3 cm long; branches terminating in 1 to several spikelets; involucral bracts 2, subulate, with a membranous base, the lower < 6 cm long, shorter to longer than inflorescence, erect. **Spikelets** 5–12 × 2–4 mm, ovoid to ovoid-ellipsoid, acute to subacute, mid-brown to dark reddish-brown. **Glumes** 2.5–3.7 × 1.5–3 mm, spirally arranged, broadly ovate, mid brown to red-brown, with numerous minute red papillae especially towards apex; apex emarginate and shortly apiculate; lateral lobes ± rounded with membranous, ciliate-denticulate margins. **Flowers** bisexual; perianth bristles 4–5, ± equalling nut, retrorsely scabrid; stamens (2–)3, with anthers 2–2.5 mm long; stigmas 2(–3). **Nuts** 2–2.5 × 1.2–1.7 mm, broadly obovoid, compressed, rarely compressed-trigonous, greyish-brown, somewhat shiny, ± smooth to minutely papillose. **Fr.** 8–9.

This plant is usually found near the coast in shallow brackish water and marshes with *Agrostis stolonifera, Bolboschoenus maritimus, Juncus bufonius, Ranunculus sceleratus* etc. (**S20**), but it is scarce in pure *Bolboschoenus* swamp (**S21**). It does occur inland, especially in C and S England, in eutrophic ponds (with *Typha* spp.: **S12, S13**), slow rivers, dykes, canals, marshes and flooded sand- and gravel-pits.

S. tabernaemontani is closely related to **9** *S. lacustris* and some authors (e.g. Sell & Murrell 1996) treat the two as conspecific, this plant being subsp. *tabernaemontani* (C.C. Gmel.) Å. & D. Löve of *S. lacustris*. This taxon differs in having minute reddish papillae on the glumes, especially near the apex, and their lateral lobes obtusely rounded and less hyaline on the margins; in addition it usually has 2 stigmas and nuts that are 2–2.5 mm long.

A hybrid with *S. triqueter* (**11 × 10** *S.* × *kuekenthalianus* (Junge) D.H. Kent) has been recorded in England but not yet in Ireland. See **9** *S. lacustris* for a putative but unproven hybrid with that species.

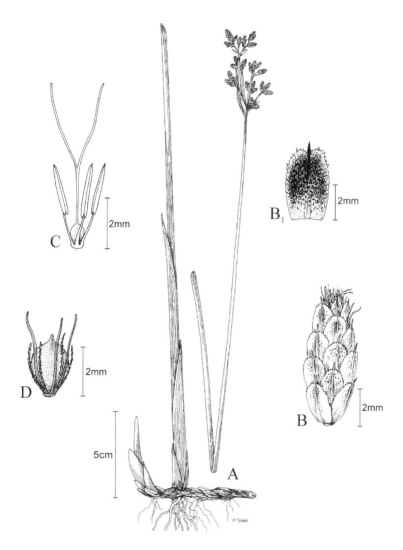

A Plant habit and flowering stem; **B** Spikelet; **B₁** Glume (*drawn by R.M.W.*);
C Floret; **D** Nut.

M10 *Schoenoplectus tabernaemontani*

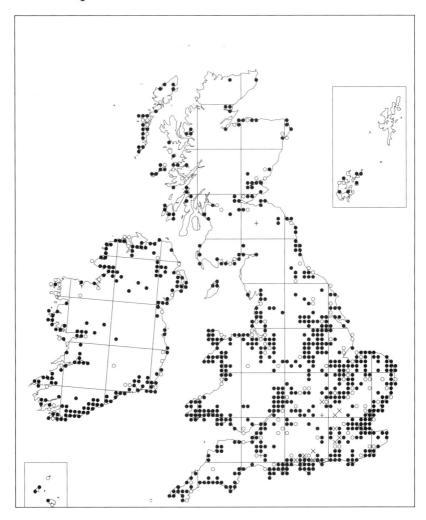

Schoenoplectus tabernaemontani is usually found near the coast in both Britain and Ireland but is infrequent in N Scotland. It also occurs inland, especially in C and S England, possibly in areas with a higher content of magnesium, potassium and sodium. It is sometimes planted.

Schoenoplectus triqueter has been recorded on the River Tamar (v.cc. 2 and 3) and from the Thames/Medway (v.cc. 16, 17 and 21), but mainly as a consequence of river engineering it is now extinct in the latter (Preston & Croft 1997; Rich & FitzGerald 2002). In Ireland it still occurs in Co. Limerick (v.c. H8).

11 *Schoenoplectus triqueter* (L.) Palla

Triangular Club-rush   *Map 11*

Rhizomes creeping. *Stems* up to 150 cm × 2–8 mm, triquetrous, smooth, solid, green or rarely glaucous, with base ± thickened by leaf-sheaths. *Leaves* mostly reduced to bladeless sheaths, with a blade present on uppermost sheath only, 1–20 cm × 2–8 mm, linear-subulate; sheath up to 18 cm long, pale to mid brown, membranous and splitting early; ligule present, membranous. *Inflorescence* with few to numerous spikelets, capitate or with 2–5 primary branches up to 2 cm long; secondary branches 0; involucral bracts 2, linear-subulate, the lower up to 11 cm long, always longer than inflorescence, erect. *Spikelets* 5–10 × 2–4 mm, ovoid, subacute, dark reddish-brown. *Glumes* 3.5–4 × 1.5–3 mm, spirally arranged, broadly obovate, membranous, reddish-brown, with narrow hyaline and ciliate margins; apex obtuse, mucronate with truncate or obtuse lobes on either side of mucro. *Flowers* bisexual; perianth bristles 6, ± equalling nut, retrorsely scabrid; stamens 3, with their anthers 1.4–1.5 mm long; stigmas 2. *Nuts* 2.5–3 × 1.5–2.5 mm, ellipsoid to obovoid, compressed, reddish-brown, shiny, smooth.

Fr. 8–9.

S. triqueter is a plant of brackish, nutrient-rich mud in estuaries and tidal rivers, often in places where it may become completely submerged owing to tides, although not by highly saline water (Rich & Fitzgerald 2002). Often associated with freshwater seepage lines (N.F. Stewart in Wigginton 1999) and can be found associated with *Bolboschoenus maritimus*, *Phragmites australis*, *Schoenoplectus lacustris* and *S. tabernaemontani*.

S. triqueter is recognised by its triquetrous stem, the presence of a leaf-blade on the uppermost leaf-sheath only, glumes with an emarginate, mucronate apex with obtuse lobes on either side of the mucro, and six perianth bristles that are more than half as long as the nut.

The species hybridises with *S. lacustris* (**11** × **9** *S.* × *carinatus* (Sm.) Palla) and *S. tabernaemontani* (**11** × **10** *S.* × *kuekenthalianus* (Junge) D.H. Kent.

Schoenoplectus triqueter is a **Red Data List** species in Great Britain; *Status*: **Critically Endangered** (Cheffings & Farrell 2005). It is also protected under Schedule 8 of the Wildlife and Countryside Act 1981. It is protected under the Flora (Protection) Order 1999 in the Republic of Ireland.

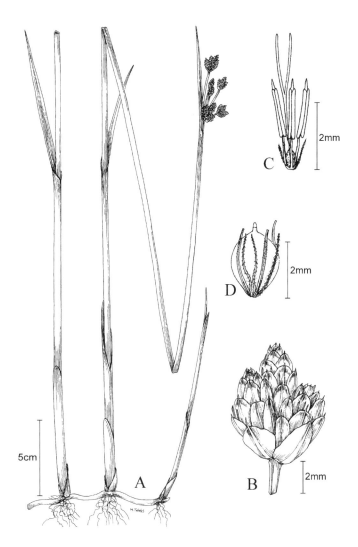

A Plant habit and flowering stem; **B** Spikelet; **C** Floret; **D** Nut.

11 × 9 *Schoenoplectus* × *carinatus* (Sm.) Palla

Schoenoplectus triqueter × *S. lacustris*   *Map 11 × 9*

S. × *carinatus* is similar in general macrostructure to *S.* × *kuekenthalianus*, but see the account of the latter for detailed differences. It differs from *S. lacustris* in its lesser stature, bluntly trigonous stems, stouter lower bracts, inflorescences with shorter primary branches and no secondary branches and the truncate or obtuse lateral lobes of its glumes. It may be distinguished from *S. triqueter* by its taller stems which are terete below and its inflorescences with longer, more numerous primary branches. It differs from both in its sterility.

Schoenoplectus triqueter	*Schoenoplectus* × *carinatus*	*Schoenoplectus lacustris*
Stems to 150 cm × 2–8 mm, triquetrous.	**Stems to 200 cm × 4–8 mm, terete below, bluntly trigonous above**, more slender than those of *S. lacustris*.	Stems to 350 cm × 5–15 mm, terete.
Lower bract often stout, always longer than inflorescence.	**Lower bract** variable but **often rather stout**, shorter or longer than inflorescence.	Lower bract often rather slender, shorter or longer than inflorescence.
Inflorescence with 2–5 primary branches, up to 2 cm long; secondary branches absent.	Inflorescence with 3–7 primary branches, 3–7 cm long; **secondary branches usually absent.**	Inflorescence with 3–10 primary branches up to 10 cm long; secondary branches sometimes present.
Glumes not papillate, but short mucro sometimes has papillae; lateral lobes truncate or obtuse.	Glumes variably sparsely papillate with hyaline-ciliate margins; apex shallowly emarginate, with a short mucro; lateral lobes truncate or obtuse.	Glumes with no or few papillae on surface; apex emarginate, with a substantial mucro and acutely pointed ciliate lateral lobes.
Stigmas 2.	Stigmas 3.	Stigmas (2–)3.
Nuts present.	**Sterile**; nuts rare.	Nuts present.

Schoenoplectus × *carinatus* (*S. triqueter* × *lacustris*) 11 × 9
S. × *kuekenthalianus* (*S. triqueter* × *tabernaemontani*) 11 × 10

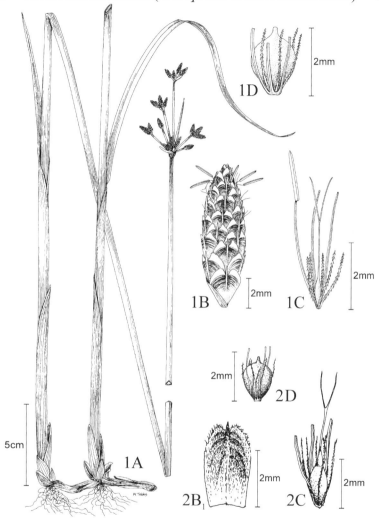

1 *Schoenoplectus* × *carinatus*   **2** *Schoenoplectus* × *kuekenthalianus* (*drawn by R.M.W.*)
A Plant habit and flowering stem; **B** Spikelet; **B₁** Glume; **C** Floret; **D** Nut.

M11 × 9 *Schoenoplectus* × *carinatus*

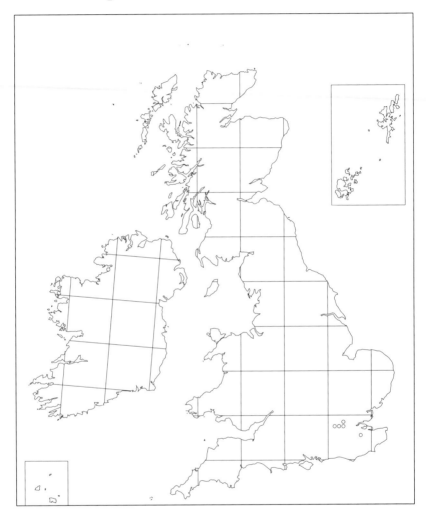

Schoenoplectus × *carinatus* has been recorded from tidal mud on the River Tamar (v.cc. 2 and 3) and from the Thames Estuary (v.cc. 16, 17 and 21) but may now be extinct in all its English sites (N.F. Stewart in Wigginton 1999).

Schoenoplectus × *kuekenthalianus* 11 × 10
(Junge) D.H. Kent

Schoenoplectus triqueter × *S. tabernaemontani*   *Map 11 × 10*

S. × *kuekenthalianus* differs from *S. triqueter* in its glaucous stems, which are terete or occasionally subtrigonous below, in the often more numerous primary inflorescence branches and in the reddish papillae found in varying quantities on the glumes. From *S. tabernaemontani* it differs in its stems that are trigonous above and in its generally stouter bracts that always exceed the inflorescence. Fertility appears to be variable, with at least some plants in the population on the Arun producing fertile seed (F. Abraham pers. comm.).

    S. × *kuekenthalianus* is similar in general macrostructure to the other British *Schoenoplectus* hybrid, *S.* × *carinatus*, but differs from it in having glaucous stems, two stigmas and, above all, reddish papillae on the glumes.

Schoenoplectus triqueter	*Schoenoplectus* × *kuekenthalianus*	*Schoenoplectus tabernaemontani*
Stems up to 150 cm × 2–8 mm, triquetrous, green or rarely glaucous.	**Stems up to 200 cm × 2–10 mm, ± terete, trigonous above, glaucous.**	Stems up to 150 cm × 3–9 mm, terete, glaucous.
Inflorescence with 2–5 primary branches up to 2 cm long; secondary branches absent.	Inflorescence with 2–8 primary branches up to 3 cm long; secondary branches usually absent.	Inflorescence with 3–10 primary branches up to 5 cm long, sometimes with secondary branches.
Bracts always longer than inflorescence.	Bracts always longer than inflorescence.	Bracts shorter or longer than inflorescence.
Glumes not papillate, but short mucro sometimes has papillae; lobes on either side of midrib truncate or obtuse.	**Glumes with variable quantities of minute reddish papillae; lateral lobes ± rounded.**	Glumes with numerous minute reddish papillae, especially towards apex; lateral lobes ± rounded, membranous.
Stigmas 2.	Stigmas 2.	Stigmas 2(–3).
Nuts 2.5–3 mm, smooth, reddish-brown, biconvex, ellipsoid to obovoid.	Nuts (when present) 2.5 mm, smooth, light brown, biconvex, obovoid to spherical.	Nuts 2–2.5 mm, ± smooth to minutely papillose, dark greyish-brown, compressed, broadly obovoid.

M11 × 10 Schoenoplectus × kuekenthalianus

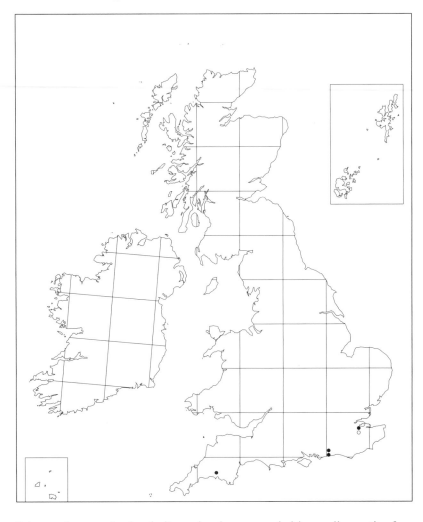

Schoenoplectus × kuekenthalianus has been recorded in small quantity from mud banks near tidal limits on the Arun (v.c. 13) and the Medway (v.c. 15) and is described as very locally frequent on the Tamar (v.cc. 2 and 3) but not in ecological competition with *S. triqueter* (N.F. Stewart in Wigginton 1999).

Schoenoplectus pungens M12

Schoenoplectus pungens used to occur in Jersey, where it is assumed to have been native but has not been seen since the 1970s. It was first collected at Ainsdale Sand Dunes (v.c. 59) in 1909 but remained unidentified until refound there in 1929, where it persisted until 1956. Thereafter it was introduced from original stock held in cultivation into local sand-dune slacks; it is presently treated as an alien (see also P.H. Smith 2005).

119

12   *Schoenoplectus pungens* (Vahl) Palla

Sharp Club-rush   *Map 12*

Rhizomes creeping. *Stems* up to 60 cm × 2–5 mm, triquetrous, smooth, green, with base thickened by leaf-sheaths. *Leaves* mostly reduced to bladeless sheaths; blade 3–20 cm × 0.8–1.5 mm, sometimes present on upper 2–3 sheaths; ligule present, membranous, brown. *Inflorescence* pseudolateral, capitate, with 1–6, tightly clustered, sessile spikelets; involucral bracts 2, linear-subulate, the lower up to 13 cm long, much longer than inflorescence, erect. *Spikelets* 8–11 × 4–6 mm, ovoid, subacute, mid brown to dark reddish-brown. *Glumes* 3.5–4 × 2.5–3 mm, spirally arranged, broadly ovate, reddish-brown, ± emarginate, mucronate, with acute lobes on either side of mucro; sides membranous and margins hyaline, sometimes fringed. *Flowers* bisexual; perianth bristles 0–6, less than half as long as nut; stamens 2, with anthers 2.5–3 mm long; stigmas 2. *Nuts* 2–2.5 × 1–1.5 mm, obovoid, compressed, greyish-brown, shiny, smooth.   *Fr.* 8–9.

Schoenoplectus pungens grows in wet sand-dune slacks and coastal lakes, but in North America it can grow inland and in freshwater mires (Flora of North America Editorial Committee 2002).

S. pungens is distinct in having a pseudolateral, capitate inflorescence with clusters of 1–6 sessile spikelets and glumes that are ± emarginate at the apex with acute lobes on either side of the mucro. In addition, the perianth bristles, when present, are less than half as long as the nut.

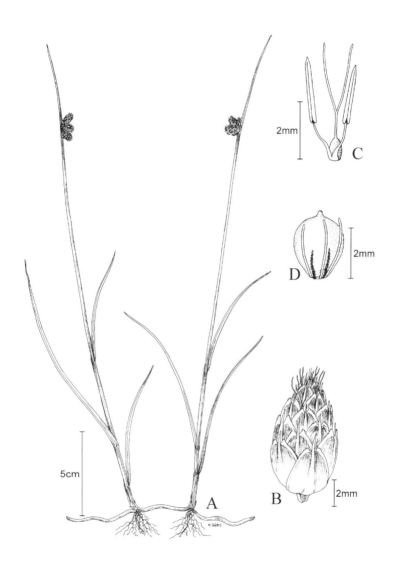

A Plant habit and flowering stem; **B** Spikelet; **C** Floret; **D** Nut.

13 *Eleocharis palustris* (L.) Roem. & Schult. sensu lato

Common Spike-rush   *Map 13*

Rhizomes thick, long-creeping. **Stems** 8–95 cm × 0.6–4 mm, sparsely to densely tufted, terete, smooth to indistinctly longitudinally ridged; stomata guard cells (Figure A₁) shorter than adjacent subsidiary cells. **Leaves** reduced to bladeless sheaths at base of stem, up to 25 cm long, yellowish to dark reddish-brown; apex ± truncate. **Inflorescence** a single, terminal, ovoid to lanceoloid-ovoid spikelet, 5–30 × 3–6 mm, usually with up to 70 flowers. **Glumes** 1.5–3.5 × 2–2.5 mm (from middle of spikelet), ovate, reddish-brown with pale brown midrib and narrow hyaline margins; apex obtuse to acute; the 2 lowest glumes empty, subequal, each surrounding not more than 2/3 of the base of the spikelet. **Flowers** bisexual; perianth bristles 0–4, shorter to longer than nut; stamens 3, with anthers 1.6–2.5 mm; stigmas 2. **Nuts** (1.2–) 1.5–2.0* × 1.3–1.5 mm, obovate, biconvex, yellowish to dark brown, finely punctate; style-base conical, not confluent with nut but strongly constricted beneath the cone base to form a rim.   **Fr.** 7–9.

This species is indifferent to soil types although more frequent in richer and slightly basic soils (Preston & Croft 1997). It is found, for example, by the side of or in water in ponds, ditches and river margins and in marshy edge communities with *Schoenoplectus* spp., *Carex rostrata*, *Equisetum fluviatile*, *Glyceria* spp., *Menyanthes*, *Potentilla palustris* etc. (**S8, S9, S12, S14, S20** etc.), often forming large and dense populations in upland pools and lakes with *Littorella*, *Lobelia dortmanna* and *Agrostis stolonifera* (**S19**) where there is little competition, and in spring 'soaks' such as those with *Potamogeton polygonifolius* (**M29**). Not at all frequent round reservoirs and other water-bodies subject to fluctuation of water level (Grime *et al.* 1988). Recorded up to 550 m at Tyne Head, v.c. 70 (Porter & Foley 2002).

Eleocharis palustris is characterised by long-creeping rhizomes which lead to the formation of large clones, its relatively large spikes, the two sterile lower glumes which do not completely surround the base of the spikelet (as also in **14** *E. mamillata* subsp. *austriaca*, which see for the differences) and the smaller number (0–4) of perianth bristles.

The two subspecies have been separated mainly on microcharacters (see p. 125). See also the Biological Flora account (Walters 1949).

***Note**: Measurements of nut length do not include the length of the style-base.

122

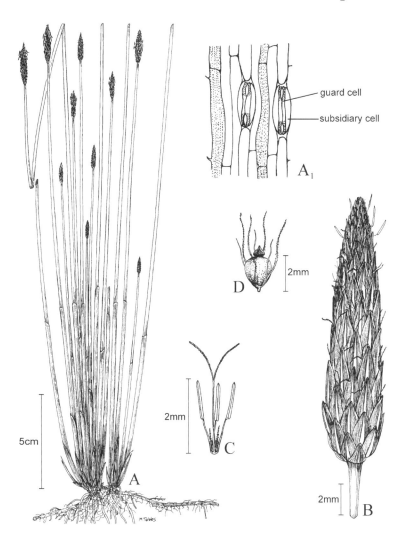

A Plant habit and flowering stems; **A₁** Stem epidermis and stomata (*drawn by V.M. Jermy, after Strandhede 1966*); **B** Spikelet; **C** Floret; **D** Nut.

M13 *Eleocharis palustris* sensu lato

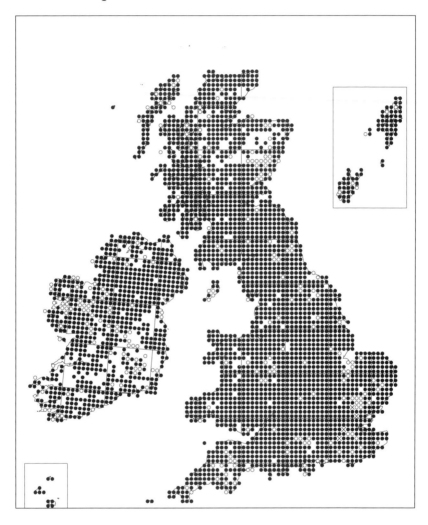

Eleocharis palustris sensu lato is widespread and common throughout most of the British Isles, but the distribution of the two subspecies still needs to be studied in detail. We expect most records mapped here to be of **13b** *E. palustris* subsp. *vulgaris*.

Eleocharis palustris sensu lato (*continued*)   **13a & b**

The species described on p. 122 has been found with a range of chromosome numbers, the more common numbers ranging from 2n = 37–40 with the mean at 38, the less common one being 2n = 16. In their gross morphology they are ± identical but they differ as shown below. Little sampling has been done in the field and, if ecological differences exist, they are not yet clear.

Eleocharis palustris subsp. *palustris* (*Map 13a*)   **13a**

Stomatal length 35–56 μm. *Spikelets* with 40–70 flowers. *Glumes* (from middle of spikelet) 2.5–3.5 mm long, rather pale whitish brown or straw-coloured, usually more easily detached. *Nuts* 1.2(–1.4)–1.5 mm long.[*]

Eleocharis palustris subsp. *vulgaris* Walters (*cf. Map 13*)   **13b**

Stomatal length 50–77 μm. *Spikelets* shorter, with 20–40 flowers. *Glumes* (from middle of spikelet) 3.5–4.5 mm long, variable in colour but usually brown becoming grey and remaining attached to the rhachis. *Nuts* (1.3–)1.5–2.0 mm long.[*]

Eleocharis palustris subsp. *vulgaris* × *E. uniglumis*   **13b × 15**

(*neither mapped nor illustrated*)

This putative hybrid may be found in more open communities in areas where *Eleocharis palustris* subsp. *vulgaris* and *E. uniglumis* are present together. Such plants appear to be morphologically intermediate between the parents and, as they often show little reduction in fertility, can present problems to identify (G.A. Swan pers. comm.). Recent studies into *E. palustris* and related species (Series *Palustriformes*) by G.A. Swan have revealed the possible presence of a further species, *E. mitracarpa* Steud., in the British flora. This species is distinguished from *E. palustris* by having the style-base wider than long and mitriform and by the glumes having a very wide hyaline margin (Walters 1980). Detailed work on these three species, *E. mitracarpa*, *E. palustris* and *E. uniglumis*, and on *E. mamillata* agg. is urgently needed, at both a British and a European level.

---

*Note: Measurements of nut length do not include the length of the style-base.

M13a *Eleocharis palustris* subsp. *palustris*

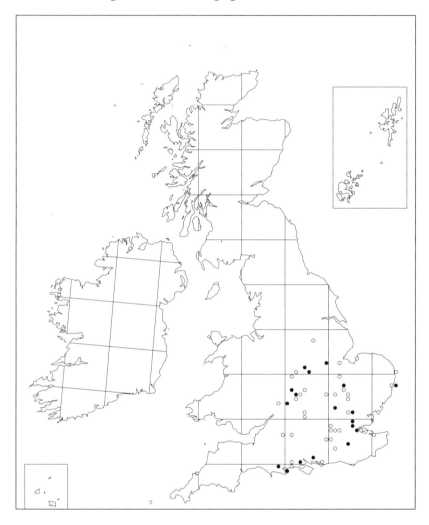

The distribution of *Eleocharis palustris* subsp. *palustris* is poorly recorded and the above map, based on Perring & Sell (1968) and Preston & Croft (1997), may change considerably when further records are made.

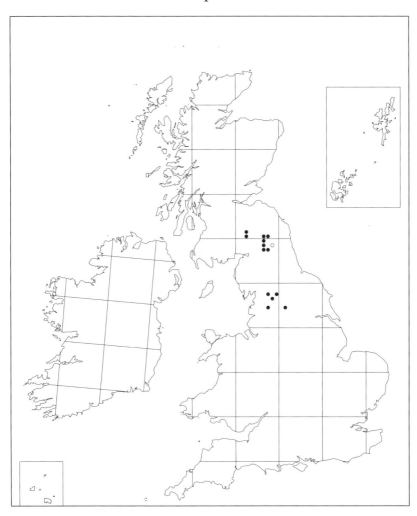

Eleocharis mamillata subsp. *austriaca* was first found in Wharfedale in 1947 (although not recognised until 1960: Walters 1963) and has its main centre now in Ribblesdale (sites in v.cc. 59 and 64); also in several sites in the far north of England (v.cc. 67 and 70) and in southern Scotland by Tima Water and the River Ettrick (v.c. 79).

14 *Eleocharis mamillata* (H. Lindb.) H. Lindb. subsp. *austriaca* (Hayek) Strandh.

Northern Spike-rush   Map 14

Rhizomes far-creeping, dark purplish. ***Stems*** up to 60 cm × 1.1–2.2 mm, tufted, ± terete, smooth, ± inflated, brittle, circular in cross-section, bright green, becoming ridged when dry; stomata guard cells (Figure A_1) longer than adjacent subsidiary cells. ***Leaves*** reduced to bladeless sheaths up to 9 cm long, brownish with reddish tinge, paler above; apex ± truncate. ***Inflorescence*** a single, terminal, ovoid, lanceoloid-ovoid or often distinctly conical spikelet; spikelet, 5–20 × 3–8 mm. ***Glumes*** 2–3 × 1–1.5 mm, *c.* 40 but up to 107 per spikelet, ovate, obtuse, often caducous when in fruit, with sides dark reddish-brown, paler towards base; margins narrowly hyaline; midrib pale brown; the 2 lowest glumes empty, each surrounding ± half the base of the spikelet. ***Flowers*** bisexual; perianth bristles (4–)5(–6), usually much longer than nut; stamens 3, with anthers 0.9–1.2 mm long; stigmas 2. ***Nuts*** 1–1.5[*] × 1.1–1.5 mm, obovate or elliptic-obovate, biconvex, yellowish to pale brown; style-base persistent, deltoid or more narrowly triangular in outline, flattened, with an acute apex, not confluent with nut.   ***Fr.*** 7–9.

This plant grows along the margins of upland rivers, particularly on gravel with silt and where there is some protection from spates, e.g. in oxbow pools. Its rootstock is usually submerged. It moves into open habitats and has colonised old limestone quarries and a gravel-pit, but it rarely persists long.

It resembles **13** *E. palustris* but is much rarer and is distinguished by its bright green stems, circular in cross-section and with longer stomata guard cells, its narrower glumes and usually 5 perianth bristles (compared with 0–4 in *E. palustris*). Detailed studies (Swan & Richards 2007) have shown most Northumbrian and Cumbrian specimens to be typical of subsp. *austriaca*. Similar plants also occur in NW Yorkshire and a distinctive and invariable morphology occurs there, showing signs of hybrid vigour, with untypically high density of fruits and number of vascular bundles. Some plants in Yorkshire and Selkirk could be referred to subsp. *mamillata*, having a short, broad style-base, but much variation in style-base shape occurs within the spikelet (*fide* F.J. Roberts pers. comm.). Further work on the group is needed.

---

[*] **Note**: Measurements of nut length do not include the length of the style-base.

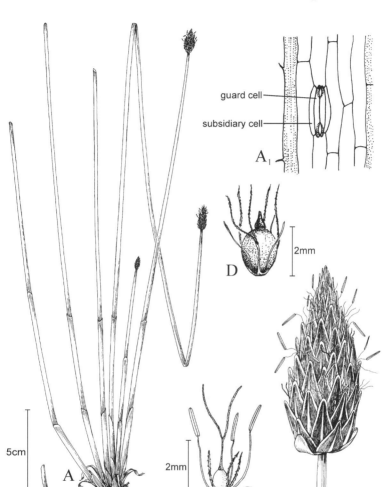

A Plant habit and flowering stems; **A₁** Stem epidermis and stomata (*drawn by V.M. Jermy, after Strandhede 1966*); **B** Spikelet; **C** Floret; **D** Nut.

15 *Eleocharis uniglumis* (Link) Schult.

Slender Spike-rush   *Map 15*

Rhizomes creeping, dark purplish. ***Stems*** up to 60 cm × 0.8–1.5(–1.9) mm, tufted, ± terete, smooth to indistinctly ridged when dry. ***Leaves*** reduced to bladeless sheaths up to 9.5 cm long, dark reddish or purplish, paler above; apex ± truncate, often with a narrow purple ring. ***Inflorescence*** a single, terminal, ovoid or lanceoloid-ovoid spikelet, 5–12 × 3–5 mm. ***Glumes*** 2.5–5 × 1.3–1.7 mm, *c.* 10–30 per spikelet, ovate to ovate-lanceolate, obtuse, with dark reddish-brown sides, paler towards the base, with paler brown or indistinct midrib and narrowly hyaline margins; only the lowest glume empty, more or less completely surrounding the base of the spikelet and with the inflorescence often tilted obliquely away from the point of insertion. ***Flowers*** bisexual; perianth bristles 0–5, mostly shorter than nut, often poorly developed; stamens 3, with anthers 2.2–2.3 mm long; stigmas 2. ***Nuts*** 1.4–2.2* × 1.1–1.5 mm, narrowly obovate, biconvex, yellowish-brown to dark brown; style-base broadly triangular, flattened, acute to obtuse, constricted at base, not confluent with nut.   ***Fr.*** 7–9.

Eleocharis uniglumis is mostly a coastal species, occurring in depressions and pools on the upper parts of rocky coasts and tidal flats with *Blysmus rufus*, *Triglochin maritimum*, *Agrostis stolonifera*, *Glaux maritima* and *Juncus gerardii* (**SM19**) and dominant, with the last three species and *Carex extensa*, in **SM20**; also in brackish and surrounding marshes, often within the spray zone. It occasionally occurs inland in lowland *Juncus subnodulosus* fen-meadows with *Carex elata* (**M22**) and in upland calcareous marshes, especially associated with higher than normal sodium content of soils (Walters 1943).

Eleocharis uniglumis resembles both **13** *E. palustris* and **14** *E. mamillata* subsp. *austriaca* but has only one sterile lower glume that more or less completely surrounds the base of the spikelet, which is frequently inserted obliquely.

---

*Note: Measurements of nut length do not include the length of the style-base.

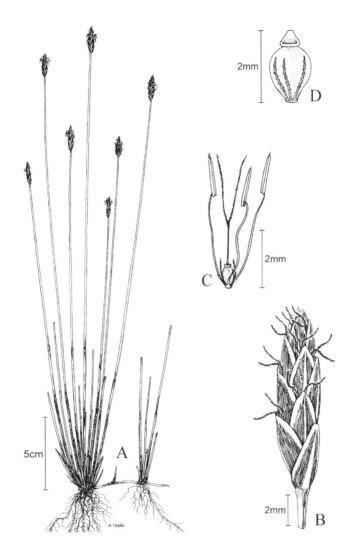

A Plant habit and flowering stems; **B** Spikelet; **C** Floret; **D** Nut.

M15 *Eleocharis uniglumis*

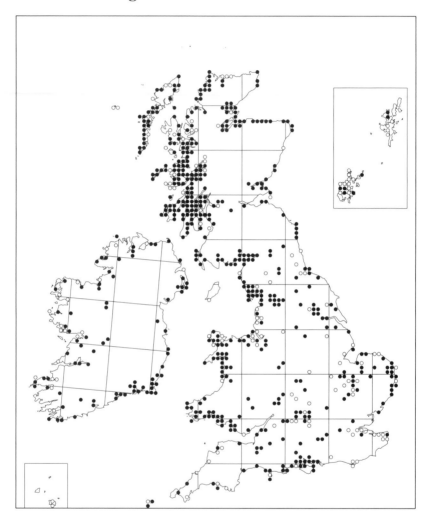

Eleocharis uniglumis is scattered throughout Britain but is being lost from many inland sites. In Ireland it is rarely recorded inland.

Eleocharis multicaulis M16

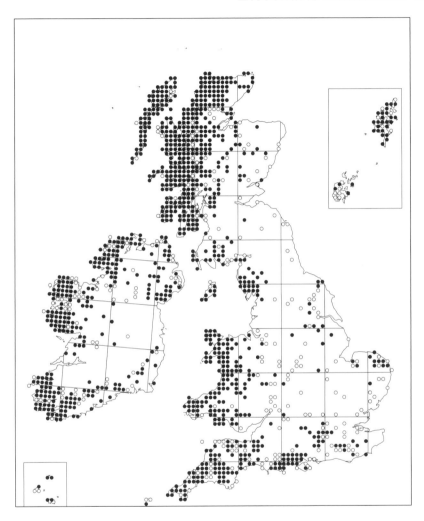

Eleocharis multicaulis occurs throughout Britain and Ireland but is more frequent in the west, from sea level to 610 m on the Macgillycuddy's Reeks, v.c. H1 (Porter & Foley 2002).

16   *Eleocharis multicaulis* (Sm.) Desv.

Many-stalked Spike-rush   *Map 16*

Rhizomes stout, shortly creeping. **Stems** 15–40 cm × 1–1.5 mm, densely clustered, ± terete, smooth to minutely ridged when dry, minutely striate or dotted, often recurved. **Leaves** reduced to bladeless sheaths up to 9.5 cm long, pale yellowish or brownish to purplish; apex obliquely acute. **Inflorescence** a single, terminal, ovoid, lanceoloid-ovoid or ellipsoid spikelet, 5–15 × 2–4 mm, often viviparous. **Glumes** 2.5–5(–7) × 1.2–1.8(–2.2) mm, *c.* 10–30 per spikelet, ovate-lanceolate, obtuse to acute, with dark reddish-brown sides, paler and often striate towards the base, with green or indistinct midrib; the lowest glume empty, *c.* 1/4 as long as the spikelet, not completely surrounding its base. **Flowers** bisexual; perianth bristles 4–6, longer than nut; stamens 3, with their anthers 1.9–2.3 mm long; stigmas 3. **Nuts** 1.2–1.5* × 0.8–1 mm, narrowly obovoid, trigonous, yellowish-brown to olive-brown; style-base triangular, trigonous, acute, constricted at base, not confluent with nut.   ***Fr.*** 6–8.

Eleocharis multicaulis is usually found on more acidic soils than **18** *E. quinqueflora*, e.g. around S*phagnum auriculatum* pools (**M1**), in upland mires (**M14** and **M16**) and occasionally in *Narthecium–Sphagnum* valley mires (**M21**). Mainly a plant of moderately enriched soligenous mires with *Hypericum elodes–Potamogeton polygonifolius* (**M29**) and of seasonally inundated habitats, e.g. in New Forest and Cornwall, with *Baldellia* (**M30**). It can also be found on wet sandy heaths and forming a sub-community with *Schoenus nigricans*, *Erica tetralix*, *E. vagans* and *Molinia caerulea* (**H5**).

Dalby & Dalby (1989) suggest that the apex of the lower glume is usually bilobed whereas that of **18** *E. quinqueflora* is not and this may be, in some areas, a useful character. The latter species has fewer (up to 7) glumes in the spikelet (whereas *E. multicaulis* may have 15 or more); also the lowest glume is more than half as long as the spikelet, which it completely surrounds at its base.

---

*Note: Measurements of nut length do not include the length of the style-base.

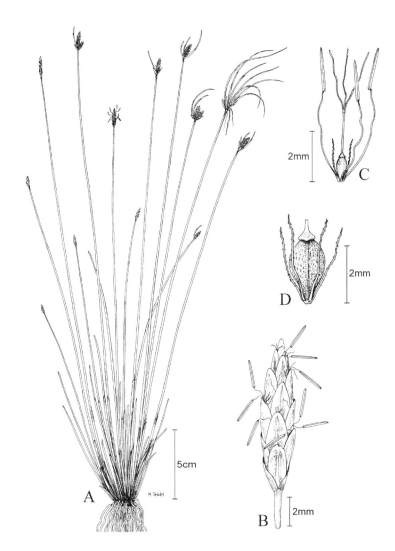

A Plant habit and flowering stems; **B** Spikelet; **C** Floret; **D** Nut.

135

17 *Eleocharis acicularis* (L.) Roem. & Schult.

Needle Spike-rush   *Map 17*

Rhizomes shortly creeping, brown. **Stems** 1–15 cm × 0.2–0.3 mm, tufted or sometimes solitary, 4-angled, smooth. **Leaves** reduced to bladeless sheaths up to 1 cm long, pale brown to reddish-brown; apex obliquely truncate. **Inflorescence** a single, terminal, ovoid to narrowly cylindric spikelet, 2.2–7.5 × 0.6–1.8(–2.2) mm. **Glumes** 1.5–3 × 1 mm, up to 15 per spikelet, ovate-lanceolate, obtuse to acute, sometimes emarginate, with pale brown to reddish-brown sides, green midrib and scarious margins; the lowest glume usually empty and up to 1/2 as long as the spikelet, completely surrounding its base. **Flowers** bisexual; perianth bristles 0–1(–4), up to 1/2 as long as nut; stamens 3, with anthers 0.9–1.2 mm long; stigmas 3. **Nuts** 0.7–1.05[*] × 0.5 mm, narrowly obovoid to obovoid-cylindric, obscurely trigonous, whitish or pale brown, finely trabeculate with longitudinal ridges and vertical lines of horizontally oblong epidermal cells; style-base small, conical, not confluent with nut.   **Fr.** 9–11.

Eleocharis acicularis is found in wet muddy and sandy places on the margins of still water with *Callitriche stagnalis* and *Zannichellia palustris* in the *Nuphar lutea* community (**A8b**) and in rich *Potamogeton* assemblages with *Myriophyllum alterniflorum* (**A13**). Less commonly it grows in bays in slow-flowing water, often forming a turf as a submerged aquatic, when it does not flower or fruit.

This species is characterised by its narrow stems with spikelets that have the lowest glume up to half as long as the spikelet. It shows a wide range of variation, particularly in stem length. The description above applies to emergent fruiting plants only. Submerged plants remain vegetative, with long stems up to 50 cm long that may branch into numerous secondary stems at the apex.

Fruiting plants with long stems in deeper water have been called var. *longicaulis* H.C. Watson, but these are probably no more than phenotypic variants resulting from this habitat.

---

*Note: Measurements of nut length do not include the length of the style-base.

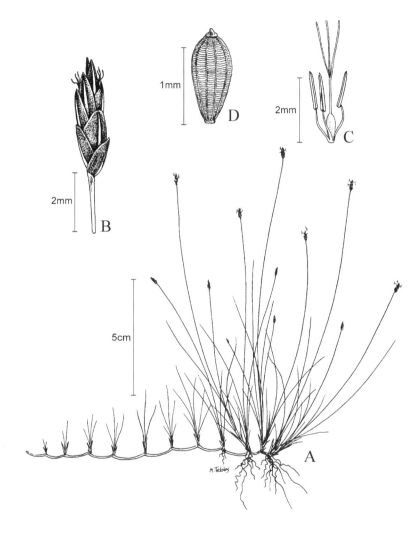

A Plant habit and flowering stems; **B** Spikelet; **C** Floret; **D** Nut.

M17 *Eleocharis acicularis*

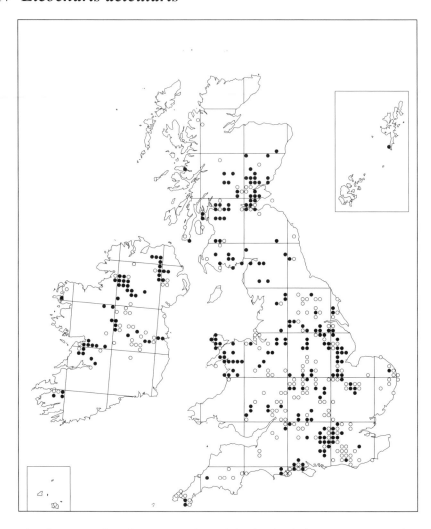

Eleocharis acicularis is scattered through lowland Britain, N to the Grampian foothills, reaching 390 m in Drumore Loch, v.c. 89 (Porter & Foley 2002). There are old records in v.cc. 105 and 108 but an extant population in S Shetland (v.c. 112). Scattered in Ireland and absent from the south.

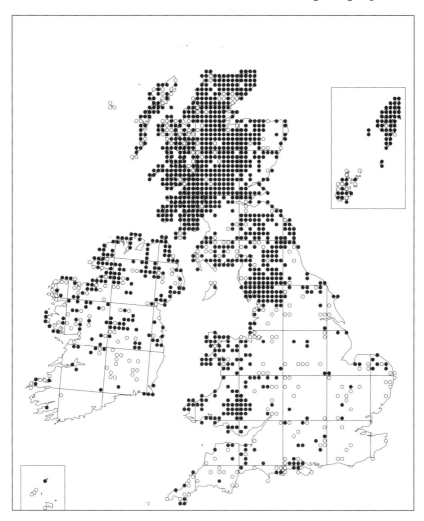

Eleocharis quinqueflora is mainly an upland and northern plant in the British Isles, reaching 915 m in Atholl, v.c. 89 (Porter & Foley 2002).

18   *Eleocharis quinqueflora* (Hartm.) O. Schwarz

Few-flowered Spike-rush   *Map 18*

Rhizomes stout, shortly creeping. **Stems** 3.5–40 cm × 0.4–1 mm, loosely to densely tufted, terete, smooth. **Leaves** reduced to bladeless sheaths up to 11 cm long, pale yellowish to brownish; apex obliquely obtuse to truncate. **Inflorescence** a single, terminal, ovoid to ellipsoid spikelet, 4–10 × 3–5 mm. **Glumes** 2.5–7 × 1.2–2.2 mm, up to 7 per spikelet, lanceolate to oblong-lanceolate, obtuse to acute, with mid to dark brown sides, green midrib and scarious margins, the lowest glume half or more as long as the spikelet and completely surrounding it at its base. **Flowers** bisexual; perianth bristles 4–6, shorter to longer than nut; stamens 3, with their anthers 1.8–2.1 mm long; stigmas 3. **Nuts** 2–3* × 1–1.2 mm, narrowly obovoid to obovoid, trigonous, blackish to grey, reticulate with rectangular epidermal cells; style-base narrowly triangular, confluent with nut.   **Fr.** 7–8.

Eleocharis quinqueflora is a plant of wet peaty mires, particularly in base-rich habitats such as spring-heads and calcareous flushes, giving its name to a distinct variant in the *Carex dioica–Pinguicula vulgaris* mires (**M10**) and a sub-community with *Palustriella commutata* in mires characterised by *Carex viridula* subsp. *oedocarpa* and *Saxifraga aizoides* (**M11b**). Also in sedge communities of dune-slacks (**SD14, SD16**) and in seepage areas with *Blysmus rufus* and *E. uniglumis* (**SM19, SM20**) in the upper part of saltmarshes. It is a plant of open vegetation and is helped by grazing and minor disturbance. Scattered throughout the British Isles but commonest in the north and west.

This species has the largest and darkest glumes of the three *Eleocharis* species in which the lowest glume in the spikelet is half as long as the spikelet or more. From **15** *E. uniglumis* it can be distinguished further by its three stigmas and/or trigonous nut, whereas **16** *E. multicaulis* has the lowest glume usually less than half the length of the spikelet.

---

*Note: Measurements of nut length do not include the length of the style-base.

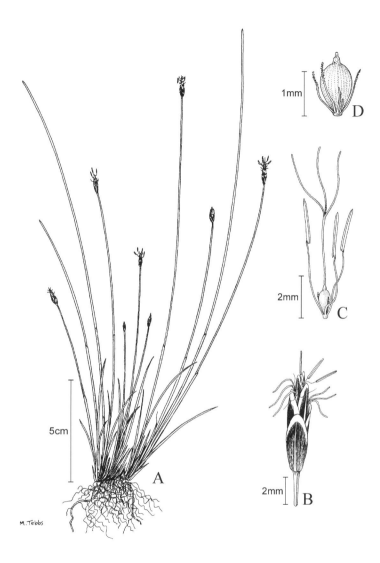

A Plant habit and flowering stems; **B** Spikelet; **C** Floret; **D** Nut.

19   *Eleocharis parvula* (Roem. & Schult.) Link ex Bluff, Nees & Schauer

Dwarf Spike-rush   *Map 19*

Plants connected by whitish capillary stolons creeping on the surface, often terminating in a small whitish tuber. *Stems* 2–8 cm × 0.3–0.5 mm, sparsely tufted, terete, often spongy, smooth to minutely septate-nodulose when dry, often flowerless and leaf-like. *Leaves* reduced to bladeless sheaths up to 1 cm long, translucent, indistinct. *Inflorescence* a single, terminal, ovoid to ovoid-ellipsoid spikelet, 1.9–4 × 1–1.5 mm. *Glumes* 1.2–2.5 × 1–2 mm, up to 9 per spikelet, ovate, with an obtuse to acute apex and greenish to yellowish-brown striate margins and indistinct midrib, the lowest glume usually empty and half or more as long as the spikelet, completely surrounding its base. *Flowers* bisexual; perianth bristles usually 3, equalling or longer than nut; stamens 3, with their anthers 1.0–1.2 mm long; stigmas 3. *Nuts* 1.0–1.4 mm[*] long, obovoid, trigonous, pale yellowish, smooth to very minutely reticulate, shiny; style-base small, conical, confluent with nut.   *Fr.* 6–7.

Eleocharis parvula is a plant of firm muddy places in the upper reaches of estuaries, avoiding strongly saline areas; it also occurs in tidal pans in brackish grazing-marshes. Its associates include *Bolboschoenus maritimus*, *Juncus foliosus*, *Limosella australis*, *Ranunculus sceleratus* and *Veronica anagallis-aquatica*. It often forms a close carpet in which other associates cannot easily establish themselves, a community briefly described by Rodwell (2000) as **SM3**. Grazing animals often poach areas, breaking the mat and thus spreading the population. Flowering and fruiting are apparently very poor in many areas: see A.J. Byfield in Wigginton (1999).

This species is superficially similar to smaller plants of **17** *E. acicularis* but is characterised by having stolons often terminating in a small tuber, slightly broader stems and inconspicuous leaf-sheaths.

---

*Note: Measurements of nut length do not include the length of the style-base.

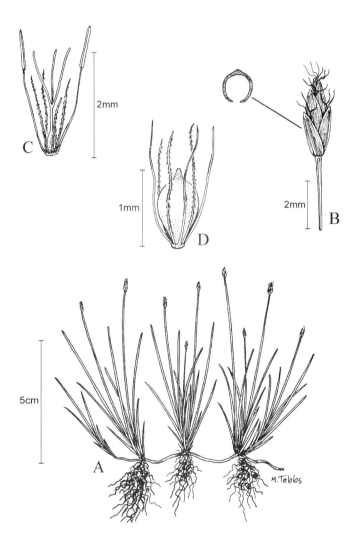

A Plant habit and flowering stems; **B** Spikelet; **C** Floret; **D** Nut.

M19 *Eleocharis parvula*

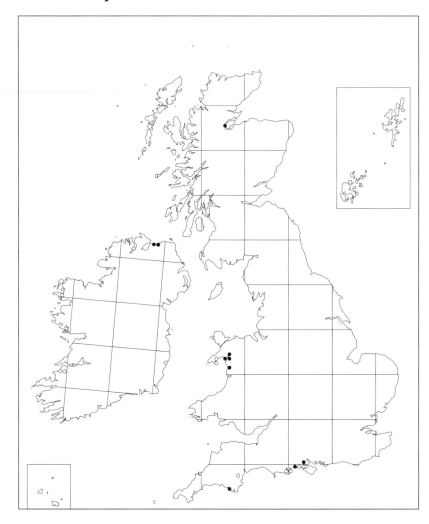

Eleocharis parvula has two main centres of distribution – the south coast of England (v.cc. 3 and 13) and the north Cardigan Bay area in Wales (v.cc. 48 and 49). In Scotland, found only in E Ross (v.c. 106). In Ireland, recently found in two sites in Co. Londonderry (v.c. H40), but there are old records in N Kerry (v.c. H2) and Co. Wicklow (v.c. H20).

144

Scirpoides holoschoenus is considered to be native only at Braunton Burrows (v.c. 4), at Watchet (v.c 5) and at Berrow Dunes (v.c. 6). Other scattered populations in South Wales (mainly in dock areas), the Usk estuary, in Kent and at Poole Harbour, Dorset, are treated as introductions. The records for Northern Ireland (Preston *et al.* 2002) are erroneous.

20 *Scirpoides holoschoenus* (L.) Soják

Round-headed Club-rush   *Map 20*

Rhizomes far-creeping, woody, with sand-binding roots. *Stems* 30–90 cm ×
2–4 mm, densely clustered, erect, glaucous, terete, with two opposite
longitudinal grooves. *Leaves* mostly basal, rarely one cauline, mostly reduced
to sheaths; blade (when present) up to 20 cm × 1.5–2 mm, acuminate, hard,
channelled, becoming flattened near apex, with margins scabrid; sheath up to
14 cm long, herbaceous to coriaceous, brown to reddish-brown, becoming
fibrous at margins. *Inflorescence* terminal but appearing lateral, compound
with 2–8 primary branches, up to 8 cm long, flattened; secondary branches
(when present) 1–2; branches terminated by 1(–3) spikes; involucral bracts 2,
leaf-like, the longest one 10–40 cm long, erect and appearing ± continuous
with stem. *Spikes* globose, 2–12 mm in diameter, composed of numerous
densely packed spikelets; spikelets 2–3.5 × 1–2 mm, broadly ovoid and
obtuse. *Glumes* 1.2–2 × 0.8–1.2 mm, obovate, brown to reddish-tinged,
membranous towards margins; apex broadly obtuse, whitish, scabrid, shortly
mucronate; midrib acutely keeled, greenish. *Flowers* bisexual; perianth
bristles absent; stamens 3; anthers 0.8–1.5 mm long; stigmas 3. *Nuts* 1–1.75
× 0.5–0.75 mm, broadly ellipsoid, compressed-trigonous, minutely reticulate,
greyish.   *Fr.* 9–10.

This plant occurs in damp, sandy areas by the sea. The only extant native
populations occur in dune-slacks at Braunton Burrows (v.c. 4) with *Salix
repens*, *Agrostis stolonifera*, *Carex flacca*, *Juncus acutus*, *Mentha aquatica*
and *Pulicaria dysenterica* (**SD14**, **SD15**), where it is extensive but the
community is under threat from scrub encroachment, and at Berrow Dunes
(v.c. 6) on the edge of a golf course (J.H.S. Cox in Wigginton 1999). It is a
common species of Mediterranean coasts, but its requirement for high
summer temperatures for regeneration by seed (Willis 1985) may be
restricting its spread in the British Isles.

Scirpoides holoschoenus is distinct from all other British and Irish sedges
in having an inflorescence of 2–8 branches terminating in densely globose
spikes, each comprising numerous spikelets.

Scirpoides holoschoenus is a **Red Data List** species in Great Britain;
Status: **Endangered** (Cheffings & Farrell 2005).

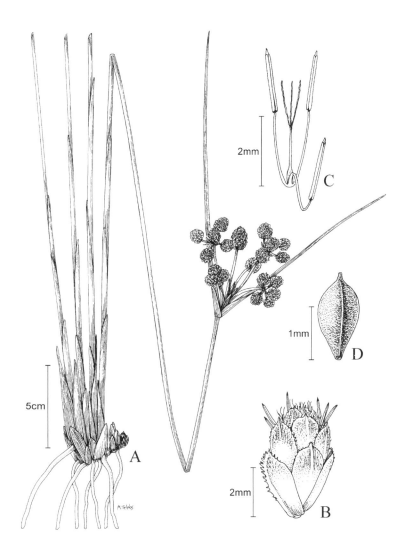

A Plant habit and flowering stem; **B** Spikelet; **C** Floret; **D** Nut.

21 *Isolepis setacea* (L.) R. Br.

Rhizomes short, ascending or occasionally spreading, knotted, forming an
annual or short-lived perennial tuft; roots whitish, capillary. **Stems** 1.2–25 cm
× 0.2–0.5 mm, terete, ridged, without nodes. **Leaves** shorter than the stems,
lower ones reduced to a setaceous point; blade of upper leaves 0.5–9.8 cm ×
0.1–0.7 mm, linear-setaceous, crescent-shaped in cross-section; apex obtuse;
sheath up to 3.3 cm long, closed, membranous, brown; ligule absent.
Inflorescence pseudolateral, ovoid to oblong, with 1–4 spikelets; involucral
bract 1, leaf-like, 2–23 mm long, usually longer than inflorescence. **Spikelets**
1.5–6.5 × 0.5–3 mm, ellipsoid. **Glumes** 1–2.5 × 0.4–1.2 mm, 4–35 per
spikelet, acute, green, sometimes with brown to dark brown patches; midrib
green, with mucro < 0.1 mm long. **Flowers** bisexual; perianth bristles 0;
stamens 1–3; anthers 0.2–0.6 mm, crested; stigmas (2–)3. **Nuts** 0.5–1.3 ×
0.4–0.9 mm, brown to dark brown; surface shiny, with longitudinal ribs and
densely set transverse bars connecting the ribs.   **Fr.** 7–9.

Isolepis setacea is found in open, damp, generally acidic sites, especially
those subject to winter flooding. It is characteristic of cattle-grazed water-
meadows and rough *Agrostis–Lolium* grassland, on poached trackways
and on the margins of ditches and ponds, being a pioneer species
of disturbed ground (Foley & Porter 2002). It occurs also in dune-slacks
and the upper zones of saltmarshes, as well as in calcareous mires,
e.g. some stands of the *Briza media–Pinguicula vulgaris* sub-community of
Schoenus nigricans–Juncus subnodulosus mire (**M13b**) and *Ranunculus
omiophyllus–Montia fontana* rills and spring-heads (**M35**).

This species differs from **22** *I. cernua* in having darker glumes and shiny
nuts with distinct longitudinal ribs; less reliable is the involucral bract that is
usually longer than the inflorescence.

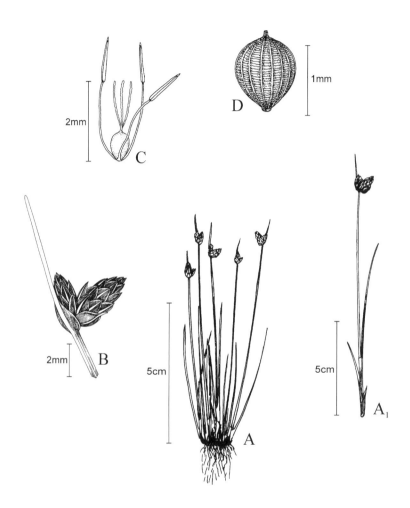

A, **A₁** Plant habit and flowering stems; **B** Spikelet; **C** Floret; **D** Nut. (**A**, **A₁** *drawn by R.M.W.*, **B**, **C**, **D** *by M. Tebbs*)

M21 *Isolepis setacea*

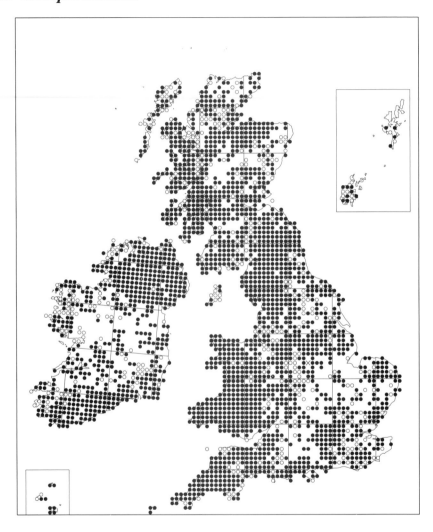

Isolepis setacea occurs throughout most of the British Isles, becoming less common in highly arable areas.

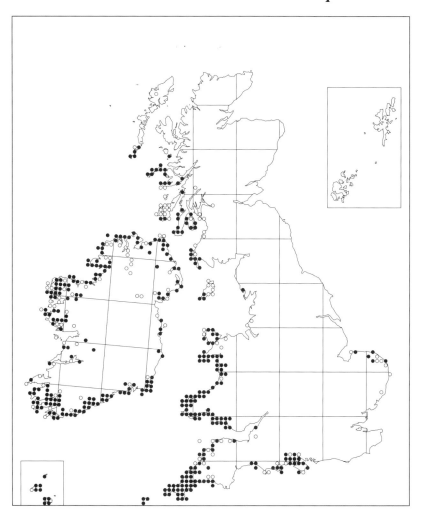

Isolepis cernua grows round most of the coast of Ireland but in Great Britain mainly on the west coasts of England, Wales and Scotland, where recent discoveries have extended its known range northwards. It also occurs in Norfolk and is locally common in the New Forest.

22   *Isolepis cernua* (Vahl) Roem. & Schult.

Slender Club-rush   *Map 22*

Rhizomes up to 2 cm × 0.3–1.5 mm, ascending, forming an annual or short-lived perennial tuft; roots whitish, capillary. **Stems** 1–30 cm × 0.2–1 mm, without nodes. **Leaves** much shorter than stems, at least lower ones reduced to a short, blunt point; blade (when present) 0.5–12 cm × 0.1–0.7 mm, linear-setaceous, crescent-shaped in cross-section; apex obtuse; sheath up to 3 cm long, brown or green; ligule absent. **Inflorescence** pseudolateral, ovoid to oblong, with 1–4 spikelets; involucral bract 1, leaf-like, 2–22 mm long, usually shorter to slightly longer than the inflorescence. **Spikelets** 1.4–9 × 1–2.4 mm, terete, ovoid. **Glumes** 0.8–2.1 × 0.4–1.6 mm, 4–27 per spikelet, obtuse, pale greenish-white to mid green, sometimes with brown to dark brown patches; midrib green, with mucro < 0.1 mm long. **Flowers** bisexual; perianth bristles 0; stamens 2–3; anthers 0.2–1 mm, crested; stigmas 3. **Nuts** 0.5–1.2 × 0.4–1 mm, 3-sided, dull brown to blackish; surface dull, smooth, minutely tuberculate to finely reticulate.   **Fr.** 7–9.

Isolepis cernua is found mostly near the sea in wet ground that is often peaty or sandy, especially on steep slopes below cliff-tops; also in maritime marshes, beside ditches and in dune-slacks, especially where disturbed by grazing animals.

Compared to **21** *I. setacea*, this species is characterised by having nuts with a surface that is smooth and minutely tuberculate to finely reticulate and glumes that tend to be much paler. The involucral bract is usually shorter to only slightly longer than the inflorescence, but this character alone is unreliable.

Isolepis cernua is of horticultural interest, often being sold as a house or conservatory plant as well as for the margins of garden ponds.

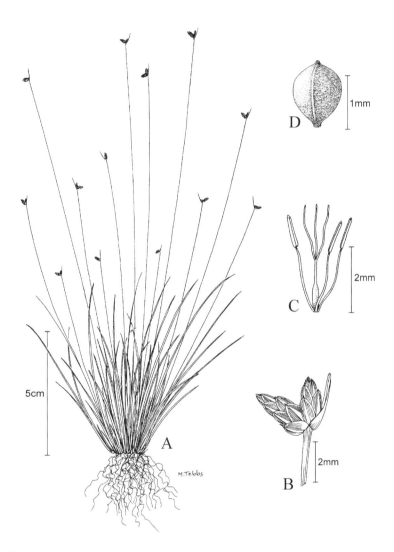

A Plant habit and flowering stems; **B** Spikelet; **C** Floret; **D** Nut.

23   *Isolepis fluitans* (L.) R. Br.

Floating Club-rush   *Map 23*

Rhizomes perennial but short-lived, or often only an annual, ascending or horizontal, usually floating or submerged, rarely terrestrial; leafless sheaths absent. **Stems** 1–50(–130) cm × 0.2–1.1 mm, compressed, pale greenish-yellow, often repeatedly branched, with one or more internodes from which culms or leaves arise; culms 1–19 cm × 0.2–0.9 mm. **Leaves** up to 10 cm × 0.2–2 mm, flat in cross-section; sheath 3–25 × 0.3–1.7 mm, green or brown; ligule absent. **Inflorescence** a solitary terminal spikelet; peduncles up to 10 cm, terete below, trigonous above; involucral bracts 2–8 × 0.3–1.3 mm, glume-like. **Spikelet** 2.4–9.4 × 0.7–2.7 mm, with 4–12(–28) glumes. **Glumes** 1.5–3.4 × 0.5–1.3 mm, acute to obtuse, green or with scarious or brown patches; midrib green, with mucro < 0.1 mm long. **Flowers** bisexual; perianth bristles 0; stamens 2–3; anthers 0.4–1.5 mm, crested; stigmas 2(–3). **Nuts** 0.9–1.8 × 0.5–1.2 mm, 2- to 3-sided, brown; surface minutely reticulate. **Fr.** 7–10.

Isolepis fluitans is essentially an aquatic plant that is virtually confined to acidic and oligotrophic habitats in peaty streams and ditches. Found with *Potamogeton* spp. and other submerged aquatics in the *Potamogeton perfoliatus–Myriophyllum alternifolium* community (**A13**) and in the similar but more species-poor association **A14**. It also occurs with *Eleocharis acicularis*, *Littorella uniflora* and *Lobelia dortmanna* (**A22**), with *Isoetes lacustris* and/or *I. echinospora* and *Subularia aquatica* (**A23**) and on silty substrates with *Juncus bulbosus* (**A24**), as well as in *Hypericum elodes–Potamogeton polygonifolius* soakways (**M29**) and related vegetation of seasonally inundated habitats (**M30**). In Ireland, near Lough Fingall in the Burren, it is found in highly calcareous but nutrient-poor sites on fen marl (Webb & Scannell 1983).

This species is quite distinct from all other British and Irish sedges in having branched, leafy stems. From the other *Isolepis* species it is also distinguished by the glume-like involucral bract and single terminal spikelet. It has often been placed in a separate genus, as *Eleogiton fluitans* (L.) Link, but a recent monograph of *Isolepis* (Muasya & Simpson 2002) shows that *Eleogiton* cannot be upheld as a distinct genus.

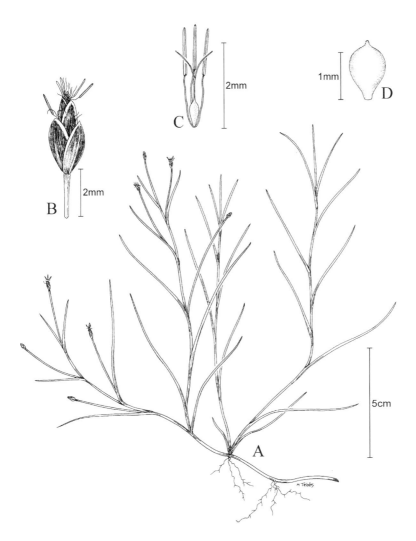

A Plant habit and flowering stems; **B** Spikelet; **C** Floret; **D** Nut.

155

M23 Isolepis fluitans

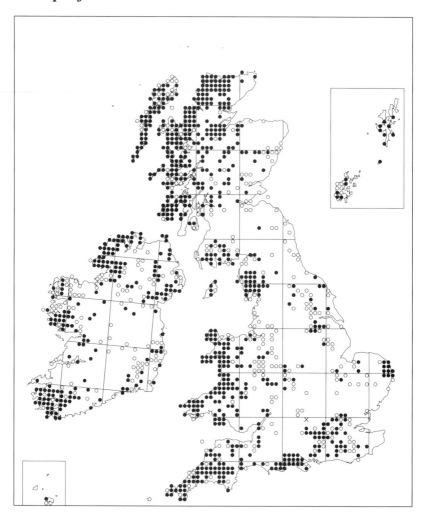

Isolepis fluitans is local throughout Britain, being more frequent in the west; apart from in the lower Bure/Waveney estuaries in East Norfolk and East Suffolk (v.cc. 27 and 28) it is scattered in eastern England and Scotland, where it has been lost to drainage (Preston & Croft 1997). In Ireland it is scarce in the central plain.

Cyperus longus M24

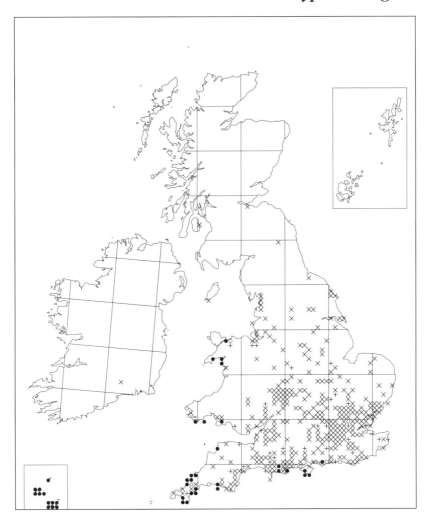

Cyperus longus, when naturally occurring, is predominantly southern in distribution, growing in the Channel Isles and in scattered localities from Cornwall eastwards to the Isle of Wight and through Wales as far north as the Conwy estuary. As an introduction it is frequent in central southern England and scattered north to outliers in Arran and Midlothian. Absent as a native from Ireland but introduced in Co. Waterford (v.c. H6).

24 *Cyperus longus* L.

Galingale

Map 24

Rhizomes shortly creeping. *Stems* 50–140 cm × 1–3.5 mm, not or slightly swollen at base, trigonous to subtriquetrous, smooth, often reddish below. *Leaves* shorter than or equalling inflorescence; blade linear, 35–85 cm × 3.5–7 mm, markedly W-shaped to flattish, acuminate; upper surface rough; sheath 18–45 cm long, pale to mid brown; vegetative shoots forming a pseudostem; ligule absent. *Inflorescence* 14–35 × 10–25 cm, compound; primary branches 5–12, 3–20 cm long, clustered and umbel-like, often branched; secondary branches 0–5, 0.5–7 cm long, arising from the upper section of the primary branches; branches terminated by a solitary spike; involucral bracts 3–5, 7–70 cm long, leaf-like, the longest usually exceeding the inflorescence. *Spikes* 1.5–5 cm long, obovoid; peduncles 0.1–0.7 cm long; spikelets 7–20 × 1–1.7 mm, 2–15 per spike, narrowly oblong to linear-lanceoloid, flattened, suberect to patent; axis broadly winged. *Glumes* 2.7–3.5 × 1.7–1.8 mm, distichously arranged, 15 or more on the longest spikelets, ovate-lanceolate, obtuse, 1–3-nerved, reddish-brown with membranous sides and pale green keel. *Flowers* bisexual; perianth bristles 0; stamens 3; anthers 1 mm long, with prominent connective; stigmas 3. *Nuts* ± 1 mm long, narrowly obovoid-cylindric, trigonous, minutely punctate, brown. *Fr.* 7–9.

C. longus is a lowland species of marshy pond margins, ditches and flushes, mainly in coastal areas, where it sometimes occurs in base-rich flushes on sea-cliffs. It is very local and has decreased in recent years through drainage of suitable habitats. It is also planted in many sites away from the coast. Once established, it can spread by vigorous rhizome growth.

This species is distinct in having a creeping rhizome and an umbel-like inflorescence with basal leaf-like bracts subtending a number of long inflorescence branches. It differs from **25** *C. fuscus* in being a larger, perennial plant, usually with a compound inflorescence. Vegetatively it can be confused with **57** *Carex acutiformis* and possibly **98** *C. acuta*, but they have ligules, vegetative shoots without a pseudostem and a blue-green tinge to the leaves in contrast to the brighter green of *C. longus*.

C. longus seems rarely to set fruit in Britain. British material belongs to subsp. *longus*, although Collins *et al.* (1988) noted that some specimens were visually intermediate with the southern European subsp. *badius*.

Cyperus longus is a **Red Data List** species in Great Britain; *Status*: **Near threatened** (Cheffings & Farrell 2005).

A Plant habit and flowering stem; **B** Spikelet; **C** Floret; **D** Nut.

25 *Cyperus fuscus* L.

Brown Galingale   *Map 25*

Plant a tufted annual; roots fibrous. *Stems* 4–25(–46) cm × 1–3 mm, triquetrous, smooth, soft. *Leaves* shorter than inflorescence; blade linear, 2.5–17 cm × 1.5–4 mm, flat, acuminate; sheath 0.3–5 cm long, rather loose, pale to mid brown, often reddish-tinged; ligule *c.* 1 mm. *Inflorescence* 0.5–2 × 0.6–2.8 cm, simple, or compound with 2–4 primary branches, 1–15 mm long and bearing capitate to umbel-like clusters of spikes; involucral bracts 3, leaf-like, 1–11 cm long, the longest exceeding the inflorescence. *Spikes* 4–6 mm long, broadly ovoid; spikelets 2–5 × 1.5–2 mm, 2–10 per spike, in ± sessile clusters or with a peduncle 1 mm long, oblong to lanceoloid, ± flattened, suberect to spreading; axis not winged. *Glumes* 1–1.5 × 0.6–1 mm, distichously arranged, imbricate, 18 or more on the longest spikelets, ovate, obtuse with a minute excurrent mucro, nerveless, dark purplish-brown with membranous sides and greenish keel. *Flowers* bisexual; perianth bristles 0; stamens 2; anthers 0.2–0.3 mm long, with minute connective; stigmas 3. *Nuts* 0.7–0.8 × 0.3–0.4 mm, narrowly obovoid, trigonous, minutely punctate, greenish- to golden-brown with paler ridges.   *Fr.* 7–9.

A very rare annual of moist, open, muddy or stony ground with a humus-rich substrate around the margins of small ponds and ditches; associated with *Agrostis stolonifera*, *Alopecurus geniculatus*, *Bidens tripartita*, *Ranunculus sceleratus* and *Rorippa palustris* (**OV28–31**). Such areas are often subject to winter flooding but dry out in summer, when they need to be kept open by soil disturbance and grazing by animals. Since seed appears to be long-lived, populations may be revived with suitable conservation management (Foley & Porter 2002). Population sizes increase in hot summers. See Rich (1999).

C. fuscus is easily distinguished from other species of *Cyperus* in being a rather small annual with dark purplish-brown spikelets.

Cyperus fuscus is a **Red Data List** species in Great Britain; *Status*: **Vulnerable** (Cheffings & Farrell 2005). It is protected under Schedule 8 of the Wildlife and Countryside Act 1981.

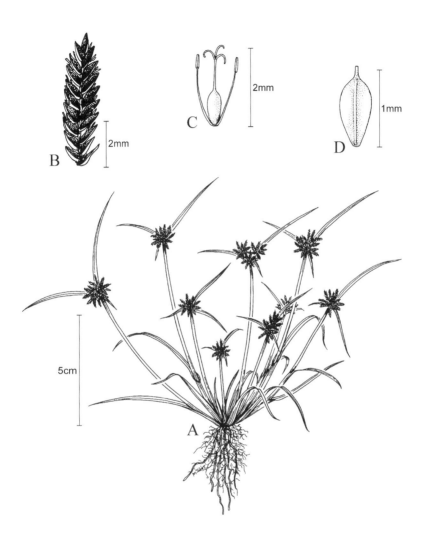

A Plant habit and flowering stems; **B** Spikelet; **C** Floret; **D** Nut.

M25 *Cyperus fuscus*

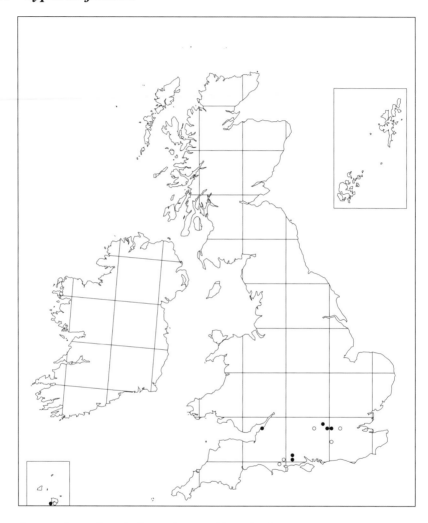

Cyperus fuscus is entirely southern and local in distribution and used to occur from North Somerset eastwards to Middlesex and on Jersey. It is now very rare, occurring naturally only in Somerset, Hampshire, Surrey and Jersey, though it is occasionally grown as an ornamental.

Cyperus eragrostis M26

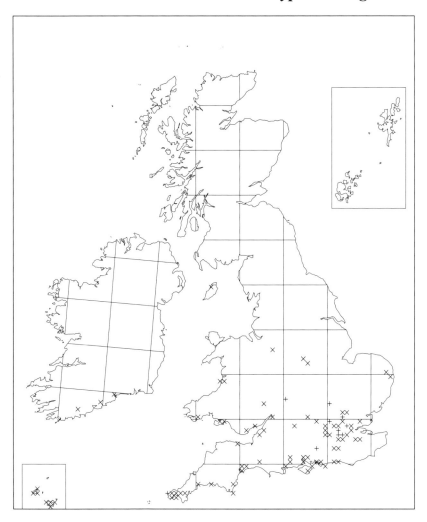

Cyperus eragrostis is native to tropical America and was possibly introduced to cultivation in Britain in 1790. It is occasionally found in southern England, the Isle of Man, the extreme south of Ireland and the Channel Islands as a garden escape as well as a wool and grass-seed alien. It is naturalised in Guernsey, where it was first recorded in the wild in 1909.

26   *Cyperus eragrostis* Lam.

Pale Galingale   *Map 26*

Rhizomes short, thick. **Stems** 20–60 cm × 1.2–2.5 mm, triquetrous, smooth. **Leaves** shorter than to exceeding inflorescence; blade linear, 10–45 cm × 5–10 mm, flattish, acuminate; sheath 2–15 cm long, pale brown to reddish; ligule absent **Inflorescence** 3–11 × 9–16 cm, compound and umbel-like; primary branches 8–11, 2–12 cm long; secondary branches 0–3, 0.5–1 cm long; branches terminated by dense clusters of few to numerous spikelets; involucral bracts 5–11, 13–47 cm long, leaf-like, all exceeding inflorescence. **Spikelets** 5–13 × 1–3 mm, narrowly lanceoloid, flattened; axis not winged. **Glumes** 2–3 × 1–1.5 mm, distichously arranged, 10–30 per spikelet, ovate-lanceolate to lanceolate, acute to subacuminate, indistinctly 1–3-nerved, pale yellowish- to greenish-brown with membranous sides and pale green keel. **Flowers** bisexual; perianth bristles 0; stamen 1; anthers 1.2 mm long, with prominent connective; stigmas 3. **Nuts** 1–1.5 × 0.5–0.6 mm, narrowly obovoid to obovoid, trigonous, minutely punctate, pale to dark greyish-brown. **Fr.** 8–10.

The species is native to tropical America and naturalised in Britain and Ireland, where it is regarded as a stable or increasing neophyte (Porter & Foley 2002). It occurs on waste ground and roadsides, by ponds and other water-bodies and on ballast and rough ground where introduced with grass-seed or wool shoddy.

Cyperus eragrostis is recognised by its dense clusters of pale yellowish- or greenish-brown spikelets.

A Plant habit and flowering stem; **B** Spikelet; **C** Floret; **D** Nut.

27 *Blysmus compressus* (L.) Panz. ex Link

Flat-sedge   *Map 27*

Rhizomes long-creeping. *Stems* 4–45 cm × 0.5–1.5 mm, solitary or tufted, terete to trigonous above, yellow-green, smooth, striate. *Leaves* 6–20 cm × 1.2–2.9 mm, linear, flat, gradually narrowed to an obtuse apex, mid green to bluish-green; sheath up to 8 cm long, pale brown to reddish-brown. *Inflorescence* a terminal, flattened, ± compact ovoid to oblong-ellipsoid head, 1.6–3.5 cm × 5–10 mm, with (4–)8–25 crowded, distichously arranged spikelets, often obscured by their subtending bracts; lowest involucral bract 1.7–7 cm long, shorter than or exceeding inflorescence, setaceous to narrowly leaf-like; upper bracts glume-like, yellowish- to reddish-brown. *Spikelets* 4–10 × 2–3 mm, ovoid-lanceoloid. *Glumes* 3–5 × 2–3 mm, ovate to lanceolate, narrowly obtuse to acute, 2–9-nerved, yellowish- or reddish-brown with narrow hyaline margins; midrib pale brown. *Flowers* bisexual; perianth bristles 3–6, exceeding nut, retrorsely scabrid; stamens 3; anthers 2.5–3.5 mm long, with scabrid connective tip; stigmas 2. *Nuts* 1.5–2 × 1–1.4 mm, obovoid, obscurely trigonous or ± plano-convex, smooth, shiny, mid grey to dark brown; beak *c.* 0.2 mm.   *Fr.* 8–9.

Blysmus compressus grows in open, wet, grassy or sedgy places, especially where flooding occurs, and in drainage channels, on relatively base-rich soils, though highly eutrophic conditions can be detrimental. It reaches 490 m in Co. Durham, v.c. 66 (Foley & Porter 2002). It is not mentioned by Rodwell (1991–2000).

This species is easily distinguished by the compact terminal inflorescence with distichously arranged spikelets. It differs from **28** *B. rufus* principally in its flat, grass-like leaves.

Blysmus compressus is a **Red Data List** species in Great Britain; *Status*: **Vulnerable** (Cheffings & Farrell 2005).

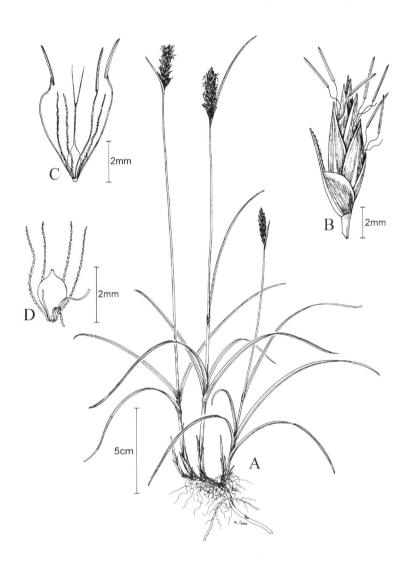

A Plant habit and flowering stems; **B** Spikelet; **C** Floret; **D** Nut.

M27 *Blysmus compressus*

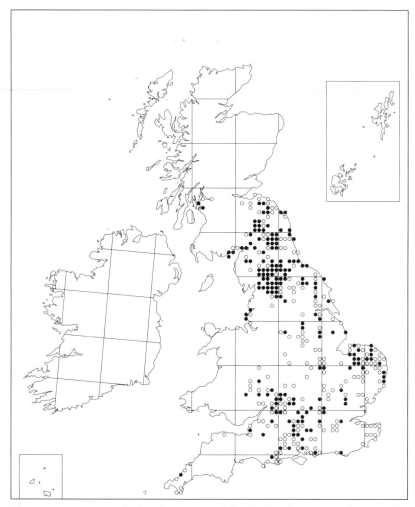

Blysmus compressus is locally scattered in England, very rarely recorded from Wales and in Scotland found only in the south. It has suffered a severe decline, being lost from more than half its pre-1930 10-km squares by 1962 and now also from some 40% of its post-1930 squares (Preston *et al.* 2002), mainly as a result of drainage or over-enrichment. It has not been recorded from Ireland.

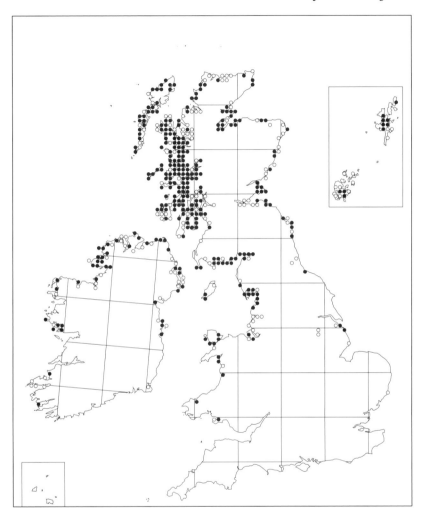

Blysmus rufus is locally frequent on the coasts of England and Wales south to Lincolnshire (v.c. 54) and Glamorgan (v.c. 41) respectively. It is common in western Scotland, often extending inland. In Ireland it is scattered around the north coast but rare in the Republic.

169

28 *Blysmus rufus* (Huds.) Link

Saltmarsh Flat-sedge *Map 28*

Rhizomes short- to medium-creeping. *Stems* 3–45 cm × 0.4–1.6 mm, solitary or tufted, terete to trigonous above, smooth. *Leaves* 1.5–15 cm × 0.4–1 mm, linear, gradually narrowed, obtuse, involute, bluish-green; sheath up to 10 cm long, pale to dark brown; ligule *c.* 1 mm. *Inflorescence* a terminal, flattened, ± compact ovoid to ellipsoid head, 1.2–2.3 cm × 2–9 mm, with 3–9 crowded, distichously arranged spikelets, often obscured by their subtending bracts; lowest involucral bract 0.6–8.6 cm long, shorter than or exceeding inflorescence, glume-like to leaf-like; upper bracts glume-like, dark brown. *Spikelets* 5–10 × 2–4 mm, ovoid-lanceoloid. *Glumes* 3–6 × 2–3 mm, ovate to lanceolate, narrowly obtuse to acute, indistinctly nerved, dark brown; midrib pale brown. *Flowers* bisexual; perianth bristles 0–6, shorter than or equal to nut, antrorsely scabrid; stamens 3; anthers 2.4–3.1 mm long, with ± smooth connective tip; stigmas 2. *Nuts* 3–4.5 × 1.5–1.6 mm, obovoid-ellipsoid, obscurely trigonous or ± plano-convex, ± smooth, ± shiny, mid-grey to yellowish-brown; beak 0.5 mm. *Fr.* 8–9.

Blysmus rufus forms a short turf community (**SM19**) in depressions on raised beaches and in freshwater runnels in upper saltmarshes with *Agrostis stolonifera*, *Glaux maritima*, *Juncus gerardii* and *Triglochin maritimum* as constant associates. It occurs frequently in grazed areas, but *B. rufus* itself does not appear to be much eaten (Rodwell 2000).

Blysmus rufus is easily recognisable by its combination of involute leaves and distichously arranged spikelets, which are darker and generally fewer than in **27** *B. compressus*; the nuts are also considerably larger.

This species has been placed in a separate genus, as *Blysmopsis rufa* (Huds.) Oteng-Yeboah, by some authors (e.g. Flora of North America Editorial Committee 2002).

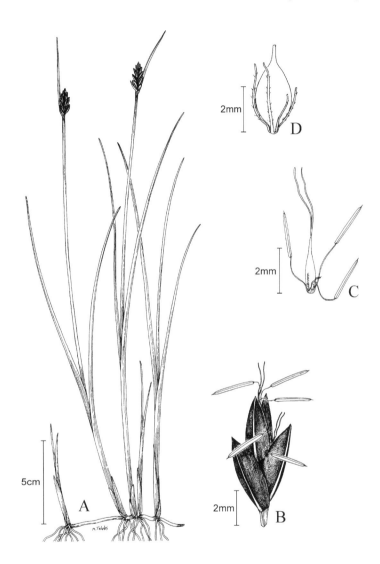

A Plant habit and flowering stems; **B** Spikelet; **C** Floret; **D** Nut.

29 *Schoenus nigricans* L.

Black Bog-rush   Map 29

Rhizomes short, densely tufted; roots fleshy, dark purplish, often growing between leaf-sheaths. **Stems** 15–80 cm × 0.9–1.4 mm, erect, rarely recurved or prostrate, terete to somewhat flattened above. **Leaves** up to 40 cm × 0.5–2 mm, basal, at least 1/2 as long as stems; blade narrowly linear, wiry, gradually tapering to an obtuse, trigonous apex, subterete to channelled, bright green to greyish-green; sheath up to 8 cm long, open, stiff, shiny dark reddish-brown to dark chocolate brown; ligule present, short, hard, often minutely ciliate. **Inflorescence** a single, dark brown to blackish, capitate head, comprising crowded fascicles each of up to 10 spikelets, each fascicle subtended by a glume-like bract; involucral bracts 2–3, leaf-like, with an open, dark brown to blackish sheathing base, the lowermost 2–5 times longer than inflorescence. **Spikelets** 10–12 × 2–4 mm, flattened, lanceoloid, acute, dark brown to blackish; rachilla thick, zigzagged, winged. **Glumes** 7–8, 5–7 × 2–2.5 mm, distichously arranged, the lowest two sterile, the remainder fertile, lanceolate, acute, shortly apiculate, strongly keeled, with sides membranous-leathery, dark reddish-brown to dark chocolate brown; keel minutely ciliate on upper glumes. **Flowers** bisexual; perianth bristles 3–4, much shorter than nut, often dropped as nut ripens; stamens 3; anthers 3.5–4 mm long, with connective tip 0.5–0.8 mm, yellow; stigmas 3. **Nuts** 1–1.9 × 0.8–1.2 mm, ovoid to ovoid-ellipsoid, obtusely trigonous, smooth, shiny, creamy-white to grey.   **Fr.** 7–8.

The plant occurs in damp or wet, peaty but base-rich areas, e.g. *Carex dioica–Pinguicula vulgaris* (**M10**), *S. nigricans–Juncus subnodulosus* (**M13**) and *S. nigricans–Narthecium* (**M14**) mires and less calcareous bogs and heaths in SW Britain, where it can be codominant with *Erica vagans* (**H5**) and occasional with that species and *Molinia* in **H6d**. Also on more acid heaths near the coast and affected by salt-laden winds, e.g. *Trichophorum germanicum–Erica tetralix, Carex panicea* sub-community (**M15a**). Found in coastal maritime grassland of *Festuca rubra–Plantago* spp. in a sub-community (**MC10c**) with *Carex panicea, C. viridula* subsp. *viridula* and *Molinia caerulea*; also codominant with the last species on oceanic cliffs of western shores. See also the Biological Flora account (Sparling 1968).

Schoenus nigricans is characterised as a densely tufted plant with stiff, erect (rarely recurved or prostrate) stems, stiff wiry leaves with shiny dark brown sheaths and a dark brown to blackish capitate inflorescence.

172

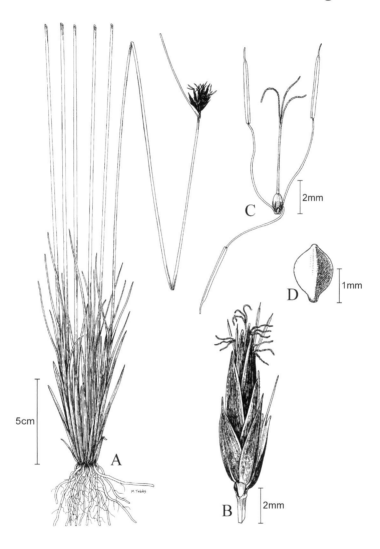

A Plant habit and flowering stem; **B** Spikelet; **C** Floret; **D** Nut.

M29 Schoenus nigricans

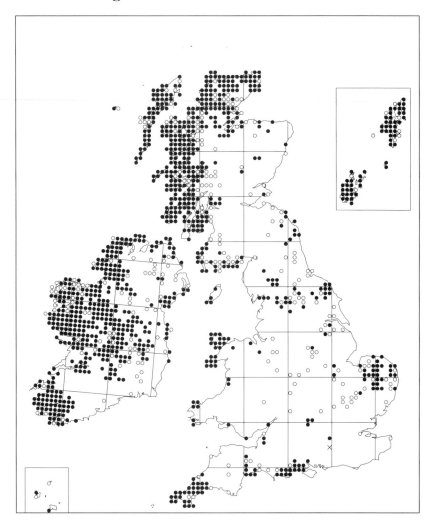

Schoenus nigricans is found mostly in western parts of the British Isles and on the deeper peat of East Anglia, the New Forest and the SW peninsula, where it can be locally frequent. Absent from large parts of England, Wales and eastern Scotland. In Ireland very common and often dominant in western and central bogs; absent in SE and rare in NE.

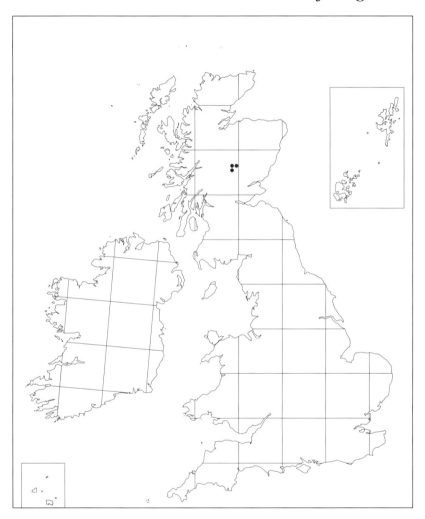

Schoenus ferrugineus was feared to have become extinct when in 1950 its original site on the edge of Loch Tummel (v.c. 88) was flooded; it was transplanted to nearby localities and still exists in one such site (Ben Vrackie). Since 1970, however, some 10 further sites on the Loch Tay limestones in Perthshire have been recorded.

30 *Schoenus ferrugineus* L.

Brown Bog-rush   *Map 30*

Rhizomes short, tufted; roots fleshy, dark brown. *Stems* 10–40 cm ×
0.5–0.7 mm, erect, terete to somewhat flattened above. *Leaves* 1–8 cm × 0.5–
0.7 mm, basal, up to 1/3 as long as stems; blade narrowly linear, wiry, obtuse
to acute at apex, channelled, pale green; sheath up to 3 cm long, open, stiff,
shiny dark reddish-brown to dark chocolate brown; ligule present,
< 1 mm. *Inflorescence* a single, dark brown to blackish, capitate head,
comprising 1–4 spikelets; involucral bracts 1–2; lower bract always present,
shorter than to equalling inflorescence, with an open, dark reddish-brown to
chocolate brown sheathing base and short blade; upper bract glume-like.
Spikelets 7–10 × 1.5–2.5 mm, flattened, lanceoloid, blackish or very dark
brown; rachilla thick, zigzagged. *Glumes* 6–7, 5–7 × 1–2 mm, distichously
arranged, the lowest two sterile, the remainder fertile, lanceolate, acute, with
sides membranous, dark reddish-brown to dark chocolate brown, with a
smooth keel. *Flowers* bisexual; perianth bristles (3–)6, exceeding nut;
stamens 3, anthers 2.5–3 mm long; stigmas 3. *Nuts* 1 × 0.7 mm, ovoid,
trigonous, smooth, shiny, whitish.   *Fr.* 6–8.

Schoenus ferrugineus occurs in base-rich flushes (small sedge mires),
often forming large, dense tufts in semi-open, often stony areas with water
running between them in a mosaic of *Carex dioica–Pinguicula vulgaris*
(**M10**) and *Carex viridula* subsp. *oedocarpa–Saxifraga aizoides* (**M11**)
communities. Often on the edges of small hummocks with the above species
and *Carex panicea, C. pulicaris, C. viridula* subsp. *brachyrrhyncha,
Eleocharis quinqueflora, Festuca ovina, Juncus alpinoarticulatus, Kobresia
simpliciuscula, Trichophorum cespitosum* and calcicolous mosses, e.g.
Ctenidium molluscum and *Scorpidium* spp. See also Wheeler *et al.* (1983).

Schoenus ferrugineus often stands out with its densely packed stems and
black heads. It differs from **29** *S. nigricans* in having much shorter leaves, a
lowermost involucral bract that is shorter than or equals the inflorescence and
an inflorescence that comprises up to four spikelets. Depauperate material of
S. nigricans has a superficial resemblance to *S. ferrugineus* but always has
longer leaves and a lowermost involucral bract exceeding the inflorescence.

Hybrids between the two species have been recorded in Europe (Stace
1975; Hedrén 1997) but not so far in Britain.

176

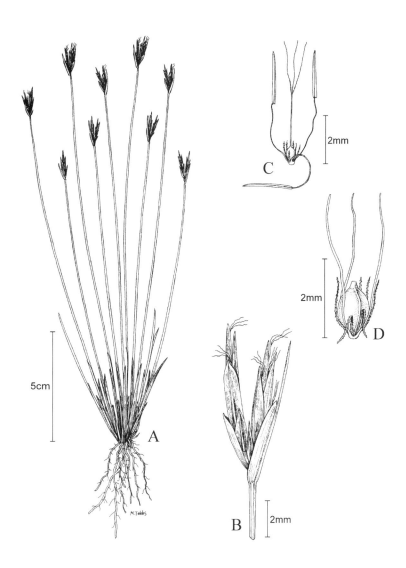

A Plant habit and flowering stems; **B** Spikelet; **C** Floret; **D** Nut.

31 *Cladium mariscus* (L.) Pohl

Great Fen-sedge *Map 31*

Rhizomes ± creeping, *c.* 8 mm in diameter, covered in purplish-brown scales. ***Stems*** up to 200 cm × 3–8 mm, solitary to loosely tufted, hollow, terete, finely ridged. ***Leaves*** mostly basal, 2–3 cauline, up to 200 cm × 5–20 mm, gradually narrowed, acute, flat, somewhat glaucous; margins and keel sharply serrate; sheath up to 20 cm long, reddish-brown, splitting early; ligule absent. ***Inflorescence*** paniculate, 30–70 × 5–12 cm; nodes up to 7, rather distant, each subtending a corymbose partial inflorescence, with dense to rather open branches; primary branches 1–2, 3.5–12 cm long; secondary branches up to 12, 0.5–7 cm long, subtending compact, ovoid to ± globose clusters of spikelets 4–10 × 10 cm; involucral bracts leaf-like, lowest up to 95 cm long. ***Spikelets*** up to 15 per cluster, 2–5 × 0.7–2 mm, ovoid, terete, 2–4-flowered. ***Glumes*** 2–4 × 1.5–3 mm, increasing in size towards spikelet apex, ovate, papery, nerveless except for indistinct midrib, mid brown; apex obtuse to acute. ***Flowers*** bisexual; perianth bristles 0; stamens 2; anthers 2–3 mm long, with prominent, reddish, densely papillose connective tip; stigmas 3. ***Nuts*** 1.5–3 (excluding style-base) × 1.5–1.7 mm, ellipsoid to ovoid, terete, shiny, smooth, with a small saucer-shaped disk at base and conical apex; style-base persistent, *c.* 0.5 mm. ***Fr.*** 7–8.

Cladium mariscus is found in base-rich to mesotrophic areas, where it can form beds consisting almost solely of *Cladium* (**S2a**) or with greater or lesser amounts of *Phragmites* (**S2a, S4a**), sometimes with *Menyanthes trifoliata* and *Potentilla palustris* (**S2b**); also associated with *Carex elata* (e.g. in **S1**). Also in mires, e.g. in the *Schoenus nigricans–Juncus subnodulosus* community (**M13**), where with *Molinia caerulea* and the moss *Calliergonella cuspidata* it can occasionally be dominant. Present, but less frequent, with *Peucedanum palustre* and other sedges in *Juncus subnodulosus–Cirsium palustre* fen-meadow (**M22d**) and in wetter situations, especially in Broadland, in tall-herb fens of *Phragmites–Peucedanum* (**S24**) and *Phragmites–Eupatorium* (**S25**), being co-dominant in sub-community **S25c**. See also the Biological Flora account (Conway 1942).

When dried, *Cladium mariscus* forms a strong thatch used for capping the ridges of cottages thatched with 'Norfolk reed' (*Phragmites australis*). It was formerly an important fuel, especially for bakers' ovens (Rowell 1986), and was also used as a source of cheap paper.

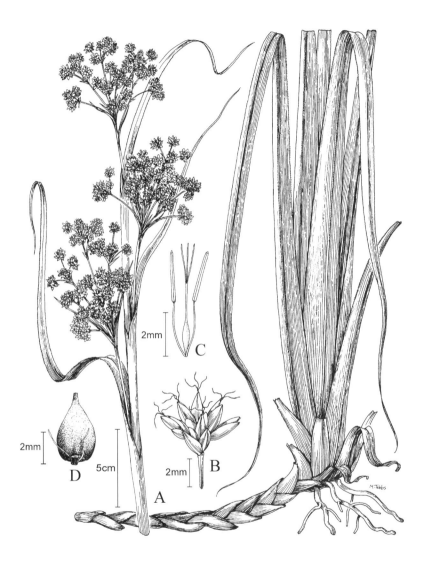

A Plant habit and flowering stem; **B** Spikelet; **C** Floret; **D** Nut (*drawn by R.M.W.*).

M31 Cladium mariscus

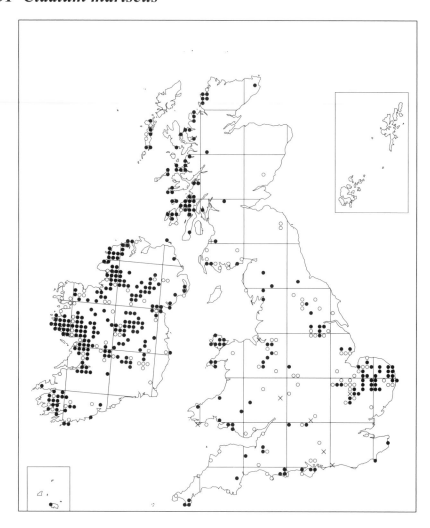

Cladium mariscus is scattered throughout Britain and is still locally common in East Anglia and on the western seaboard of Scotland, though there have been many losses elsewhere. In Ireland it is a frequent plant of mires in western and central areas but absent from much of the NE and SE.

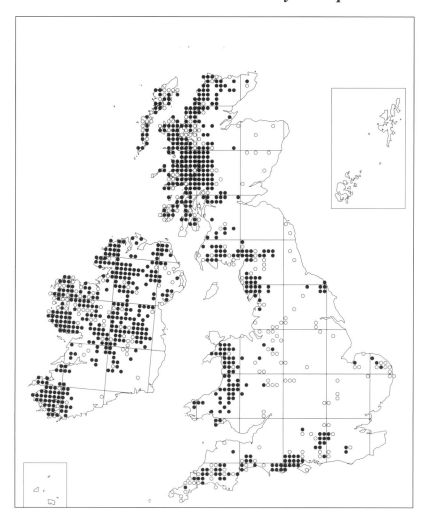

Rhynchospora alba has occurred through much of the British Isles in scattered localities, but it is absent or has disappeared from large parts of central and eastern England, eastern and southern Wales and eastern Scotland. In Ireland it is most common in the north and west.

32 *Rhynchospora alba* (L.) Vahl

White Beak-sedge   *Map 32*

Rhizomes short. *Stems* 10–60 cm × 0.3–0.5 mm, tufted, erect, terete to trigonous above. *Leaves* mostly cauline, reduced to bladeless sheaths near base; blade narrowly linear, up to 15 cm × 1–2 mm, channelled, gradually narrowing to an obtuse apex, grey to yellowish-green; sheath up to 3.5 cm long, greenish to pale brown; lower sheaths often subtending bulbil-like buds; ligule absent. *Inflorescence* comprising 1–4, distant, pedunculate, capitate heads of spikelets; involucral bracts leaf-like, that subtending the lowermost head not exceeding the terminal head. *Spikelets* 3.5–5 × 0.8–1.3 mm, fusiform to ellipsoid, acute, whitish to pale brown. *Glumes* 4–5, 2–5 × 0.7–1 mm, ovate-lanceolate, with an acute to aristate apex and membranous sides, whitish to pale brown, the lowest one or two sterile, the uppermost three fertile, sterile and fertile respectively. *Flowers* bisexual; perianth bristles 9–13, with minute retrorse hairs, shorter than or equalling the nut; stamens 2–3; anthers 0.8–1.2 mm long; stigmas 2. *Nuts* 1.5–2 (excluding style-base) × 0.9–1 mm, obovate, biconvex, smooth to minutely papillose, pale to mid brownish; style-base persistent, conical, quickly tapering to a 1 mm beak.   *Fr.* 8–9.

Rhynchospora alba is characteristic of the shallower parts of bog-pools dominated by *Sphagnum auriculatum* (**M1**), found in the far W of Britain where the annual rainfall exceeds 1200 mm (Climatological Atlas 1952) and similarly in W Ireland (Horsfield *et al.* 1991), and of similar pools with *S. cuspidatum* (**M2a**). In *Schoenus nigricans–Narthecium* mire (**M14**), with *Erica tetralix–Sphagnum compactum*, forming, in wetter areas, a sub-community with *Drosera* spp. (**M16c**), and, in wetter hollows of blanket mires (**M17**, **M18**), with *Carex echinata*, *C. limosa* and *C. pauciflora*. Also in New Forest valley mires dominated by *Narthecium ossifragum* and several *Sphagnum* species, especially *S. auriculatum* (**M21a**), and in *Hypericum elodes–Potamogeton polygonifolius* soakways (**M29**).

R. alba is distinguished by having a short rhizome, spikelets in 1–4 heads with the bract subtending the lowermost head not exceeding the terminal head, whitish to pale brown glumes and 9–13 perianth bristles which are shorter than or equal to the nut and bear minute retrorse hairs. The arrangement of fertile and sterile glumes is characteristic of *Rhynchospora*.

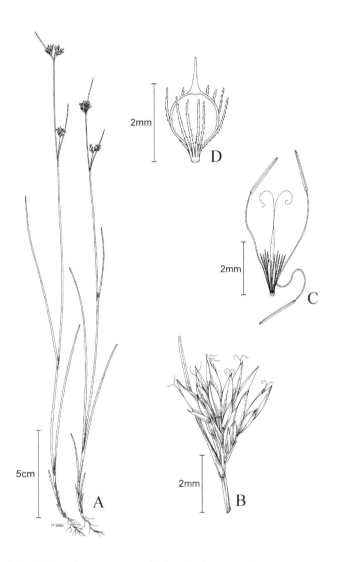

A Plant habit and flowering stems; **B** Spikelet; **C** Floret; **D** Nut.

33 *Rhynchospora fusca* (L.) W.T. Aiton

Brown Beak-sedge   *Map 33*

Rhizomes long-creeping. *Stems* 10–40 cm × 0.4–0.7 mm, distant, erect, terete to trigonous. *Leaves* basal and cauline, up 15 cm × 0.8–1 mm; blade narrowly linear, channelled, gradually narrowing to an obtuse apex, pale greyish-green; sheath up to 4 cm long, greeenish to pale brown; lower sheaths with short blade, without bulbil-like buds: ligule absent. *Inflorescence* comprising 1–2(–3), usually distant, pedunculate, capitate heads of spikelets; involucral bracts leaf-like, that subtending the lowermost head usually exceeding the terminal head. *Spikelets* 5–6 × 1–1.8 mm, oblong-ovoid, acute, dark reddish-brown. *Glumes* 4–5, 2–5 × 0.8–2.2 mm, lanceolate to ovate-lanceolate, acute, aristate, with membranous sides, dark reddish-brown, the lowest one or two sterile, the uppermost three fertile, sterile and fertile respectively. *Flowers* bisexual; perianth bristles 5–6, with minute antrorse hairs, twice as long as the nut or more; stamens 2–3; anthers 1.6–2.2 mm long; stigmas 2. *Nuts* 1.5–2 (excluding style-base) × 0.8–1 mm, obovate, biconvex, smooth, shiny, pale to mid brownish; style-base *c.* 0.5 mm long, conical, truncate at apex.   *Fr.* 8–9.

Rhynchospora fusca occurs on wet peaty soils with a pH between 3 and 5 (Averis *et al.* 2004) and especially in shallow pools and soakways in blanket mires with floating *Sphagna* (with *S. auriculatum* usually dominant), *Eriophorum angustifolium* and *Menyanthes trifoliata* (**M1**), preferring open areas where competition is minimal. Also, in southern England, in *Erica tetralix–Sphagnum compactum* mires in a sub-community with *R. alba* and *Drosera* spp. (**M16c**).

R. fusca is distinguished from **32** *R. alba* by having distant stems on a long-creeping rhizome, dark reddish-brown spikelets, the bract subtending the lowermost head usually exceeding the terminal head and 5–6 perianth bristles which are much longer than the nut and bear minute antrorse hairs.

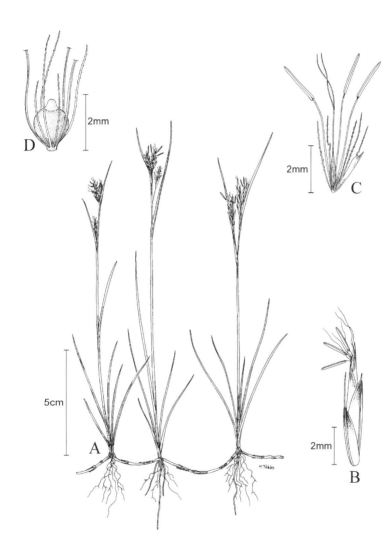

A Plant habit and flowering stems; **B** Spikelet; **C** Floret; **D** Nut.

M33 *Rhynchospora fusca*

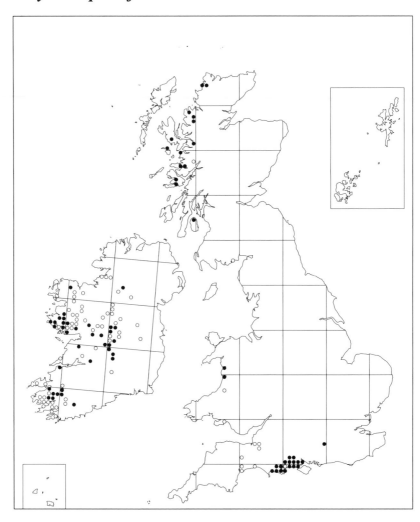

Rhynchospora fusca is very local in Britain, occurring only in Wiltshire, Dorset, Hampshire, Surrey, Cardiganshire and Merioneth and in oceanic areas in NW Scotland, but some populations in Dorset and NW Scotland are very large. In Ireland there has been a widespread decline and it now occurs mainly in the SW, W and centre.

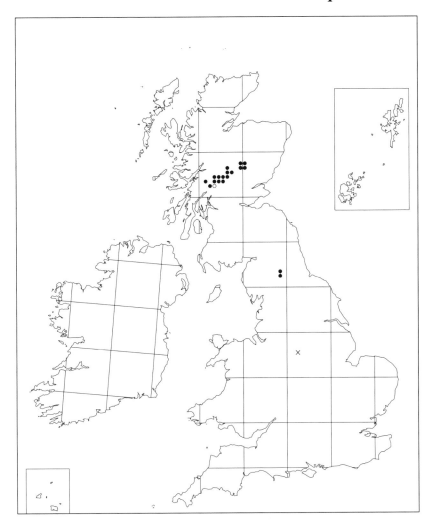

Kobresia simpliciuscula is very locally distributed, being known only from Teesdale, Mid and East Perthshire (v.cc. 88 and 89) and Argyll (v.c. 98), but some populations contain tens of thousands of plants (Porter & Foley 2002).

34   *Kobresia simpliciuscula* (Wahlenb.) Mack.

False Sedge   *Map 34*

Rhizomes very short, densely tufted. *Stems* 5–20 cm × 0.4–0.7 mm, trigonous, rough, stiff, greyish-green, leafy at base. *Leaves* mostly basal, narrowly linear, 3–12 cm × 0.5–1.5(–2) mm, shorter than stems, gradually narrowed to a shortly trigonous, ± obtuse apex, channelled, greyish-green, with margins scabrid near apex; sheaths 1–3 mm long, dull orange-brown to mid brown; ligule *c.* 0.4 mm long, truncate at apex. *Lowest involucral bract* comprising a sheath with a short (*c.* 3–5 mm) greenish to brown lamina. *Inflorescence* a cylindric to ovoid-cylindric, 1–2.5 mm long terminal cluster of 3–10 spikes. *Spikes* 0.4–0.8 mm long, usually crowded, rarely the lowest somewhat distant, mid brown to mid reddish-brown, with male florets above and female below in each spike. *Glumes* 4–5 × 1.3–1.6 mm, those of male and female florets similar, elliptic-ovate, with reddish-brown keel and greenish membranous sides with scarious margins; apex obtuse to acuminate-aristate. *Flowers* unisexual; perianth bristles 0; stamens 3; anthers *c.* 2 mm long; stigmas 3; prophyll (utricle) open at least towards the top, leaving nut exposed, frequently also open down the side, often more so as nut matures. *Nuts* 2–3 × *c.* 1.5 mm, oblong, trigonous, pale dull brown. **Fr.** 7–8.

Kobresia simpliciuscula is characteristic of highly calcareous, somewhat hummocky open flushes within the *Briza media–Primula farinosa* sub-community of the *Carex dioica–Pinguicula vulgaris* mire (**M10b**), and there distinguished as a variant, **M10biii**, best seen in Teesdale, in which *Racomitrium lanuginosum* and *Carex capillaris* are often prominent with the dominant *Kobresia*. In Scottish localities *Carex dioica*, *C. hostiana*, *C. panicea*, *C. pulicaris* and *C. viridula* subspp. *brachyrrhyncha* and *oedocarpa*, *Eleocharis quinqueflora*, *Juncus articulatus* and the bryophytes *Aneura pinguis*, *Ctenidium molluscum* and *Palustriella commutata* amongst others, are common and *Equisetum hyemale* and *Schoenus ferrugineus* locally frequent.

Kobresia is closely related to *Carex*, the former being distinguished by the fact that the utricle does not fully enclose the nut, being open at least at its apex and often down its side. In addition each spike has a male floret at the top and a female one below.

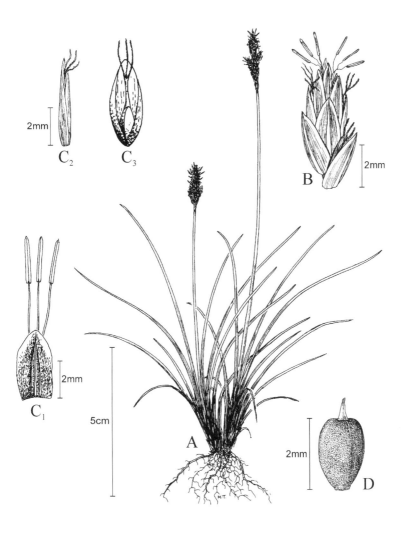

A Plant habit and flowering stems; **B** Spikelet; C_1 Male floret; C_2 Young female floret with folded prophyll (utricle); C_3 Older female floret exposing young nut (*drawn by R.M.W.*); **D** Nut.

35 *Carex paniculata* L.

Rhizomes very short and ascending, forming dense tussocks up to 1.5 m high and 1 m in diameter; roots thick, dark brown, felty; scales dark brown, shiny, ribbed, persistent. **Stems** 60–150 cm, rough, trigonous, spreading. **Leaves** 20–120 cm × (2–)4–7 mm, stiff, channelled or involute, dark green, smooth, rounded and shiny beneath, with many transverse septa, distinctly impressed on upper leaf-face, tapering abruptly to a trigonous apex; margins serrulate; overwintering; hypostomous; sheaths persistent, the lowermost brown, with lateral faces ribbed, herbaceous, often overlapping margins of hyaline inner face, reducing it to a narrow central strip; apex brown, concave; ligule 2–5 mm, rounded. **Inflorescence** a compact panicle, 5–15 cm (except in forma *simplex*, in which some spikes are separated); bracts setaceous or glumaceous with broad hyaline margin and excurrent midrib. **Spikes** numerous, mostly compound, made up of clusters of spikelets 5–8 mm, male at top, female below; some lower spikelets all female, pedunculate, yellow-brown and grass-like. **Male glumes** 3–4 mm, ovate-lanceolate, orange-brown, hyaline, with a pale midrib; apex acute. **Female glumes** 3–4 mm, ovate-triangular, appressed to utricle, orange-brown to greyish with wide hyaline margin; apex acute or acuminate. **Utricles** 3–4 mm, ovoid, ± trigonous, ventricose at base, ribbed, green to dark brown; beak 1–1.5 mm, broadly winged, serrulate; stigmas 2; nut ovoid, biconvex.   **Fr. 6–8.**

C. paniculata is a species of peaty, medium base-rich swamps and mires where water levels are at least seasonally high (e.g. **M9, M27, S24a, S25b**); occasionally in spring-heads; frequently on edges of lakes, ponds, canals and ditches; dominant in **S3** sedge-swamp. An important component of the early hydrosere in open fen-carr; its tussocks facilitate establishment of tree species such as birch and sallow (**W1, W2, W5**). It can withstand some shade, but becomes less vigorous, flowering only sparsely. Mainly lowland, but to over 600 m on Gylchedd, v.c. 50 (Preston & Croft 1997; Porter & Foley 2002).

C. paniculata can be confused only with **36** *C. appropinquata*, with which it hybridises (**36** × **35** *C.* × *rotae* De Not.). Hybrids are found also with *C. remota* (**35** × **48** *C.* × *boenninghausiana* Weihe), *C. canescens* (**35** × **54** *C.* × *ludibunda* J. Gay) and *C. diandra* (**37** × **35** *C.* × *beckmannii* Keck ex F.W. Schultz). A hybrid with **43** *C. arenaria* has recently been found in Merioneth, v.c. 48, by P.M. Benoit (specimen not available for examination).

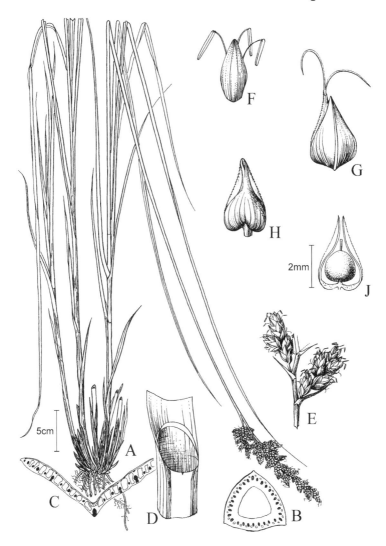

A Fertile shoot; **B** T.S. stem (culm); **C** T.S. leaf; **D** Inner face of leaf-sheath and ligule; **E** Upper spikes; **F** Male floret; **G** Female floret; **H** Utricle (abaxial view); **J** Section through utricle, showing nut.

M35 Carex paniculata

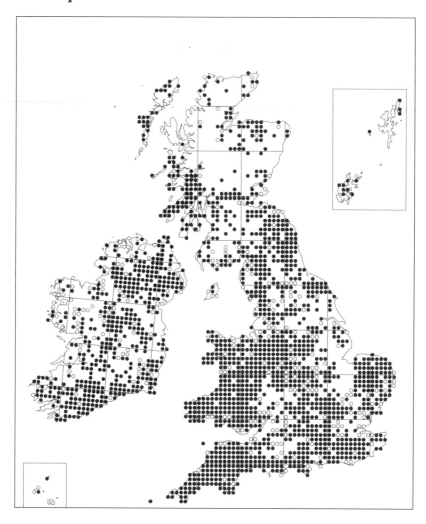

Carex paniculata is widespread and common throughout most of the British Isles but less frequent in Scotland owing to lack of suitable lowland habitats. However, its frequency has decreased and it is threatened in some sites, such as in Broadland, where 'tussock-fens' have ceased to develop.

Carex × *boenninghausiana*   *M35 × 48*
(*C. paniculata* × *C. remota*)

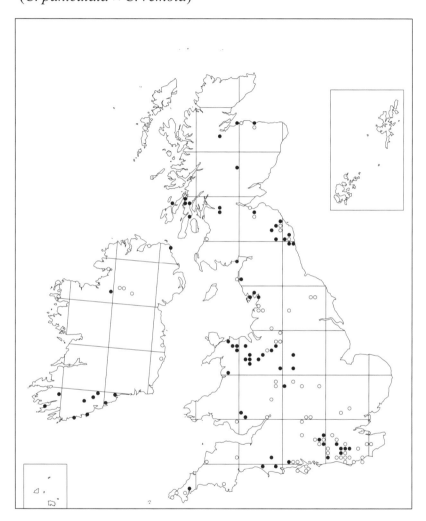

Carex × *boenninghausiana* is one of the more common hybrids, occurring with the parents in damp shady habitats, pool margins and wet woodland, e.g. alder and willow carr. It is scattered throughout much of the British Isles.

35 × 48 *Carex* × *boenninghausiana* Weihe

Carex paniculata × *C. remota*   *Map 35 × 48*

This hybrid is intermediate between the parents in habit, stem length, leaf width, presence and length of bracts, and inflorescence characters. It is most readily distinguished by its long inflorescence, the small, neat spikes of which are distant below, then contiguous and finally crowded above, and usually by the presence of a single, long lowest bract. Male florets usually occur at the base of the spike, as in *C. remota*. *C. paniculata* forma *simplex* is superficially similar but has hard, fertile utricles and lacks the long bract. Best separated from *C.* × *pseudoaxillaris* by its longer inflorescence with more frequent, more spaced-out, narrower, somewhat longer spikes.

Carex paniculata	*C.* × *boenninghausiana*	*Carex remota*
Forms dense tussocks up to 150 cm high.	Forms dense tussocks up to 50 cm high.	Forms dense tussocks up to 30 cm high.
Stem 60–150 cm.	**Stem 70–120 cm.**	Stem 30–75 cm.
Leaves (2–)4–7 mm wide, tapering abruptly, dark green.	**Leaves 2–5 mm wide,** tapering ± gradually to a fine tip, mid green.	Leaves 1.5–2 mm wide, tapering gradually, mid green to yellow-green.
Ligule 2–5 mm, not tubular.	Ligule 1–2 mm, tubular.	Ligule 1–2 mm, tubular.
Spikes up to 15, usually compound, lax, each up to 3 cm long, forming a compact panicle 5–15 cm long; spikelets ♂ at top, ♀ below, or all ♀.	**Spikes 10–15, narrowly ellipsoid to broadly triangular,** 5–10 mm long, **upper crowded, lower distant,** decreasing in size upwards; **spikelets ♀ above, ♂ below, or all ♀.**	Spikes 4–9, ovoid, 3–10 mm long, upper ± contiguous, lower remote, ♀ at top, ♂ below.
Bracts glumaceous or setaceous, never exceeding the inflorescence.	**Lowest bract setaceous to leaf-like, as long as or exceeding the inflorescence, rarely shorter.**	Bracts leaf-like, those of the lower spikes exceeding the inflorescence.
Utricle 3–4 mm, ovoid, ± trigonous, green to dark brown, ribbed; beak winged, serrulate.	Utricle *c.* 4 mm, ellipsoid, plano-convex, pale brown; veining or ribbing weak; beak not winged, serrulate, usually sterile.	Utricle 2.5–3.5 mm, ovoid-ellipsoid, plano-convex, green, veined, shiny; beak not winged, minutely toothed.

194

Carex × boenninghausiana (*C. paniculata* × *C. remota*)   35 × 48
Carex × ludibunda (*C. paniculata* × *C. canescens*)   35 × 54

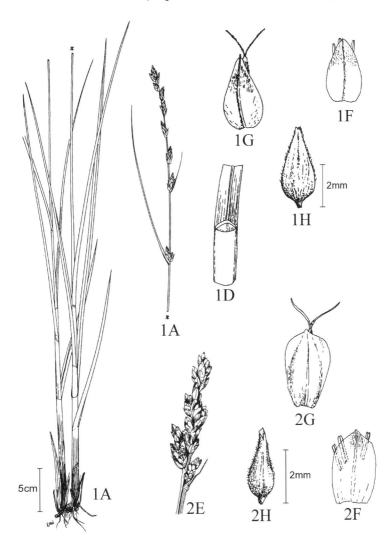

1 *Carex* × *boenninghausiana* **2** *C.* × *ludibunda*
A Fertile shoot; **D** Inner face of leaf-sheath and ligule; **E** Upper spikes; **F** Male floret; **G** Female floret; **H** Utricle.

M35 × 54 *Carex* × *ludibunda* (*Carex paniculata* × *C. canescens*)

Carex × *ludibunda* has been confirmed, growing with both parents, at Newbridge Bog, Ashdown Forest (v.c. 14), in Brecknockshire (v.c. 42) and, most recently in 1989, at Dowrog Common (v.c. 45).

Carex × *ludibunda* J. Gay

Carex paniculata × *C. canescens*   *Map 35 × 54*

This hybrid is closer to *C. canescens*, especially in its medium to small stature. It differs further from *C. paniculata* in its pale basal sheaths, its much shorter, separated inflorescence and its smaller, unwinged utricles. From *C. canescens* it can be distinguished by its tussocky habit, its generally greater height, its broader, thicker leaves, and its ovate-triangular female glumes. It differs from both in its often shrivelled and empty utricles.

Carex paniculata	*Carex* × *ludibunda*	*Carex canescens*
Forming large, dense tussocks; basal sheaths dark brown, persistent.	**Forming tussocks**; basal sheaths pale yellow-brown, persistent.	Shoots loosely tufted; basal sheaths pink-brown.
Leaves 20–120 cm × (2–)4–7 mm, dark green, stiff, channelled or involute.	**Leaves 15–25 cm × 2.5–4 mm**, pale green, ± flat.	Leaves 15–55 cm × 2–3 mm, pale green, soft, flat or ± keeled.
Ligule 2–5 mm, rounded.	Ligule *c.* 2 mm, rounded.	Ligule 2–3 mm, acute.
Inflorescence 5–15 cm; spikes numerous, usually compact.	**Inflorescence 2.5–5 cm**; spikes 8–12, contiguous above, separated below.	Inflorescence 3–5 cm; spikes 4–8, contiguous or ± distant.
♀ glumes 3–4 mm long, ovate-triangular, appressed to utricle, orange-brown with a wide hyaline margin.	♀ glumes 2–3 mm long, ovate-triangular, tightly appressed to utricle, pale brown with a broad hyaline margin.	♀ glumes *c.* 2 mm long, ovate-oblong, hyaline with green midrib.
Utricles 3–4 mm long, ovoid, green to dark brown; beak winged, serrulate.	**Utricles 2.5–3 mm long**, narrowly ovoid, pale green, **tightly appressed, empty**; beak occasionally with a serrate membranous margin but not significantly winged.	Utricles 2–3 mm long, ovoid-ellipsoid, pale green or blue-green to yellow; beak not winged.

36 *Carex appropinquata* Schumach.

Fibrous Tussock-sedge   *Map 36*

Rhizomes very short, ascending, usually forming dense tussocks up to 1 m high and 80 cm in diameter; roots thick, dark brown, felty; scales dark brown-black, eventually breaking up into wiry fibres. *Stems* 40–80 cm, rough, trigonous. *Leaves* 20–80 cm × 1–3 mm, stiff, keeled, yellow-green; hypostomous; sheaths of sterile shoots forming a false stem, the lowermost dark brown with shorter blades, with inner face hyaline; apex brown, concave; ligule 2–3 mm, rounded. *Inflorescence* a compact panicle 4–8 cm; bracts setaceous or glumaceous. *Spikes* made up of spikelets 4–7 mm, male at top, female below; lower spikelets pedunculate and compound, some all female. *Male glumes* 3–4 mm, ovate, reddish-brown, with hyaline margin and apex acute. *Female glumes* 3–4 mm, ovate, acuminate, red-brown, becoming hyaline in fruit. *Utricles* (2.7–)3–4 mm, ovoid to subglobose, ± abruptly narrowed into the beak; beak (0.7–)1–1.5 mm, rough, not winged, notched, sometimes split on adaxial side; stigmas 2; nut ovoid, biconvex.
Fr. 5–7.

A plant of similar habitats to *C. paniculata* (in **M9**), with which it sometimes grows, but perhaps requiring less water movement, as in *Juncus subnodulosus* mires (**M13**) and *Filipendula–Angelica–Valeriana officinalis* mires (**M27**) where grazing or cutting has ceased, and occasionally in more acid fens (e.g. at edges of *Molinia* mire (**M26**), as at Malham Tarn).

C. appropinquata has declined in its East Anglian stronghold and in its Yorkshire lowland sites as a result of drainage and recent dry summers (Porter & Foley 2002).

Possibly sometimes overlooked or confused with **37** *C. diandra* and the former record in Pembrokeshire was in error for a form of that species (forma *pseudoparadoxa*) with compound, pedunculate, proximal spikes (David 1990). It can also be confused with depauperate specimens of **35** *C. paniculata*, from which the blackish, fibrous sheaths, the red colouring of the glumes (both more pronounced on drying) and the unwinged utricle should sufficiently distinguish it.

C. appropinquata hybridises in England with *C. paniculata* (**36** × **35** *C.* × *rotae* De Not.). Hybrids with *C. canescens*, *C. diandra* and *C. remota* are recorded in mainland Europe and could occur in our area.

Carex appropinquata is a **Red Data List** species in Great Britain; *Status*: **Near threatened** (Cheffings & Farrell 2005).

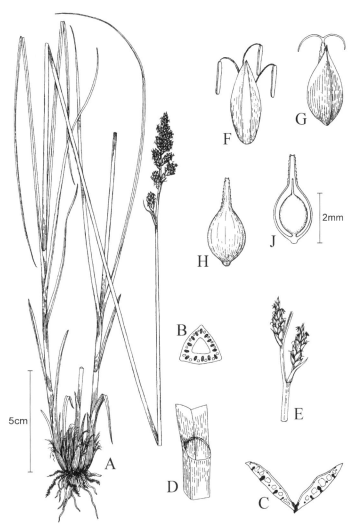

A Fertile shoot; **B** T.S. stem (culm); **C** T.S. leaf; **D** Inner face of leaf-sheath and ligule; **E** Upper spikes; **F** Male floret; **G** Female floret; **H** Utricle; **J** Section through utricle, showing nut.

M36 Carex appropinquata

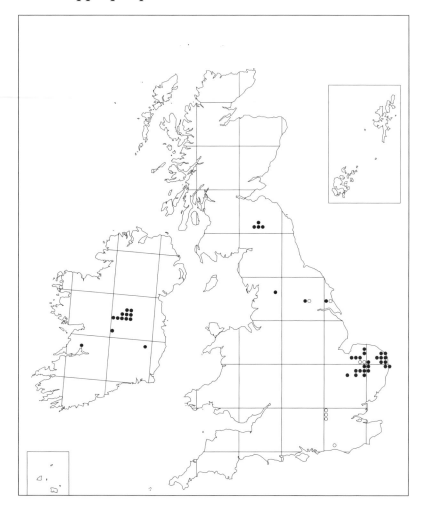

Carex appropinquata is frequent in East Anglia and very local in SE and mid-west Yorkshire and in Roxburgh and Selkirk; formerly also on the Middlesex–Herts–Bucks borders but now extinct. In Ireland it is widespread but local in the centre. See also David (1990).

Carex × rotae (*Carex appropinquata × C. paniculata*)   *M36 × 35*

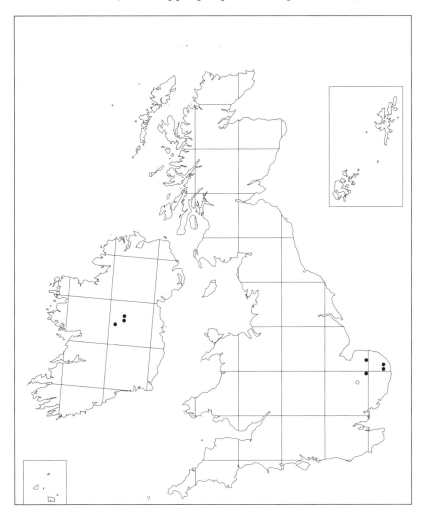

Carex × rotae has been found in East Anglia, in a swamp between Barton Mills and Icklingham (v.c. 26), at Strumpshaw and Wheatfen Broads on the R. Yare, at Upton and Ranworth on the R. Bure (v.c. 27) and at Cranberry Rough (v.c. 28). It also occurs at four sites in Co. Westmeath (v.c. H23): north of Twy Loch, at Mount Dalton, at Lough Iron and NW of Lough Owel.

36 × 35 *Carex* × *rotae* De Not.

Carex appropinquata × *C. paniculata*   *Map M36 × 35*

Although variable, *Carex* × *rotae* is intermediate between the parents in its leaf width and leaf and stem length. It can be further distinguished from *C. appropinquata* by its dark brown, rather than matt black, slightly fibrous basal sheaths, by its occasionally extremely long inflorescence (here showing a resemblance to a plant which has been called *C. paniculata* forma *simplex*) and by its often winged utricles. It further differs from *C. paniculata* in its lesser stature, darker, more fibrous, basal sheaths, shorter inflorescence and less tussocky habit. This hybrid appears to be partially fertile.

Carex appropinquata	*Carex* × *rotae*	*Carex paniculata*
Densely tufted, usually forming tussocks.	Variably, sometimes densely, sometimes loosely, tufted.	Densely tufted, forming tussocks.
Sheaths matt black, becoming fibrous.	**Sheaths dark brown, slightly fibrous, sometimes with a sheen.**	Sheaths shiny dark brown, not becoming fibrous.
Stems 40–80 cm in length.	**Stems 50–100 cm in length.**	Stems 60–150 cm in length.
Leaves 20–80 cm × 1–3 mm, yellow-green.	**Leaves 50–90 cm × 2–4 mm, grey-green.**	Leaves 20–120 cm × (2–)4–7 mm, dark green.
Inflorescence a compact panicle 4–8 cm in length.	Inflorescence variable in length, 3–5(–12) cm.	Inflorescence a compact panicle 5–15 cm in length (but longer in forma *simplex*).
♀ glumes red-brown, hyaline.	♀ glumes pale brown, often with hyaline margin.	♀ glumes greyish to orange-brown with broad hyaline margin.
Utricles grey-brown; beak not winged.	Utricles dull medium brown; beak often winged, serrulate.	Utricles green to dark brown; beak winged, serrulate.

Carex × rotae (Carex appropinquata × C. paniculata) 36 × 35
Carex × beckmannii (Carex diandra × C. paniculata) 37 × 35

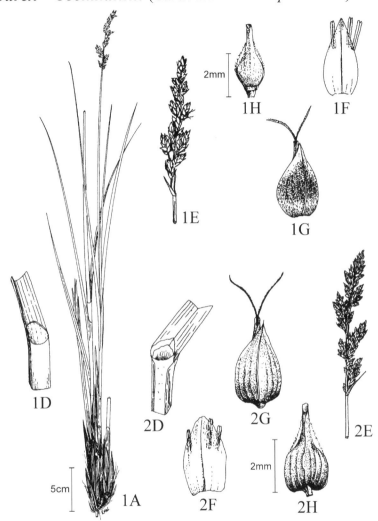

2mm

1H   1F

1E   1G

1D   2D   2G   2E

5cm   1A   2F   2mm   2H

1 *Carex × rotae* **2** *C. × beckmannii*
A Fertile shoot; **D** Inner face of leaf-sheath and ligule; **E** Upper spikes; **F** Male floret; **G** Female floret; **H** Utricle.

M37 × 35 *Carex* × *beckmannii* (*Carex diandra* × *C. paniculata*)

Carex × *beckmannii* is known from peaty marshes and pool margins, where it grows with both parents at five sites: SE Yorks. (v.c. 61), Loch Lochton (v.c. 75), two sites in Main Argyll (v.c. 98) and one site in Mid Cork (v.c. H4).

Carex diandra × *C. paniculata*   *Map 37 × 35*

Intermediate between its parents in height, leaf width and inflorescence length, this sterile hybrid can also be distinguished from *C. paniculata* by its less tussocky habit, its mid green rather than dark green leaves, its tubular ligule, its darker, more uniform inflorescence and its unwinged or slightly winged utricle beak. From *C. diandra* it further differs in its mid green, involute leaves. An additional difference can be seen at flowering time (May/June), when the inflorescence of the hybrid overtops the leaves while that of *C. diandra* is often concealed by them. From both species it can be distinguished in the field by the dull grey colour of its empty utricles contrasting with the brown of the parents' fertile utricles. It is best told from **36** × **35** *C.* × *rotae* by its greener leaves and its tubular ligule.

At its Irish site the lowest spikes of the inflorescence are compound and pedunculate and the upper surface of the leaves grey-green, the *C. diandra* parent here being sometimes referred to as forma *pseudoparadoxa* S. Gibson (T. O'Mahony pers. comm.).

Carex diandra	*C.* × *beckmannii*	*Carex paniculata*
Rhizomes shortly creeping, usually forming a loose, low tussock.	**Rhizomes shortly creeping, usually forming a loose, low tussock.**	Rhizomes very short, forming a dense, often high tussock.
Stems 25–60 cm.	Stems *c*. 40 cm.	Stems 60–150 cm.
Leaves 1–2 mm wide, grey-green, flat.	**Leaves (2–)3–4 mm wide, mid green, occasionally greenish-yellow, involute.**	Leaves (2–)4–7 mm wide, dark green, channelled.
Ligule tubular.	**Ligule tubular.**	Ligule not tubular.
Inflorescence 1–5 cm long, neat, compact, dark brown.	**Inflorescence 3–5 cm long, ± neat, compact, dull grey when mature.**	Inflorescence 5–15 cm long, rather ragged and untidy, brown.
Lowest spike sessile.	Lowest spike sessile.	Lowest spike pedunculate.
Utricles broadly ovoid or suborbicular, narrowing into an unwinged beak.	**Utricles empty**, narrowly ovoid-ellipsoid; **beak not or slightly winged.**	Utricles ovoid, ± trigonous, narrowing into a broadly winged beak.

37 *Carex diandra* Schrank

Lesser Tussock-sedge   *Map 37*

Rhizomes shortly creeping; shoots clustered, forming a loose tussock or appearing at ± regular intervals; roots grey- or orange-brown; scales black or dark grey-brown, persistent. **Stems** 25–60 cm, slender, ± sharply trigonous, rough on angles. **Leaves** 20–40 cm × 1–2 mm, rough at least above, ± flat or slightly keeled, gradually tapered to a fine ± trigonous point, grey-green, often overwintering; hypostomous; lower sheaths grey-brown or dark brown, persistent, with inner face hyaline, often with glandular dots; apex ± straight to concave; ligule 1–2 mm, obtuse, tubular with a free margin of 1–2 mm. **Inflorescence** a ± compact head, 1–5 cm; bracts glumaceous, lowest rarely setaceous. **Spikes** 6–10, 5–8 mm, sessile, male at top, female below. **Male glumes** 3–4 mm, lanceolate-elliptic, pale brown-hyaline; apex acute. **Female glumes** c. 3 mm, broadly ovate, purple-brown, with a short green midrib and broad hyaline margin; apex acute or mucronate. **Utricles** 3–4 mm, broadly ovoid or suborbicular, plano-convex, distinctly 2–5-ribbed in lower half, dark brown, shiny; beak 1.5–2 mm, broad, serrulate, bifid, split for whole length on abaxial side; stigmas 2; nut top-shaped, plano-convex, stalked.   *Fr.* 6–7.

Carex diandra is a species of very wet mires in moderately base-rich waters, forming a characteristic sub-community with *C. rostrata, Potentilla palustris, Menyanthes trifoliata, Calliergon giganteum* and *Calliergonella cuspidata* (**M9b**); also often in overgrown ditches or in more acid old peat-cuttings and mesotrophic flushes in blanket mires. It also occurs in valley fens in the Norfolk Broads, in *Schoenus nigricans–Juncus subnodulosus* mire (**M13c**), occasionally among scattered bushes or in fen-carr.

This is a distinct species rarely confused with others. Depauperate plants in shade and in stagnant water may be tussocky and appear like **36** *C. appropinquata*; that species, however, has very fibrous, black lower leaf-sheaths, reddish-brown glumes and a more compact and compound inflorescence. Robust forms have been called *C. ehrhartiana* Hoppe or *C. diandra* forma *pseudoparadoxa* S. Gibson – a taxon bearing compound, pedunculate, proximal spikes, easily confused with **36** *C. appropinquata*, but these do not warrant taxonomic recognition.

C. diandra hybridises with *C. paniculata* (**37** × **35** *C.* × *beckmannii* Keck ex F.W. Schultz) and also with *C. appropinquata* but not in our area.

Carex diandra is a **Red Data List** species in Great Britain; *Status*: **Near threatened** (Cheffings & Farrell 2005). It is not endangered in Ireland.

206

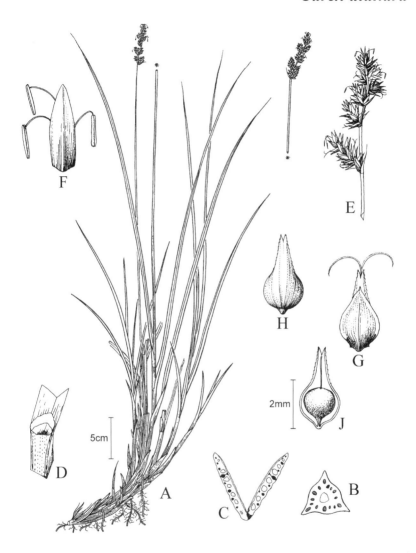

A Fertile shoot; **B** T.S. stem (culm); **C** T.S. leaf; **D** Inner face of leaf-sheath and ligule; **E** Upper spikes; **F** Male floret; **G** Female floret; **H** Utricle (abaxial view); **J** Section through utricle, showing nut.

M37 Carex diandra

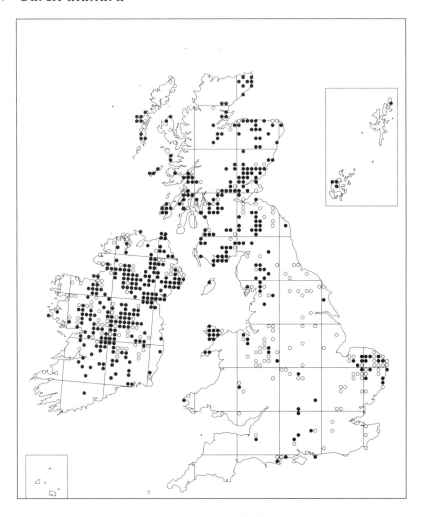

Carex diandra is predominantly a lowland plant, but reaches 370 m near Malham Tarn, v.c. 64 (Porter & Foley 2002). Throughout the British Isles north to Caithness, but absent from the SW peninsula and becoming scarcer in central and E England, other than the Norfolk Broads, as sites are drained. In Ireland, it is mainly in the centre, commonly on reworked peat areas.

Carex vulpina M38

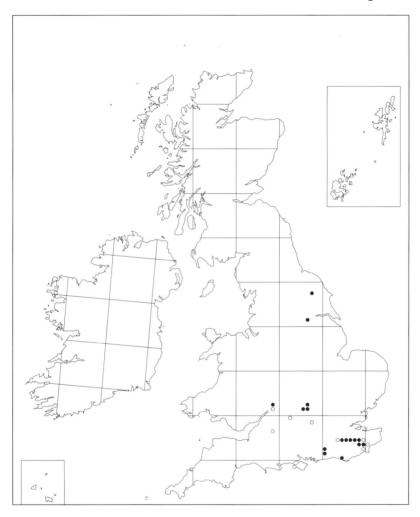

Carex vulpina is now local in SE England, Oxon, Glos and SE and NE Yorks; in the last two it has been reintroduced. Formerly also in the Isle of Wight, Berks and Somerset.

38   *Carex vulpina* L.

True Fox-sedge   *Map 38*

Rhizomes short; shoots stout, densely tufted; roots thick, grey-brown; scales dark brown, remaining only as black fibres. ***Stems*** 30–100 cm, smooth below, rough above, sharply trigonous, their faces ± concave and angles winged. ***Leaves*** up to 80 cm × 4–10 mm, ± erect, acutely keeled, ± abruptly tapering to a flat, sharp point, dark green even when dry, not auriculate at base; hypostomous; inner face of sheaths glandular, transversely wrinkled and perforated with a vertical line of small holes; apex markedly lingulate; ligule 2–6 mm, truncate, shorter than width of leaf, its free margin overlapping the edges of the leaf-blade. ***Inflorescence*** a stout, dense panicle; bracts short, setaceous, with ± prominent dark auricles. ***Spikes*** numerous, 8–14 mm, compound, all or most male above and female below. ***Male glumes*** 3.5–4 mm, oblanceolate-elliptic, dark or rusty brown with a green midrib. ***Female glumes*** 4–5 mm, ovate, acuminate, dark or rusty brown; midrib indistinct. ***Utricles*** 4–5 mm, ovoid-ellipsoid, minutely papillose, only faintly nerved, readily dropping at maturity; epidermal cells of adaxial face thick-walled, minutely papillous and ± isodiametric; beak 1–1.5 mm, split on back; stigmas 2; nut oblong-obovoid, biconvex.   ***Fr.*** 6–8.

In damp places, often standing in water in ditches and areas flooded in winter, usually on heavy clay soils and over chalk or limestone, enduring shade when encroached upon by shrubs and trees (**W1**, **W2**).

Probably overlooked as a result of confusion with **39** *C. otrubae*, from which it is distinguished by the very broad, overlapping, truncate ligule (in *C. otrubae* the ligule is ± acute and narrower than the width of the leaf), the acutely keeled leaf and the split beak to the papillose utricle. The strongly winged stem, the perforated glandular inner face of the leaf-sheaths, the dark auricles of the bracts and the dark young spikes are also diagnostic. Under the microscope *C. vulpina* has the epidermal cells of the utricle thick-walled and ± square, while those of *C. otrubae* are thin-walled and oblong (Samuelsson 1922). For other microscopic differences see pp. 10 and 11.

Hybrids with **39** *C. otrubae* have been tentatively identified from W Kent and W Sussex (see p. 212). Hybrids with *C. paniculata* and *C. remota* are also recorded, but not in the British Isles.

Carex vulpina is a **Red Data List** species in Great Britain; *Status*: **Vulnerable** (Cheffings & Farrell 2005).

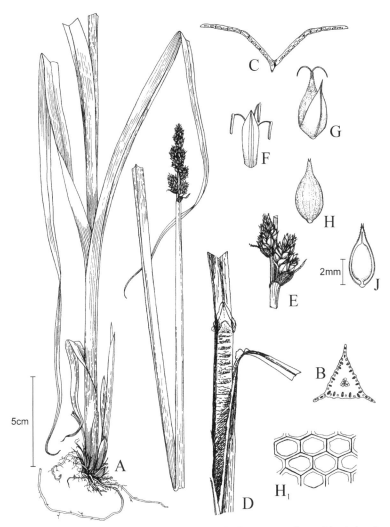

A Fertile shoot; **B** T.S. stem (culm); **C** T.S. leaf; **D** Inner face of leaf-sheath and ligule; **E** Two spikes; **F** Male floret; **G** Female floret; **H** Utricle; **H₁** epidermal cells of adaxial face of utricle; **J** Section through utricle, showing nut.

38 × 39 *Carex vulpina* × *Carex otrubae*

(neither mapped nor illustrated)

Conclusive proof of the existence of this hybrid in the Britain Isles has long been awaited. From material studied, the putative hybrid differs from *C. otrubae* in its shorter bracts and distinctly smaller, faintly ribbed utricles. From *C. vulpina* it differs in its only slightly winged stems, its longer bracts and the elongated cells on the adaxial face of the utricles. It differs from both parents in its flat, empty utricles

Tentatively identified by E. Nelmes from the River Medway, near Tonbridge (v.c. 16), and Amberley Wild Brooks (v.c. 13) (*Hall 3383*, **BM**), occurring with both parents along ditch margins. After F. Abraham and M. Briggs collected atypical specimens from Amberley, we searched the site and noted some plants showing intermediacy between the parents (cf. *Foley & Porter F. 2013*, **E**). These also demonstrate intermediacy in flowering time and only partial fertility. Molecular work on the putative hybrid carried out by C. Smith (pers. comm.) also supports the possibility of hybridisation.

Carex vulpina	*Carex vulpina* × *C. otrubae*	*Carex otrubae*
Flowering from March.	Flowering late April.	Flowering from May.
Stem faces concave, distinctly winged.	Stem faces only slightly winged.	Stem faces ± flat, only slightly winged.
Ligule truncate; free hyaline margin present.	Ligule acute; free hyaline margin absent.	Ligule acute; free hyaline margin absent.
Bracts usually very much shorter than inflorescence.	**Bracts generally shorter than inflorescence.**	Bracts half as long as or longer than inflorescence.
♀ glumes dark or rusty brown; midrib indistinct.	♀ glumes mid brown with a green midrib.	♀ glumes orange- or pale red-brown; midrib green.
Utricles 4–5 mm, ovoid-ellipsoid, faintly ribbed, yellow-brown, darkening on maturity; cells on adaxial surface ± isodiametric, minutely papillose.	**Utricles 3.9–4.2 mm,** ovoid, plano-convex, **faintly ribbed,** pale yellow-brown, **many appearing empty; cells on adaxial surface elongated.**	Utricles 4–6 mm, ovoid, plano-convex, distinctly ribbed, green, red-brown to dark brown at maturity; cells on adaxial surface distinctly elongated.

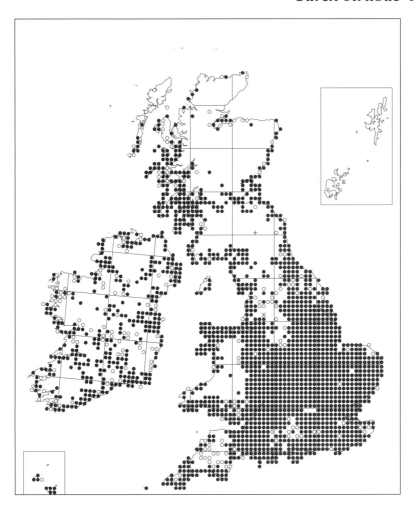

Carex otrubae is a lowland plant which is rare in mountain areas of Britain and becomes almost exclusively coastal in NW England and Scotland. It is scattered throughout Ireland but commonest near the coast.

213

39   *Carex otrubae* Podp.

False Fox-sedge   *Map 39*

Rhizomes short; shoots stout, densely tufted; roots thick, grey-brown; scales brown, remaining as black fibres. *Stems* 30–100 cm, stout, smooth below, rough above, trigonous, their faces ± flat, slightly winged on angles. *Leaves* up to 60 cm × 4–10 mm, ± erect, obtusely keeled, tapering to a flat, sharp point, bright green, becoming grey-green when dry and often spotted with pale orange-brown in decay; margins rough; hypostomous; base appearing subauriculate, as it abruptly contracts into the sheath; sheaths white with green veins, becoming brown, soon decaying, with inner face hyaline, not wrinkled; apex variable from concave to rarely lingulate; ligule 5–10 mm, ± acute, tubular, contained within the width of the leaf. *Inflorescence* an elongate panicle, becoming dense when in fruit; lower bracts setaceous, with leaf-like base, half as long as, or often longer than, the inflorescence; upper bracts glumaceous. *Spikes* numerous, 8–14 mm, compound, all or most male above and female below. *Male glumes* 3.5–4 mm, oblanceolate-elliptic, pale orange-brown with green midrib; apex acute. *Female glumes* 4–5 mm, ovate, pale red- or orange-brown with green midrib; apex acuminate-aristate. *Utricles* 4–6 mm, ovoid, plano-convex, ± shiny, strongly nerved, green, at maturity red-brown to dark brown and not readily dropping; epidermal cells of adaxial face thin-walled and elongated; beak 1–1.5 mm, rough at apex, bifid, not split at back; stigmas 2; nut oblong-obovoid, biconvex.   *Fr.* 7–9.

   C. otrubae is a species of heavy soils, usually in damp situations with *Juncus effusus* or *J. acutiflorus*, typically in **M28** and related communities, where an element of flushing occurs, and a marginal species in roadside ditches and drainage dykes (**S18**), becoming in western regions almost exclusively a coastal plant in sites that may be inundated by brackish or even saline water (e.g. **MG12**). Similar to **38** *C. vulpina* (which see for diagnostic characters) and certainly hybridises with it in mainland Europe. Narrow-leaved plants are difficult to separate from **40–42** *C. muricata* agg., but the thicker, stout stem, the distinctive veining in leaves and sheaths, the acute tubular ligule and ± auriculate leaves of *C. otrubae* will usually distinguish it.

   C. otrubae hybridises with *C. spicata* (**39** × **40** *C.* × *haussknechtii* Senay), **42a** *C. divulsa* subsp. *divulsa* (see **42a** × **39**) and *C. remota* (**39** × **48** *C.* × *pseudoaxillaris* K. Richt.). Hybrids with **38** *C. vulpina* are difficult to detect but have been tentatively identified in southern England (see p. 212).

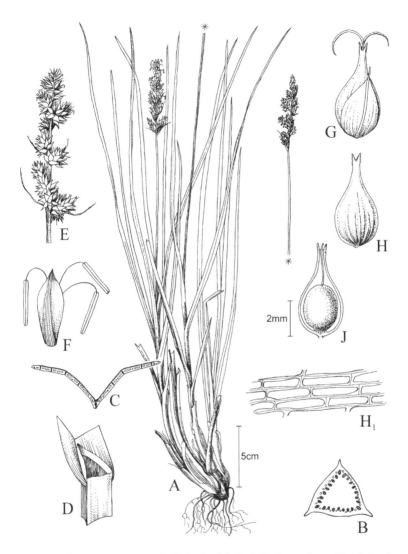

A Fertile shoot; **B** T.S. stem (culm); **C** T.S. leaf; **D** Inner face of leaf-sheath and ligule; **E** Upper spikes; **F** Male floret; **G** Female floret; **H** Utricle; **H₁** epidermal cells of adaxial face of utricle; **J** Section through utricle, showing nut.

215

39 × 40 *Carex* × *haussknechtii* Senay

Carex otrubae × *C. spicata*   (*not mapped*)

With its robust stature and stout inflorescence, this hybrid has the general appearance of *C. otrubae*. However, the stem, although trigonous, is not winged and the leaves are intermediate in width between those of the parents. It is closer to *C. spicata* in its more separated lower spikes and in utricle size. *C.* × *haussknechtii* differs from the equally rare **42a** × **39** *C. divulsa* × *C. otrubae* in its long acute ligule and its much stouter, less separated inflorescence.

This hybrid has been recorded from several localities in the British Isles, but Wallace (1975) doubted the identity of the voucher specimens from v.cc. 17 and 33. However, plants occurring on the side of a lane near Whitchurch, North Somerset (v.c. 6), in 1925 (**CGE**) are sterile and show evidence of intermediacy as described below.

Carex otrubae	*C.* × *haussknechtii*	*Carex spicata*
Stems 30–100 cm, sharply trigonous, slightly winged.	Stems 75–95 cm, trigonous, not winged.	Stems 10–85 cm, trigonous (sometimes ± rounded), not winged.
Leaves 4–10 mm wide, tapering abruptly.	**Leaves 3–7 mm wide**, usually tapering abruptly.	Leaves 2–4 mm wide, tapering gradually.
Inflorescence with up to 15, usually contiguous spikes, the lowest rarely separated.	**Inflorescence 5–9.5 cm**, with up to 12 spikes, the **lowest often separated.**	Inflorescence 1–4 cm long with 3–8 spikes, contiguous but lowest often separated.
Lower bract setaceous, half as long as to longer than the inflorescence.	Lower bract setaceous, up to twice the length of the lowest spike.	Lower bracts short and glumaceous.
♀ glumes pale brown, ovate; apex often extremely acuminate.	♀ **glumes** pale- to mid brown, ovate-lanceolate; apex **highly acuminate.**	♀ glumes red-brown, lanceolate; apex acuminate.
Utricles 4–6 mm, ribbed, narrowing abruptly to bifid beak *c.* 1–1.5 mm.	**Utricles 3.5–4.5 mm, ribbed, empty, narrowing gradually to notched beak *c.* 1 mm.**	Utricles 4–5 mm, not ribbed, narrowing gradually to notched beak *c.* 2 mm.

Carex × haussknechtii (Carex otrubae × C. spicata)   39 × 40
Carex × pseudoaxillaris (Carex otrubae × C. remota)   39 × 48

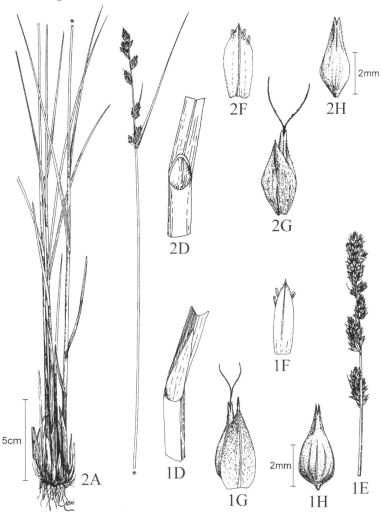

1 *Carex × haussknechtii* **2** *C. × pseudoaxillaris*
A Fertile shoot; **D** Inner face of leaf-sheath and ligule; **E** Upper spikes; **F** Male floret; **G** Female floret; **H** Utricle.

M39 × 48 *Carex × pseudoaxillaris* (*Carex otrubae* × *C. remota*)

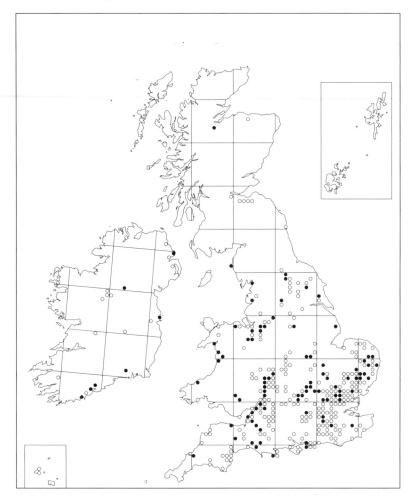

Carex × pseudoaxillaris is found in both inland and coastal sites in the south and central parts of Britain. In the north, where it may have gone from some sites, it is mainly coastal, as is its parent *C. otrubae*. In Ireland it is occasional and scattered.

218

Carex × *pseudoaxillaris* K. Richt.   **39 × 48**

Carex otrubae × *C. remota*   *Map 39 × 48*

A tall (to 150 cm), tufted plant, this usually sterile hybrid differs from *C. otrubae* in its more slender stems, its distinctly separated spikes and its long bracts that often overtop the inflorescence. It is distinguished from *C. remota* by its much stouter, ± triangular spikes, the two lowest of which are less widely separated. It differs from both parents in its unemergent anthers and usually empty utricles.

One of the more frequent hybrids, which may occur wherever the parents grow together, sometimes forming extensive patches, usually at low altitudes, in damp or seasonally wet habitats on acid soils. Found growing in hedgerows and ditches, sometimes in shade, both inland and in coastal sites, in the latter on wet cliff-ledges and muddy shores just above the strandline.

Carex otrubae	*C.* × *pseudoaxillaris*	*Carex remota*
Stem stout, slightly winged.	Stem less stout than in *C. otrubae*, sometimes sharply trigonous.	Stem very slender, not winged.
Spikes ± ovoid, the lower compound; upper part of spike ♂, the lower ♀.	**Spikes ± triangular to trapezoid, the 2 lowest separated by approximately 2–3 times their own length,** often compound; **each spike ♂ at base, ♀ above.**	Spikes ovoid to oblong-cylindric, the 2 lowest separated by at least 5 times their own length; each spike ♀ at top, ♂ at base, lowest entirely ♀.
Lowest bracts setaceous, 1/2 length of to longer than inflorescence.	Lowest bracts narrow, leaf-like, often exceeding inflorescence.	Lowest bracts very long, leaf-like, well exceeding inflorescence.
♀ glumes 4–5 mm, ovate, pale red- or orange-brown; midrib green.	♀ glumes 2.5–3.5 mm, ovate, pale green to white; midrib green.	♀ glumes *c.* 2.5 mm, ovate to lanceolate, pale; midrib green.
Utricles 4–6 mm, ovoid, green, becoming dark brown, patent; beak 1–1.5 mm.	**Utricles 3–4 mm, narrowly ovoid,** pale green-brown, **usually empty,** appressed; beak up to 1 mm.	Utricles 2.5–3.5 mm, ovoid-ellipsoid, green, ± shiny, appressed; beak 0.5 mm.

40–42 *Carex muricata* group (section *Phaestoglochin* Dumort.)

The *Carex muricata* aggregate comprises, in the British Isles, five closely related taxa (see below) whose precise taxonomic status is debatable. They are most conveniently considered as falling into three groups – a species standing a little apart from the rest and two separate pairs. The most distinct is **40** *C. spicata*, which differs in the structure of utricle and ligule and in the presence (sometimes only in the roots) of a purplish pigment wholly absent from the other taxa. **41** *C. muricata* is treated here as having two subspecies, subspp. *muricata* and *pairae*, showing small but definite differences and seeming to be ecologically and thus to some extent geographically vicarious, the one a rare early-flowering taxon confined to calcareous, mostly western, sites and the other a late-flowering and more widespread calcifuge.

From the above three taxa, **42** *C. divulsa* subspp. *divulsa* and *leersii* are separated by the markedly interrupted inflorescence and by the diamond-shape of the utricles, narrowed both above and below. The extreme form of **42a** *C. divulsa* subsp. *divulsa*, with long, lax inflorescence, appressed spikes and small utricles, is strikingly distinct from the extreme form of **42b** subsp. *leersii*, which has a shorter, stouter inflorescence and strongly patent or divaricate utricles of (in Britain) 4 to 4.5 mm. There are also differences in flowering time, as in the two subspecies of *C. muricata*. Many intermediates between these extreme forms can, however, be found. Some of these show a degree of sterility and may be hybrids between the two or between one of them and some other member of the aggregate. Furthermore, **42b** *C. divulsa* subsp. *leersii*, if severely damaged by mowing or other disturbance, may produce late depauperate flowering stems that are indistinguishable from those of **42a** subsp. *divulsa*. The two taxa, when considered over their whole geographical range, appear to represent a cline, or continuous variation, between the extreme form of subsp. *leersii* (*C. polyphylla* Kar. & Kir. of Central Asia, a much more robust plant than any seen in the west, although Karelin and Kirilov's type is far from being an extreme form and can easily be matched by British material: R.W. David pers. comm.) and the subsp. *divulsa* of Western Europe.

The taxonomy of this, the most complicated *Carex* section in our flora, has been studied morphometrically by several workers and most recently by Řepka (2003). What is needed now is a molecular approach (and see below). The similarities within the section have resulted in an extensive list of synonyms at different hierarchical levels that need not worry botanists using this book. The names used in the following pages are summarised here, with the more common synonyms used by British or Irish writers. See also David (1976).

40 *Carex spicata* Huds. (syn: *C. contigua* Hoppe; *C. muricata* auct. plur., non L.)

41a *Carex muricata* L. subsp. ***muricata*** (syn: *C. muricata* subsp. *lamprocarpa* (Wallr.) Čelak.; *C. pairae* subsp. *borealis* Hyl.)

41b *Carex muricata* L. subsp. ***pairae*** (F.W. Schultz) Čelak. (syn: *C. lamprocarpa* auct., non (Wallr.) Čelak.; *C. bullockiana* Nelmes)

42a *Carex divulsa* Stokes subsp. ***divulsa***

42b *Carex divulsa* Stokes subsp. ***leersii*** (Kneuck.) W. Koch (syn: *C. leersii* F.W. Schultz, non Willd.; *C. muricata* subsp. *leersii* Ascherson & Graebner; ? *C. polyphylla* Kar. & Kir.)

Hybrids

Hybrids within the group are rare. Those between **40** *C. spicata* and **42** *C. divulsa* have been recorded but not confirmed. **42a** *C. divulsa* subsp. *divulsa* and **41b** *C. muricata* subsp. *pairae* have been found to hybridise in Co. Cork (v.c. H5; see p. 241). Subsequently a total of eight sites was found in v.cc. H4 and H5. The first plant appeared partly fertile and its finder, T. O'Mahony, was able to grow a fertile F_2 generation (O'Mahony 1989, 2004). The plant and its offspring were vigorous, their stems often reaching to well over 100 cm. Interestingly its morphology was superficially like that of *C. divulsa* subsp. *leersii*, a plant not recorded for Ireland, but O'Mahony's thorough study has shown distinct morphological differences. The discovery of this hybrid and its potential for back-crossing, though seen in cultivation, might indicate a closer genetical relationship between *C. muricata* and *C. divulsa* than may be suggested by our present treatment here. In such a group it is inevitable that there will be conflicting views about merging taxa as subspecies or designating relict populations containing rich gene-pools as full species. Subsequent molecular study may elucidate the situation.

Outside the group, *Carex spicata* hybridises with *C. otrubae* (**39** × **40** *C. × haussknechtii* Senay) and with *C. echinata* in mainland Europe. *C. divulsa* subsp. *divulsa* hybridises with *C. otrubae* (**42a** × **39**) and *C. remota* (**42a** × **48** *C. × emmae* L. Gross.) in Britain and Ireland. A hybrid with *C. leporina* occurs in mainland Europe.

40   *Carex spicata* Huds.

Spiked Sedge   *Map 40*

Rhizomes short; shoots densely tufted; roots purple-tinged; scales brown or red-brown, with black veins, eventually becoming fibrous. *Stems* 10–85 cm, often stout, trigonous; fruiting stems often elongating considerably in wet ditch-cum-hedge-bank habitats. *Leaves* 7–45 cm × 2–4 mm, keeled, gradually tapering to a flat tip, mid green; hypostomous; sheaths forming a short false stem, sometimes stained wine-red; apex straight or concave; ligule 4–8(–10) mm, ± acute, with much soft, white, loose tissue, sometimes tinged purple-red. *Inflorescence* 1–4 cm; bracts glumaceous, with a setaceous point. *Spikes* 3–8, usually contiguous (rarely widely separated), 5–10 mm, sessile, male at top, female below. *Male glumes* 3–4 mm, lanceolate; apex acute. *Female glumes* 4–4.5 mm, lanceolate, acuminate, red-brown with a green midrib, occasionally tinged purple-red. *Utricles* 4–5 mm, with an irregularly bulbous and corky base and gradually attenuated into a scabrid beak *c.* 2 mm long, the whole bronze-green, eventually turning dull black; stigmas 2; nut rounded-cubical, set well above the base.   *Fr.* 7–8.

On roadsides and waste ground and in grasslands usually associated with **MG10**, usually on ± neutral or slightly base-rich, heavier and damper soils than the other members of the group. See also the Biological Flora account (David & Kelcey 1985).

C. spicata is sometimes confused with small specimens of **39** *C. otrubae*, but in that species the usually broader leaves appear (at least in fresh material) pinched where they emerge from the leaf-sheath, many more of the bracts subtending the spikes have long setaceous points, and the utricles are clearly ribbed. From other members of the *C. muricata* group *C. spicata* is distinguished by the long, acute, soft ligule (best observed in stem leaves) and the large bulbous-based and narrow-beaked utricles. The acuminate female glumes, which often give the young inflorescence a shaggy appearance, are also distinctive, as is the wine-red pigment which does not appear in any other member of the group and sometimes (but by no means invariably) extends to leaf-sheaths, bracts and even glumes and which, when present, is definitive.

For hybrids, see above introduction to the group.

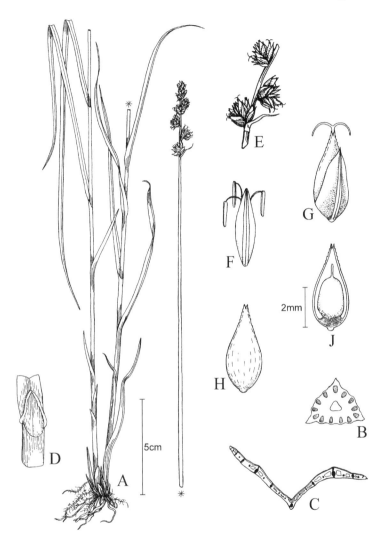

A Fertile shoot; **B** T.S. stem (culm); **C** T.S. leaf; **D** Inner face of leaf-sheath and ligule; **E** Upper spikes; **F** Male floret; **G** Female floret; **H** Utricle; **J** Section through utricle, showing nut.

M40 Carex spicata

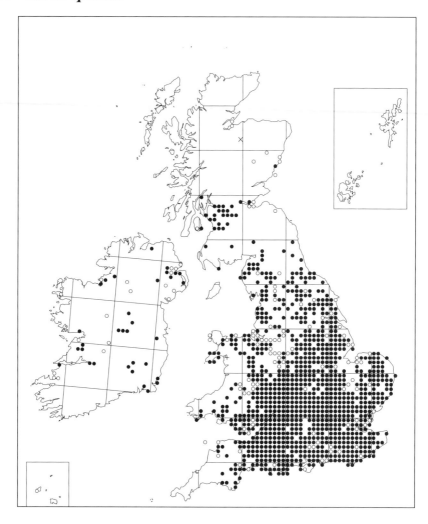

Carex spicata is frequent throughout most of southern and midland England and more common in NW England than originally thought; becoming less common towards the west coast and in Wales; absent from Cornwall. In Scotland mainly in the Clyde basin. In Ireland scattered and local.

Carex muricata subsp. *muricata*   *M41a*

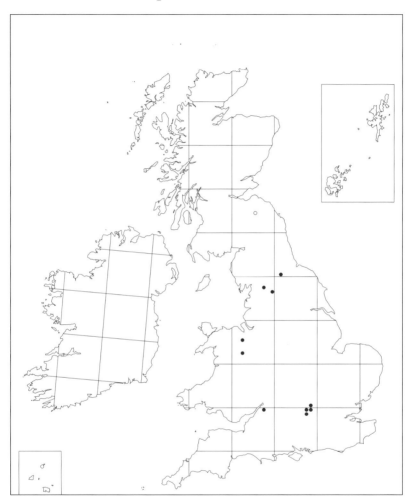

Carex muricata subsp. *muricata* is a rare taxon found at only nine sites in Great Britain: *1*, *2* near High Wycombe (v.c. 24); *3* near Nympsfield (v.c. 34), where possibly lost; *4*, *5* at Jones' Rough and Moelydd (v.c. 40); *6* near Wrexham, (v.c. 50); *7*, *8* in Gordale and Ribblesdale (v.c. 64); and *9* Downholme, Swaledale (v.c. 65). Recorded in 1878 near Lauder Castle (v.c. 81), where it was probably introduced or perhaps recorded in error.

41a *Carex muricata* L. subsp. *muricata*

Prickly Sedge *Map 41a*

Rhizomes short; shoots densely tufted; roots brown; scales brown with black veins, soon becoming fibrous. *Stems* 10–85 cm, often stout and rough just below inflorescence especially when in fruit, obtusely trigonous and even polygonal below. *Leaves* 7–45 cm × 2–4 mm, keeled, gradually tapering to a flat tip, mid green; hypostomous; sheaths forming a short false stem; apex straight or concave; ligule 2–3.5 mm, ovate. *Inflorescence* 1–4 cm × 9–11 mm; bracts glumaceous, lowest setaceous and divaricate, up to 30 mm long. *Spikes* 4–8, upper contiguous, lowest separated by up to 10 mm, 5–10 mm, globose, sessile, male at top, female below, or lower entirely male. *Male glumes* 3–4 mm, elliptic, red-brown; apex acute. *Female glumes* 2.5–3.5 mm, markedly shorter than utricles, dark or red-brown, making, at flowering time and when half-ripe, a strong colour contrast with the green utricles; apex apiculate. *Utricles* 3.8–4.6 mm, less than twice as long as wide, ovate-orbicular with a broad margin, healthy mid green, becoming dark red-brown to black and shiny as fruit matures; beak *c.* 0.75 mm, abruptly contracted, minutely toothed; stigmas 2; nut orbicular-compressed. *Fr.* 6–8.

The commoner subspecies in Scandinavia and eastern Europe, but in Britain confined to steep, dry (well-drained) limestone or chalk slopes of *Festuca ovina–Briza media–Helictotrichon pratensis* open grassland (**CG2**) in various stages of the succession towards, usually, Ash–Field Maple–*Mercurialis perennis* woodland (**W8**). A lowland species, reaching 340 m in Ribblesdale, v.c. 64 (David 1979b). See also the Biological Flora account (David & Kelcey 1985).

Differs from **41b** subsp. *pairae* in the more erect and rigid habit (stem 0.9–1.2 mm wide just below inflorescence; 0.7–0.9 mm in **41b**), the early flowering time (May, about a month before subsp. *pairae*), the marked colour contrast at this time and, when half-ripe, much shorter, dark glumes and more rounded deep green, measurably larger utricles (which become concolorous when the fruits mature), and the more globose and wider spikes, the lowest of which is often quite distinctly separated from the next above. From **40** *C. spicata* it differs in the shape and size of ligule and utricle and from **42** *C. divulsa* in the comparatively compact and dark-coloured inflorescence.

Carex muricata subsp. *muricata* is a **Red Data List** taxon in Great Britain; *Status*: **Near threatened** (Cheffings & Farrell 2005).

Carex muricata subsp. *muricata*   **41a**

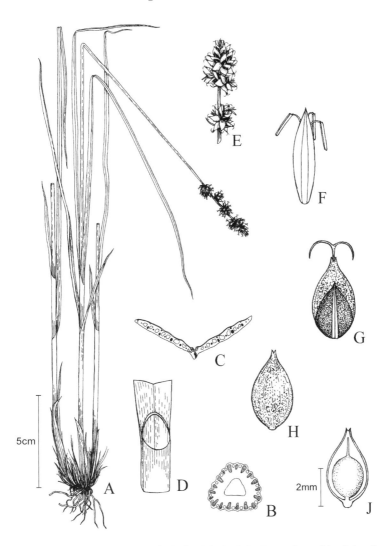

A Fertile shoot; **B** T.S. stem (culm); **C** T.S. leaf; **D** Inner face of leaf-sheath and ligule; **E** Upper spikes; **F** Male floret; **G** Female floret; **H** Utricle; **J** Section through utricle, showing nut.

41b *Carex muricata* L. subsp. *pairae* (F.W. Schultz) Čelak.[*]

Prickly Sedge   *Map 41b*

Rhizomes short; shoots densely tufted; roots brown; scales brown with black veins, soon becoming fibrous. **Stems** 10–85 cm (–160 cm when in fruit), often rigid but rarely as much as 1 mm in diameter just below inflorescence, pentagonal to bluntly trigonous. **Leaves** 7–45 cm × 2–4 mm, keeled, gradually or sometimes abruptly tapering to a flat tip, mid green, often bronzing on dying; hypostomous; sheaths forming a short false stem; apex straight or concave; ligule 2–3.5 mm, ovate. **Inflorescence** 1–4.5 cm × 7–9(–10) mm, unbranched, stiffly erect; bracts glumaceous, with a setaceous point. **Spikes** 3–8, contiguous or crowded, 5–10 mm, ovoid, sessile, male at top, female below, the proximal/subproximal spikes frequently compound, consisting of 2–6 digitately disposed spikelets often entirely female. **Male glumes** 3–4 mm, lanceolate-elliptic, hyaline or pale brown; midrib green; apex acute. **Female glumes** 3–4.5 mm, ovate, pale or golden-brown, fading to white as the fruits mature; apex acute or apiculate. **Utricles** 3–4.5 mm, usually more than twice as long as wide, ovoid with broad base or ovoid-ellipsoid, widely divaricate, giving the spikes a star-like appearance, yellow-green, becoming dark brown and shiny on maturity with short veins near base, tapering ± evenly into a minutely toothed beak *c.* 0.75 mm long; stigmas 2; nut orbicular-compressed.   **Fr.** 7–9.

A plant of road-banks and heathy, rough pasture in open situations, preferring drier, lighter and more acid soils than **40** *C. spicata* and therefore rare on the Midland clays and Carboniferous areas of the Pennines; a favourite habitat is the 'west country' turf-covered walls (called, in Cornwall, 'hedges'). See also the Biological Flora account (David & Kelcey 1985).

Robust specimens of *C. muricata* subsp. *pairae* have been regularly confused with poor specimens of **40** *C. spicata* lacking the distinctive wine-red coloration, but, even when the utricles of *C. muricata* are larger than usual, the absence of any corky padding at the base and a broad attenuated beak and a short, neatly ovate ligule (best observed on stem-leaves) should suffice for a correct determination. The differences between the two subspecies have been described under **41a** subsp. *muricata*.

A hybrid with *C. divulsa* subsp. *divulsa* (**42a** × **41b**) has been described from Cork (v.c. H5).

---

[*]*Carex muricata* subsp. *lamprocarpa* Čelak. in Edition 2

Carex muricata subsp. *pairae* 41b

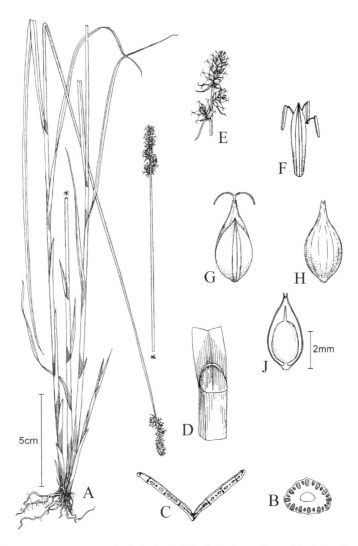

A Fertile shoot; **B** T.S. stem (culm); **C** T.S. leaf; **D** Inner face of leaf-sheath and ligule; **E** Upper spikes; **F** Male floret; **G** Female floret; **H** Utricle; **J** Section through utricle, showing nut.

M41b *Carex muricata* subsp. *pairae*

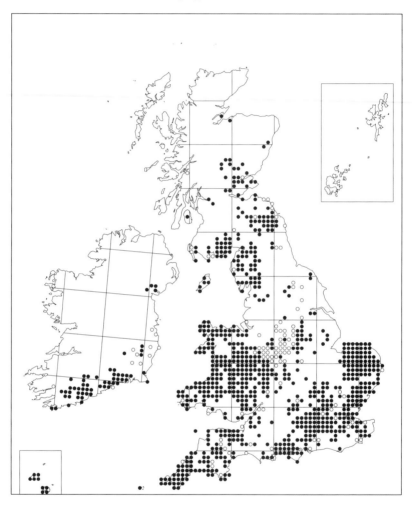

Carex muricata subsp. *pairae* is frequent in southern and SW England, East Anglia and W Wales. In the north it occurs in Cumbria and in quantity in Galloway and on the Cheviots. It becomes less common again in Scotland N of the Clyde and Forth, though it reaches Oban in the W and Inverness in the E. It is uncommon in Ireland, occurring mainly in the south.

Carex divulsa subsp. *divulsa*   *M42a*

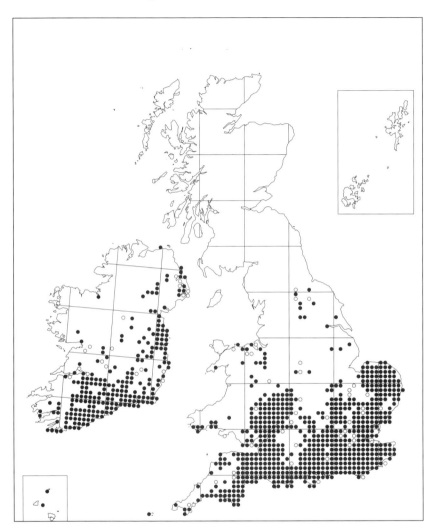

Carex divulsa subsp. *divulsa* is a lowland sedge, common throughout southern England from Kent to Cornwall and from the Channel to the Forest of Dean, the Chilterns and East Anglia, becoming rare in the Midlands but with strong colonies in north-eastern Wales and in Yorkshire east of the Pennines. It is found in similar density in S and E Ireland.

231

42a *Carex divulsa* Stokes subsp. *divulsa*

Grey Sedge   *Map 42a*

Rhizomes short; shoots in ± dense tufts 10–20 cm across; roots thick, grey-brown; scales dark brown with black veins, soon becoming fibrous. ***Stems*** 25–75 cm, slender, trigonous, striate, often drooping. ***Leaves*** up to 75 cm × 2–3 mm, flat or channelled, flaccid, gradually tapered to a fine, flat apex, grey, the upper face yellowish-green when young, bronze- or grey-green and usually very glossy when mature, often overwintering; hypostomous; sheaths forming false stems in sterile shoots, lower pale brown, ribbed; inner face hyaline; apex straight or ± concave; ligule *c.* 2 mm, obtuse, with free tissue hyaline, *c.* 0.3 mm wide. ***Inflorescence*** 6–18 cm; lower bracts setaceous, 2–3 cm, sometimes much longer, upper glumaceous. ***Spikes*** 5–8, the upper contiguous, unbranched, ovoid, 3–8 mm, with 4–10 florets, all female (or male in late-season specimens), the lower distant from each other by 2 cm or more, 5–15 mm, often branched, male at top and female below, then with fewer utricles. ***Male glumes*** 3.5–4 mm, lanceolate, ± hyaline; apex acute. ***Female glumes*** 3–3.5 mm, ovate-elliptic, ± hyaline or pale brown with hyaline margins and green midrib; apex acute, often attenuate. ***Utricles*** 3.5–4(–4.5) mm, ± erect or appressed to stem axis, ellipsoid to diamond-shaped (i.e. tapered and ± straight-sided), faintly nerved at base, shiny, pale yellow or whitish-green, turning dull greyish-black; beak *c.* 1 mm, rough, split; stigmas 2; nut obovoid, biconvex.   ***Fr.*** 7–9(–11).

This is a plant of hedge-banks, wood-borders, roadsides, rough, open grassland (**MG1**) and waste ground where competition is not too great. In N Yorkshire, field studies (Lowe 2004) indicate a plant association typical of mesotrophic swards with affinities to **MG5** of the NVC. It appears relatively indifferent as to soil, tolerating all but strongly acidic soils. See also the Biological Flora account (David & Kelcey 1985).

There is considerable variation in the size of the utricle even on the same spike and the glumes may be tinged with darker brown, but on the whole *C. divulsa* is characterised by the colourless glumes and generally pale-coloured, few-flowered spikes. From others of the *C. muricata* group, except **42b** subsp. *leersii, C. divulsa* subsp. *divulsa* is distinguished by its elongate inflorescence and diamond-shaped utricle. In **48** *C. remota* the lower bracts are longer than their spikes and often longer than the whole inflorescence.

For hybrids see **40–42** *Carex muricata* group.

Carex divulsa subsp. *divulsa* **42a**

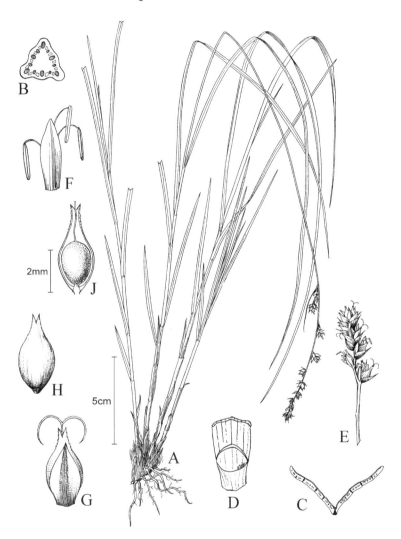

A Fertile shoot; **B** T.S. stem (culm); **C** T.S. leaf; **D** Inner face of leaf-sheath and ligule; **E** Upper spikes; **F** Male floret; **G** Female floret; **H** Utricle; **J** Section through utricle, showing nut.

42b *Carex divulsa* Stokes subsp. *leersii* (Kneuck.) W. Koch

Leers' Sedge   *Map 42b*

Rhizomes short; shoots in ± dense tufts 10–20 cm across; roots thick, grey-brown; scales dark brown with black veins, soon becoming fibrous. **Stems** 25–90 cm, robust, trigonous. **Leaves** up to 75 cm × 3–5 mm, shorter than flowering stem, flat or channelled, gradually tapered to a fine, flat apex, usually bright yellow-green till late in the season (although darker in shade), stiff; hypostomous; sheaths forming false stems in sterile shoots, lower pale brown, ribbed; inner face hyaline; apex straight or ± concave; ligule 2 mm or less, obtuse or truncate, often yellow. (The blade of the leaf is at this point so closely appressed to the stem that when pulled it parts from it with a snap.) **Inflorescence** 4–6 cm; lower bracts 2–3 cm, sometimes longer, setaceous, upper glumaceous. **Spikes** 4–8, the upper contiguous, 5–10 mm, all female, the lower up to 2 cm distant from each other, sometimes branched, 5–15 mm, male at top and female below. **Male glumes** 3.5–5 mm, lanceolate, brownish-hyaline; midrib green; apex acute. **Female glumes** 4–4.5 mm, ovate-elliptic, golden-yellow or light brown; midrib often green; apex acute to attenuate. **Utricles** 4–4.5(–4.8) mm, markedly divaricate, ovoid, tapered above and below, faintly nerved at base, shiny, yellowish, soon becoming dark red-brown; beak *c.* 1 mm, rough, split; stigmas 2; nut obovoid, biconvex.

Fr. 6–8.

    C. divulsa subsp. *leersii* is found in habitats similar to those of subsp. *divulsa*, but more commonly on chalk or limestone, where it reaches to 220 m in Wensleydale (v.c. 65); but also on acid sands, e.g. in W Norfolk (v.c. 28) (G. Beckett pers. comm.). Many populations have characters intermediate between those of subspp. *leersii* and *divulsa*. In addition, damaged plants of subsp. *leersii* may produce weak, late stems resembling those of subsp. *divulsa* (R.W. David pers. comm.). See also the Biological Flora account (David & Kelcey 1985).

    Characters separating **42** *C. divulsa* sensu lato from other sedges are given under **42a** subsp. *divulsa*. From that subspecies, subsp. *leersii* in its extreme form differs in the erect, rigid habit, the yellow-green of the leaves, which are shorter than the stem, the shorter, stouter and more compact inflorescence and the larger, very markedly divaricate utricles which soon turn a shiny red-brown. Subsp. *leersii* flowers in May and has usually shed most of its fruit by the end of August, whereas subsp. *divulsa*, beginning later, has a much longer flowering season from June to October.

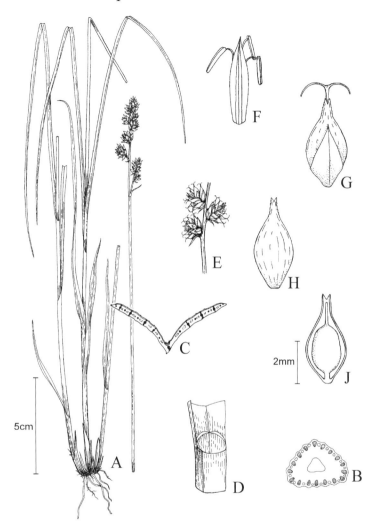

A Fertile shoot; **B** T.S. stem (culm); **C** T.S. leaf; **D** Inner face of leaf-sheath and ligule; **E** Upper spikes; **F** Male floret; **G** Female floret; **H** Utricle; **J** Section through utricle, showing nut.

M42b Carex divulsa subsp. *leersii*

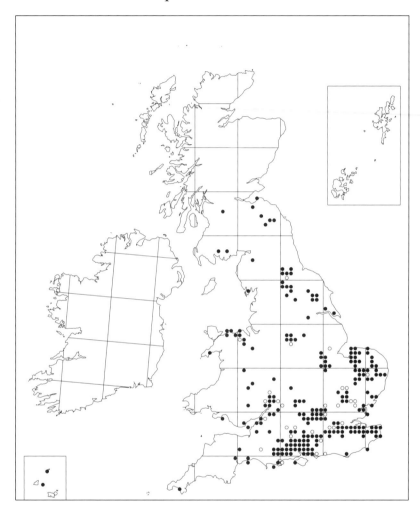

The most extreme forms of *Carex divulsa* subsp. *leersii* are found in Yorkshire, Derbyshire, Rutland, Denbighshire and the Cotswolds, but the plant is scattered over much of the rest of S and E England and north to Edinburgh.

Carex divulsa subsp. *divulsa* × *C. otrubae*　　　*M42a × 39*

Although there have been many records for this hybrid in the British Isles, most have been considered doubtful. However, several collections from ditch-sides in Worcestershire (v.c. 37) appear to be this plant and we have confirmed other records from v.cc. 13, 14 and 23.

42a × 39 *Carex divulsa* subsp. *divulsa* × *Carex otrubae*

Map 42a × 39

This hybrid has the appearance of an extremely robust *C. divulsa* with larger, well-separated spikes, similarly shaped utricles and a short ligule. It resembles *C. otrubae* in its stouter, compressible stem, its acute ligule and its broader leaves. It is intermediate between the parents in inflorescence length and utricle size.

Although most utricles are empty, some plants appear to have a small proportion of fertile utricles and this adds to the problems of identification. Populations of a putative hybrid with subsp. *leersii* should be considered where that subspecies is present in the vicinity.

Carex divulsa	*Carex divulsa* × *C. otrubae*	*Carex otrubae*
Stem 25–75 cm, not compressible (solid), unwinged.	Stem 60–90 cm, compressible (hollow), unwinged.	Stem 30–100 cm, compressible (hollow), winged.
Leaves 2–3 mm wide.	**Leaves 4–5 mm wide.**	Leaves 4–10 mm wide.
Ligule *c.* 2 mm, obtuse.	Ligule 2–3 mm, ± acute.	Ligule 5–10 mm, ± acute.
Inflorescence 6–18 cm in length.	**Inflorescence 5–10 cm in length.**	Inflorescence 2–4 cm in length.
Spikes 7.5–10 mm in diameter, ± contiguous above and distant below.	**Spikes 10–12 mm in diameter, upper often contiguous, lower distant.**	Spikes 8–14 mm in diameter, mostly contiguous.
♀ glumes 3–3.5 mm, ovate-elliptic; apex acute, pale brown with hyaline margins.	♀ glumes 4–6 mm, ovate; apex acute or acuminate, pale brown with green midrib.	♀ glumes 4–5 mm, ovate; apex acuminate-aristate, pale red- or orange-brown with green midrib.
Utricles 3.5–4(–4.5) mm, ovoid, tapered above and below, pale yellow or whitish-green, shiny, ± erect, or appressed to stem axis	**Utricles 4–5.5 mm,** ovoid, tapered above and below, ribbed, pale brown, ± patent, **usually empty.**	Utricles 4–6 mm, ovoid, plano-convex, ribbed, green, dark brown at maturity, ± patent.

Carex divulsa subsp. *divulsa* × *C. otrubae*   **42a × 39**
Carex divulsa × *C. muricata* subsp. *pairae*   **42a × 41b**
Carex × *emmae* (*C. divulsa* subsp. *divulsa* × *C. remota*)   **42a × 48**

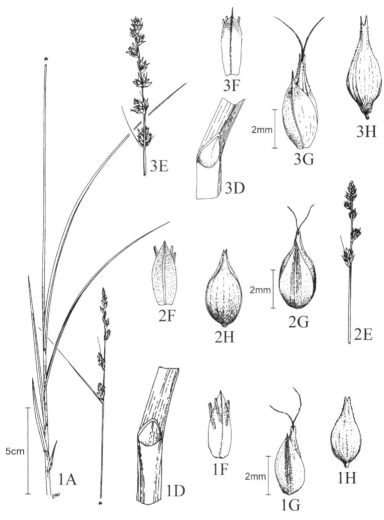

1 *C.* × *emmae* **2** *C. divulsa* × *C. muricata* subsp. *pairae* **3** *C. divulsa* × *C. otrubae*
A Fertile shoot; **D** Inner face of leaf-sheath and ligule; **E** Upper spikes; **F** Male floret; **G** Female floret; **H** Utricle.

239

M42a × 41b Carex divulsa subsp. *divulsa* × *C. muricata* subsp. *pairae*

In 1983 this taxon was first recorded in a garden in Cork (O'Mahony 1989). and it was subsequently found at eight wild sites in v.cc. H4 and H5 (O'Mahony 2004). Since the parents frequently occur together, this hybrid could be more widespread and possibly occur in southern England and Wales.

Carex divulsa subsp. divulsa ×
C. muricata subsp. pairae

42a × 41b

Map 42a × 41b

This hybrid is intermediate between its parents in inflorescence length. It resembles *Carex divulsa* subsp. *divulsa* in the shape and disposition of its utricles and *C. muricata* subsp. *pairae* in its erect inflorescence, its leaf colour and the colour and shininess of the utricles. It differs from both parents in its often empty, deformed utricles.

In 1983 the hybrid appeared spontaneously in T. O'Mahony's garden in Cork, where both parents were in cultivation (O'Mahony 1989). Fieldwork later found it in eight sites along paths, on grassy roadside verges and hedgebanks and on a limestone outcrop, usually close to both parents (O'Mahony 2004).

Carex divulsa subsp. *divulsa*	*C. divulsa* × *C. muricata* ssp. *pairae*	*Carex muricata* subsp. *pairae*
Leaves green, bright when young, dull later.	Leaves mid green, matt or slightly shiny.	Leaves mid green, matt or slightly shiny.
Inflorescences 6–18 cm long, often pendent; lower spikes spaced 2 cm or more apart.	**Inflorescences varying in length on same plant,** < **7.5 cm**, stiffly erect; **gap between lower spikes highly variable.**	Inflorescences up to 4.5 cm long, stiffly erect; lower spikes contiguous or clustered.
Spikes ovoid, with 4–10 utricles closely appressed to spike axis.	Spikes with **6–17 utricles,** (closer to *pairae*) but **appressed** to spike axis (as in *divulsa*).	Spikes star-like, with 6–22(–24) widely divaricate utricles.
Utricles 3.5–4(–4.5) mm, shiny yellow-green, becoming dull black, ellipsoid to diamond-shaped.	**Utricles** 3.7–5 mm, yellow-green, becoming dark brown and ± **shiny,** ellipsoid or rhomboid; **many malformed** but some (up to 30%) fertile.	Utricles 3–4.5(–5) mm, yellow-green, becoming dark brown and shiny, ovoid with a broad base.

M42a × 48 *Carex* × *emmae* (*C. divulsa* ssp. *divulsa* × *C. remota*)

Carex × *emmae* was first recorded in 1924 from a roadside verge near Heathfield, v.c. 14 (Salmon 1925), and more recently from two sites in Mid Cork, v.c. H4 (1982/1990), one in East Cork, v.c. H5 (2004) and one in Waterford, v.c. H6 (2003) (T. O'Mahony 1983 and pers. comm. 2004).

Carex × *emmae* L. Gross   42a × 48

Carex divulsa subsp. *divulsa* × *C. remota*   *Map 42a × 48*

Carex × *emmae* is much closer in its general appearance to *C. remota* than to *C. divulsa*. From the latter it is distinguished by its mid green leaves, its often extremely long lower bracts, its tubular ligule and its slightly shorter female glumes and utricles. It differs from *C. remota* in the variability in the length of its lower bracts, in its predominantly male subterminal spikes and in its often compound lowest spikes, with the male florets variably above or below and sometimes both above and below the female florets.

It has been found in woodland, on hedge-banks and along roadsides where drainage ditches contain the *C. remota* parent.

Carex divulsa	*Carex* × *emmae*	*Carex remota*
Leaves 2–3 mm broad, grey, bronzy or dark green.	Leaves 1.5–3 mm broad, mid green.	Leaves 1.5–2 mm broad, mid green to yellow-green.
Lowest bract usually short (less than 3 cm) but very occasionally exceeding the inflorescence.	Lowest two bracts extremely variable in length (2–25 cm), often exceeding, but sometimes much shorter than, the inflorescence.	All bracts long, at least the lowest two exceeding the inflorescence.
Ligule not tubular.	Ligule shortly tubular.	Ligule tubular.
Upper spikes contiguous, all ♀; lower distant from each other by 2 cm or more, ♂ above, ♀ below.	Upper **spikes** ± contiguous; **subterminal ones mainly** ♂, often curved; **lower** remote, ♂ **above and/or below** or all ♀.	Upper spikes ± contiguous, ♀ at top, ♂ below; lower remote, all ♀.
Lowest spike(s) often compound.	**Lowest spike(s) often compound.**	Lowest spike simple.
♀ glumes 3–3.5 mm long, ovate-elliptic.	♀ glumes 2.5–3 mm long, ± elliptic.	♀ glumes *c.* 2.5 mm long, lanceolate to ovate.
Utricles 3.5–4(–4.5) mm long, tapered above and below, pale yellow or whitish-green.	**Utricles 3–3.5 mm long**, variable in shape between the parents, sterile, pale green.	Utricles 2.5–3.5 mm long, not tapered below, green.

43 *Carex arenaria* L.

Sand Sedge   *Map 43*

Rhizomes far-creeping; shoots usually single, at about every fourth node; roots pale brown, much branched; scales dark brown, soon becoming fibrous. *Stems* 10–90 cm, rough towards the top, trigonous, often curved, varying in thickness. *Leaves* up to 60 cm × 1.5–3.5 mm, ± flat, rigid, thick, rough above, often recurved and keeled or channelled in open habitats, tapering gradually to a fine trigonous point, shiny, dark green, often dark brown on dying; base frequently with a small scarious flange on either side; hypostomous; lower sheaths pale brown or grey-brown, persistent, with inner face a loose hyaline membrane, densely mamillate (appearing as a velvet sheen), becoming brown; apex straight; ligule 3–5 mm, obtuse, tubular. *Inflorescence* a dense head up to 8 cm; bracts glumaceous, lower with setaceous points. *Spikes* 5–15, 8–14 mm, terminal male, middle male at top and female below, lower entirely female. *Male glumes* 5–7 mm, lanceolate-elliptic, pale red-brown with hyaline margins; apex acute. *Female glumes* 5–6 mm, ovate, pale red-brown, with pale or green midrib and hyaline margins; apex acute or acuminate. *Utricles* 4–5.5 mm, ovate, plano-convex, many-ribbed, broadly winged, serrate in upper half, pale green-brown; beak 1–1.5 mm, broadly winged below, bifid; stigmas 2; nut oblong-ellipsoid.   *Fr.* 7–8.

C. arenaria is principally maritime, a pioneer and often dominant plant on wind-blown sand (**SD10**) and mature, more acid dunes, forming associations with lichens (**SD11**). It also occurs in other coastal communities, e.g. with *Phleum arenarium* (**SD19**), in *Festuca ovina–Agrostis capillaris* grassland (**SD12**), in dune-slacks with *Salix repens*, *C. flacca*, *C. nigra* etc. (**SD13, SD14, SD17**) and in *Hippophae* scrub (**SD18**), as well as on sandy tracksides. See also the Biological Flora account (Noble 1982).

C. arenaria could be confused with **44** *C. disticha* when both occur at the ecotone between slack and dune. The later has herbaceous inner faces to the leaf-sheaths and the uppermost spikes female. Two close relatives occur on the West European dunes: *C. reichenbachii* Bonnet, which has all the spikes male below, and *C. ligerica* J. Gay, with fewer spikes that are usually all female at the top and male below and darker, chestnut female glumes. Either might turn up in eastern Britain.

P.M. Benoit has found a hybrid with **35** *C. paniculata* in Merioneth (v.c. 48) (specimen not available for examination). A hybrid with *C. remota* found in mainland Europe has not been recorded in the British Isles.

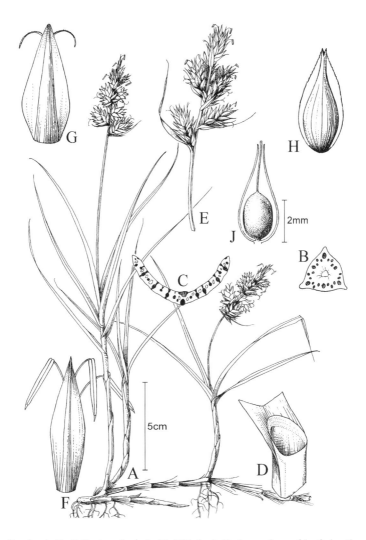

A Fertile shoot; **B** T.S. stem (culm); **C** T.S. leaf; **D** Inner face of leaf-sheath and ligule; **E** Inflorescence; **F** Male floret; **G** Female floret; **H** Utricle; **J** Section through utricle, showing nut.

M43 Carex arenaria

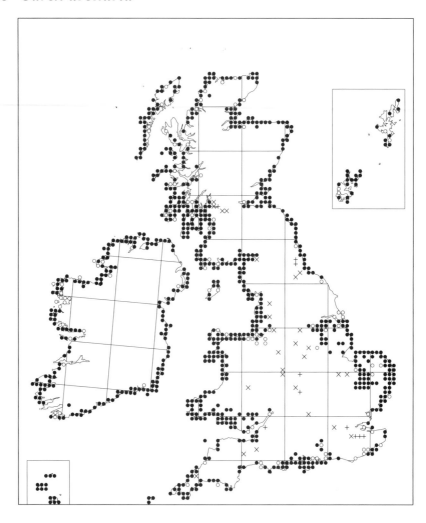

Carex arenaria is mainly a coastal plant throughout the British Isles, but it occurs naturally inland in Breckland, the Lincolnshire coversands and the Avon valley and Woolmer Forest, Hants.

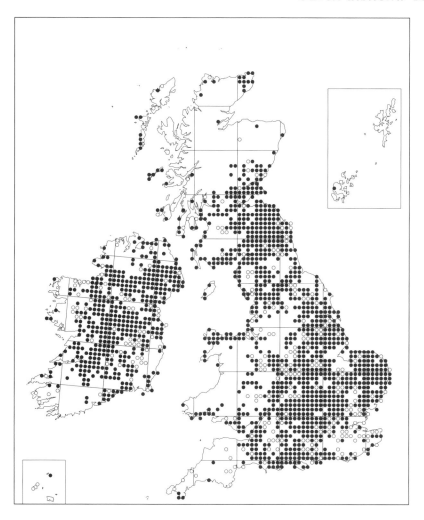

Carex disticha is found throughout most of England and S Scotland but is rare in Cornwall and Devon, Central Wales and north of the Grampians; generally lowland but reaching 455 m in Roxburghs (Porter & Foley 2002). In most of Ireland, but again rare in the SW peninsula.

44 *Carex disticha* Huds.

Brown Sedge   *Map 44*

Rhizomes far-creeping; shoots single or in pairs, often 14–16 nodes apart; roots grey-brown, much branched; scales brown, becoming dark and fibrous. *Stems* 20–100 cm, erect, rough, sharply trigonous. *Leaves* 15–60 cm × 2–4 mm, smooth on both surfaces but rough on veins beneath, thick, ± flat but with keeled midrib, gradually tapering to a flat rough tip, mid green; hypostomous; sheaths forming false stems in sterile shoots, with inner face hyaline only around concave apex, otherwise herbaceous; lower sheaths with very short blades, brown, persistent; ligule 3–7 mm, obtuse, tubular. *Inflorescence* a dense panicle, 2–7 cm, forming a broadly lanceoloid to ellipsoid head, narrowed in middle; bracts glumaceous, brown-hyaline or the lowest leaf-like and exceeding inflorescence. *Spikes* numerous, contiguous, sessile, terminal female (sometimes overtopped by male spikelets), intermediate male, lower all female or sometimes male at base. *Male glumes* 4–5 mm, lanceolate, pale red-brown, with hyaline margins; apex acute. *Female glumes* 3.5–4.5 mm, ovate-lanceolate, pale red-brown, with hyaline margins; apex acute. *Utricles* 4–5 mm, ovoid, many-ribbed, red-brown, with very narrow, ± serrate, lateral wings; beak *c.* 1 mm, rough, split; stigmas 2; nut ovate, biconvex, shortly stalked.   *Fr.* 7–8.

Carex disticha is a plant of mixed herb/sedge fens, e.g. *Epilobium hirsutum–Phragmites–Iris* (**OV26b**), and of dense grass/rush tall herb associations with *Filipendula ulmaria–Angelica sylvestris* (**M27**), preferring areas with a somewhat fluctuating water-table. Also in periodically flooded wet meadows with *Alopecurus geniculatus* (**OV29**) and in wet dune-slacks dominated by *C. nigra* (**SD17**). More frequent in the calcareous fens of the eastern half of England (e.g. in *Juncus subnodulosus* fen-meadows, **M22**). The single shoots are often overlooked if not in flower.

The scattered shoots from a monopodial rhizome distinguish this species from most other *Carex* species. When growing in a dune-slack it may intermingle with **43** *C. arenaria*. The latter species has a male terminal spike and a hyaline inner face to the leaf-sheath with dark green longitudinal veining, while the sheaths and leaf surfaces are smooth and devoid of epidermal papillae (T. O'Mahony pers. comm.).

No hybrids of *C. disticha* are recorded.

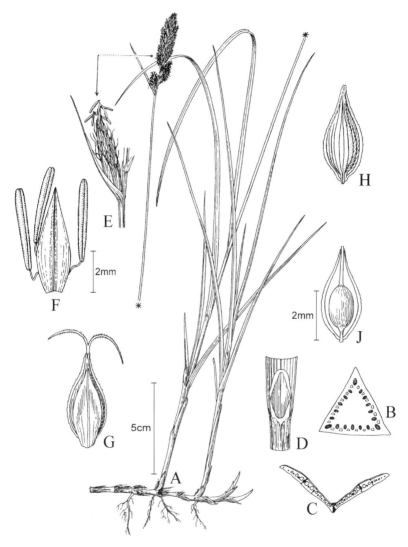

A Fertile shoot; **B** T.S. stem (culm); **C** T.S. leaf; **D** Inner face of leaf-sheath and ligule; **E** Spike from middle of inflorescence; **F** Male floret; **G** Female floret; **H** Utricle; **J** Section through utricle, showing nut.

249

45 *Carex chordorrhiza* L. f.

String Sedge   *Map 45*

Rhizomes far-creeping, often ascending; shoots solitary, arising from elongated, decumbent base of flowering stem; roots red-brown; scales pale yellow-brown, chaffy, soon decaying. **Stems** 15–40 cm, stout, ± terete, striate, with few short leaves at base. **Leaves** up to 30 cm × 1–2 mm, stiff, erect, flat or ± involute, gradually narrowed to a ± trigonous fine point, mid green; hypostomous; sheaths forming short false stem, with inner face hyaline-brown and apex concave; lower sheaths pale brown-hyaline, often darkening; ligule 1–2 mm, rounded. **Inflorescence** a compact ± ovoid head, 7–15 mm; bracts glumaceous. **Spikes** 2–4, 4–8 mm, male at top, female at base, lower often entirely female. **Male glumes** *c.* 3.5 mm, oblanceolate-elliptic, pale red-brown; apex acute. **Female glumes** 3–4 mm, broadly ovate-elliptic, pale red-brown, hyaline towards margin; apex ± acute. **Utricles** (3–)3.5–4.5 mm, ovoid-ellipsoid, ± compressed, faintly ribbed, shiny, yellow-brown or often dark brown; beak *c.* 0.5 mm, bifid; stigmas 2; nut obovoid-oblong, stalked, with truncate apex.   **Fr.** 7–8.

Carex chordorrhiza is a plant of very wet base-poor mires, growing with *C. canescens*, *C. limosa*, *C. rostrata*, *Sphagnum fallax*, *S. papillosum* etc. (**M4**), although it does not survive prolonged inundation (Legg *et al.* 1995). In the Insh Marshes locality it is found in *C. rostrata–Potentilla palustris–Menyanthes* mires (**S27**). Although it occurs in two areas only, present conditions appear to be favouring the vegetative spread of the plants, especially in the v.c. 97 locality where the plant is increasing (N.R. Cowie in Wigginton 1999). There is no appreciable difference in genotypic diversity in the British populations (Jardine 1994). See also Cowie & Sydes (1995).

Distinctive in having creeping decumbent shoots that in their second year give rise to similar shoots from the basal four or five, more or less widely spaced, nodes. The leaves are often inrolled, giving the plant the appearance of marram grass.

A hybrid with *C. canescens* has been described from Norway.

250

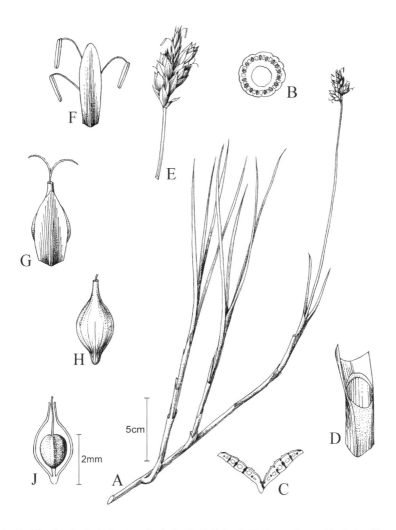

A Fertile shoot; **B** T.S. stem (culm); **C** T.S. leaf; **D** Inner face of leaf-sheath and ligule; **E** Inflorescence; **F** Male floret; **G** Female floret; **H** Utricle; **J** Section through utricle, showing nut.

M45 Carex chordorrhiza

Carex chordorrhiza was first found in 1897 by E.S. Marshall and W.A. Shoolbred at the head of Loch Naver, Altnaharra, W Sutherland (v.c. 108); since found in several places within a 5-km radius of there. Discovered in 1978, in quantity, in the Insh Marshes (v.c. 97) (Page & Rieley 1985). The record for South Uist (v.c. 110) is in error (J.E. Raven in Preston 2004).

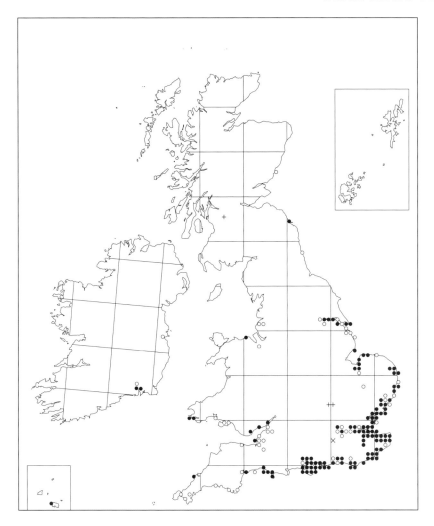

Carex divisa is found in the S and E of England, W to the Pembrokeshire coast and N to the Humber estuary, with an outlier on Holy Island, where it has become very scarce. Not seen recently in Angus or in Dublin but refound in Wexford in 1990 (Curtis & FitzGerald 1994).

46   *Carex divisa* Huds.

Divided Sedge   *Map 46*

Rhizomes thick, woody, persistent, sometimes far-creeping and branched; shoots ± densely clustered, arising from short lateral branches; roots black- or grey-brown; scales pale brown, ribbed, very soon becoming dark and fibrous. *Stems* 15–80 cm, rough at the top, wiry, trigonous. *Leaves* 15–60 cm × 1.5–3 mm, stiff, ± flat or often channelled or inrolled, tapering to a slender ± flat tip, mid green to grey-green, overwintering; hypostomous; sheaths of sterile shoots forming a false stem, lower brown, soon decaying, with inner face hyaline and apex straight or concave, brown-purple; ligule 2–3 mm, obtuse, ± tubular, with free portion 0.5 mm. *Inflorescence* 1–3 cm, purplish-brown; bracts leaf-like or setaceous, lowest usually much exceeding inflorescence. *Spikes* 3–8, contiguous, lower sometimes remote, 3–13 mm, upper male at top and female below, lower often all female. *Male glumes* 3.5–4.5 mm, lanceolate-elliptic, pale red-brown; apex acute. *Female glumes* 3.5–5 mm, ovate-lanceolate, purple-brown, with pale midrib and broadly hyaline margins; apex aristate. *Utricles* 3.5–4 mm, ovoid or broadly ellipsoid, plano-convex, faintly nerved, pale brown; beak 0.5–0.75 mm, parallel-sided, bifid; stigmas 2; nut suborbicular, biconvex.   *Fr.* 7–8.

Carex divisa flourishes in brackish conditions and is rarely found far from the coast; it may require a soil with a high magnesium content. It is found on the edges of *Festuca rubra* saltmarsh (**SM16**) and occasionally in adjacent damp pastures (**MG11**) or in marshy ground, mostly in inorganic soils with *Phragmites*, *Bolboschoenus maritimus*, *Carex distans*, *C. disticha*, *C. nigra* etc.; also beside ditches but rarely in the water.

This species has a distinct woody, fibrous rhizome system with the shoots often on short thick side branches. The inflorescence is distinctly purplish-brown with a characteristic stiff, ± setaceous, lower bract that usually overtops it.

No hybrids have been confirmed.

Carex divisa is a **Red Data List** species in Great Britain; *Status*: **Vulnerable** (Cheffings & Farrell 2005). It is protected under the Flora (Protection) Order 1999 in the Republic of Ireland.

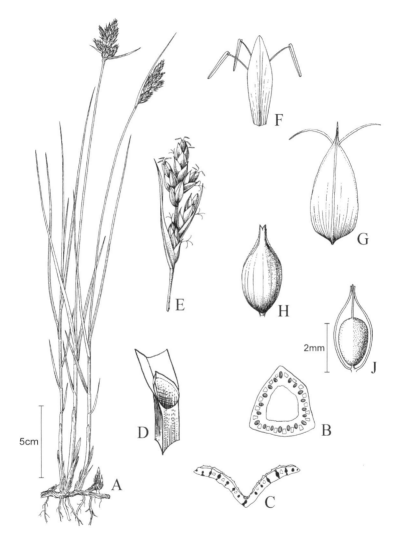

A Fertile shoot; **B** T.S. stem (culm); **C** T.S. leaf; **D** Inner face of leaf-sheath and ligule; **E** Upper spikes; **F** Male floret; **G** Female floret; **H** Utricle; **J** Section through utricle, showing nut.

47   *Carex maritima* Gunnerus

Curved Sedge   *Map 47*

Rhizomes far-creeping, much branched; shoots loosely tufted or solitary and terminal on short branches of rhizome; roots pale red-brown, with numerous branched laterals; scales dark brown, soon becoming fibrous. *Stems* 1–18 cm, solid, often curved, terete, striate. *Leaves* 3–15 cm × 0.5–2 mm, thick, stiff, channelled, often inrolled, tapering gradually to a ± trigonous point, mid green, often overwintering; hypostomous; sheaths hyaline or brown, thin, ribbed, persistent, with inner face with thin hyaline membranous strip only (see Figure **D**); apex straight; ligule 0.5–1 mm, rounded. *Inflorescence* a compact ovoid or subglobose head, 0.5–1.5 cm, on initially erect stem (but, when mature, stems bend down to soil level and the heads resemble rabbit-droppings); bracts glumaceous or 0. *Spikes* 4–8, clustered, 3–6 mm, few-flowered, upper male, often hidden, lower female with occasional male at top. *Male glumes* c. 4 mm, elliptic, dark orange-brown; apex ± acute. *Female glumes* 3–4 mm, broadly ovate, red-brown (often bleached), with midrib paler and margins narrowly hyaline; apex ± acute or obtuse and mucronate. *Utricles* 4–4.5 mm, ovoid to subglobose, faintly ribbed, brown, almost black on maturity; beak 0.5–1 mm, bifid; stigmas 2, often persistent; nut orbicular, biconvex.   *Fr.* 7–8.

    C. maritima is a rare plant of sandy coasts, able to withstand salt spray and silt accretion to a limited extent; often found with *C. distans, C. extensa, Plantago maritima, Juncus gerardii* etc. in saltmarsh such as **SM16** and **SM19**. It is likely to be in similar vegetation in the unmanaged 'rough' of coastal golf courses; e.g. it was abundant on St Andrews golf course (v.c. 85) in 1984, although not seen recently (Foley & Porter 2002). Also on almost bare sand with *Glaux maritima*. Some populations can be large, when on freshly accumulating sand, but others in saltmarsh conditions can be vulnerable to wave-wash and erosion.

    This species is perhaps superficially like a species of *Juncus* when in the vegetative state, but the thick leaves are not septate and are inserted in three rows. It is distinguished from all other sedges of its habitat by the narrow hyaline strip on the inner face of the leaf-sheath.

    Hybrids between *C. maritima* and *C. dioica* have been recorded in northern Europe.

    Carex maritima is a **Red Data List** species in Great Britain; *Status*: **Endangered** (Cheffings & Farrell 2005).

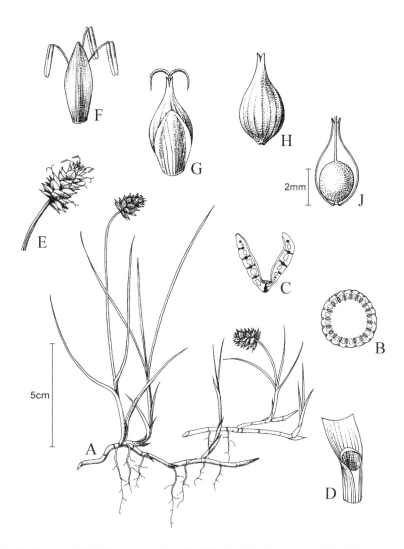

A Fertile shoot; **B** T.S. stem (culm); **C** T.S. leaf; **D** Inner face of leaf-sheath and ligule; **E** Inflorescence; **F** Male floret; **G** Female floret; **H** Utricle; **J** Section through utricle, showing nut.

M47 Carex maritima

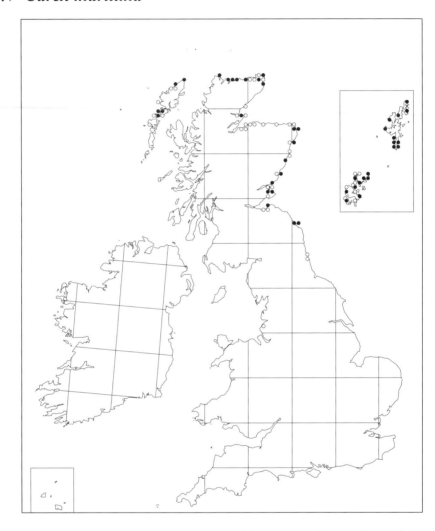

Carex maritima is found around the Scottish coast, reaching as far south as
Holy Island, where it is very scarce (Swan 1993). See also David (1982).
Fieldwork in 2005 and 2006 has added new records and confirmed almost all
the old sites in N and W Scotland. The record for Westmorland was shown
by A.O. Chater (pers. comm.) to be in error.

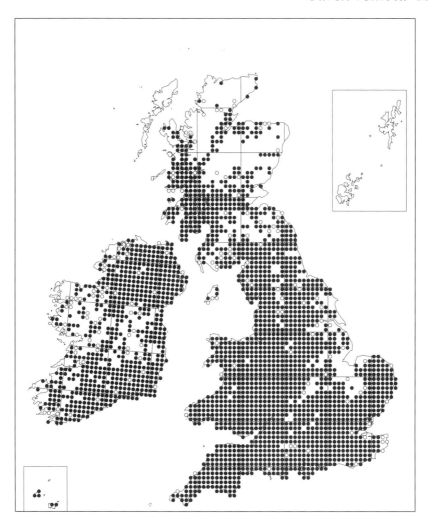

Carex remota is common throughout England and Wales except in the winter-cold Fenland–Breckland basin. Found in lowland Scotland and the west, but very rare in the extreme north and absent from the Outer Hebrides. Throughout Ireland, sometimes on calcareous soils, but rarer in the west.

48 *Carex remota* L.

Rhizomes short; shoots densely tufted, often forming stools up to 30 cm high; roots pale purple-brown; scales brown, persistent or more rarely becoming fibrous. ***Stems*** 30–75 cm, spreading, slender, trigonous or with two serrulate angles towards top. ***Leaves*** 25–60 cm × 1.5–2 mm, channelled, gradually tapering to a long slender pendulous point, mid green to yellow-green, overwintering; sheaths pale yellow-brown, persistent, forming false stems in sterile shoots, hyaline; apex shallowly concave to deeply V-shaped, protruding up to 1.8 mm above blade/sheath union; ligule 1–2 mm, long-tubular, rounded or obtuse, with free tissue *c.* 0.6–1 mm wide. ***Inflorescence*** 1/4–1/3 length of stem, up to 30 cm, often curved; lower bracts leaf-like, exceeding inflorescence, upper glumaceous. ***Spikes*** 4–9, 3–10 mm, sessile, ovoid to oblong-cylindrical, upper ± contiguous, simple, female at top, male at base, lower remote, rarely branched, entirely female, the latter commonly with 17–30(–40) utricles (T. O'Mahony pers. comm.). ***Male glumes*** 2.5–3 mm, ovate-elliptic, pale brown-hyaline, with green midrib; apex acute. ***Female glumes*** *c.* 2.5 mm, lanceolate to ovate, pale brown or hyaline, with green midrib; apex acute. ***Utricles*** 2.5–3.5 mm, ovoid-ellipsoid, plano-convex, green, ± shiny, distinctively veined on abaxial face; beak 0.5 mm, broad, minutely toothed, split; stigmas 2; nut ovoid, biconvex. ***Fr.*** 7–8.

C. remota is a species of shady situations on peaty or siliceous soils with a high water level for at least part of the year. Commonly found in alder, sallow or wet birch carr, often with *Phragmites*, *C. laevigata*, *C. paniculata* etc. (**W1**, **W2**, **W5** and **W7**). Mainly a lowland plant, reaching 320 m in Swaledale, NW Yorks (Porter & Foley 2002).

This species is not easily confused with any other; the remote spikes, long bracts and tussocky habit distinguish it. The ligule and the inner face of the sheaths are very distinctive and clearly separate *C. remota* from all members of the *C. muricata* group (**40–42**).

C. remota hybridises with *C. paniculata* (**35** × **48** *C.* × *boenninghausiana* Weihe), *C. otrubae* (**39** × **48** *C.* × *pseudoaxillaris* K. Richt.) and *C. divulsa* (**42a** × **48** *C.* × *emmae* L. Gross); in all cases the tubular ligule, long bract and larger number of utricles are to be seen in the hybrids. Hybrids with *C. arenaria*, *C. canescens*, *C. echinata*, *C. elongata* and *C. leporina* are reported from mainland Europe.

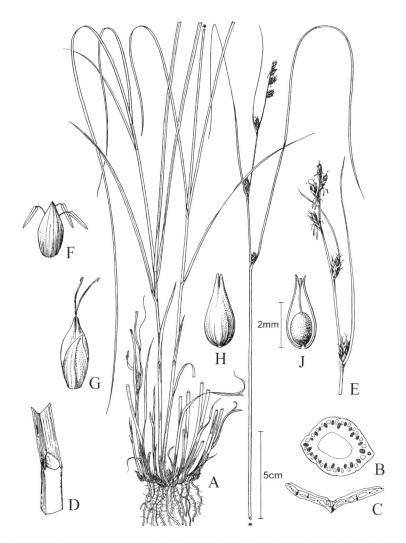

A Fertile shoot; **B** T.S. stem (culm); **C** T.S. leaf; **D** Inner face of leaf-sheath and ligule; **E** Upper spikes; **F** Male floret; **G** Female floret; **H** Utricle; **J** Section through utricle, showing nut.

49   *Carex leporina* L.[*]

Oval Sedge   Map 49

Rhizomes short; shoots densely tufted, often ± prostrate; roots pale brown or purple-brown; scales dark brown, becoming fibrous. ***Stems*** 10–90 cm, ± solid, rough at top, stiff, trigonous, usually spreading at an angle of 45°. ***Leaves*** up to 50 cm × 1–3 mm, thin, ± soft, with rough margins, ± flat, gradually tapering to a ± fine trigonous point, mid to dark green, often overwintering; hypostomous; sheaths forming a false stem in sterile shoots, becoming pink- or grey-brown, persistent, with inner face narrow, hyaline; apex ± straight; ligule *c.* 1 mm, obtuse, tubular. ***Inflorescence*** a compact, yellow-brown, ovoid head; lower bracts often setaceous, occasionally longer than head, upper bracts glumaceous. ***Spikes*** 2–9, contiguous or overlapping, 5–15 mm, sessile, upper female at top, male at base, lower all female or with a few male flowers at very base. ***Male glumes*** 4–5 mm, broadly lanceolate, pale orange-brown, with keeled midrib and broadly hyaline margin; apex acute. ***Female glumes*** 3–4.5 mm, lanceolate-elliptic, dark brown or red-brown, with green or paler midrib and narrowly hyaline margin; apex acute. ***Utricles*** 4–5 mm, ellipsoid-ovoid, plano-convex, narrowly winged at top, distinctly nerved, light brown, very divaricate on maturity; beak *c.* 1 mm, winged, rough, bifid; stigmas 2; nut obovoid to elipsoid, biconvex, shortly stalked.   ***Fr.*** 7–8.

C leporina is a species of moderately acid soils with impeded drainage, although occasionally in moderately base-rich flushes and dune-slacks. Often along trackways, where it can tolerate trampling. Found in woodland rides, grassy heathland where water accumulates, various grasslands (e.g. **MG5, MG9, MG10, MG13**), flood-meadows (**MG8**) and *Festuca–Agrostis* grassland (**U4**) up to 1005 m on Lochnagar (v.c. 92) (Foley & Porter 2002).

The prostrate shoots with elongated basal nodes and coarse leaves, which often form tufts with open centres, are distinctive. When in fruit, the ± ovoid heads with rather divaricate utricles, giving a 'spiky' appearance to the inflorescence, are easily recognisable.

C. leporina hybridises with *C. remota* in mainland Europe but no hybrids are recorded from our area. A North American species, *C. crawfordii* Fernald, similar in appearance but with a narrowly lanceoloid utricle longer than the acute and lanceolate female glumes (Figures G_1, H_1), has in the past become established in Britain with introduced crop-seed.

---

[*]*Carex ovalis* Gooden. in previous editions

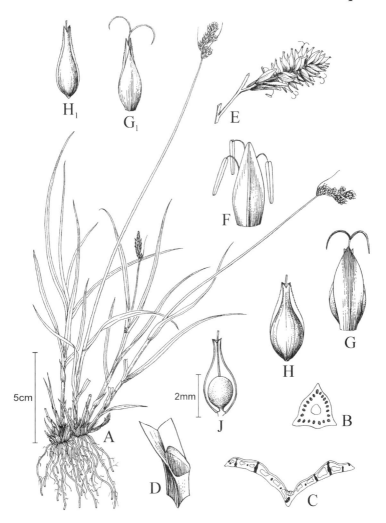

A Fertile shoot; **B** T.S. stem (culm); **C** T.S. leaf; **D** Inner face of leaf-sheath and ligule; **E** Upper spike; **F** Male floret; **G** Female floret (**G₁** *C. crawfordii*); **H** Utricle; (**H₁** *C. crawfordii*); **J** Section through utricle, showing nut.

M49 *Carex leporina*

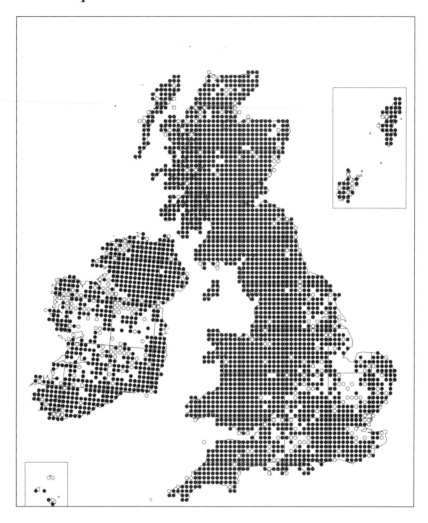

Carex leporina is common throughout the British Isles, although local in the East Anglian fens and less frequent in central Ireland.

264

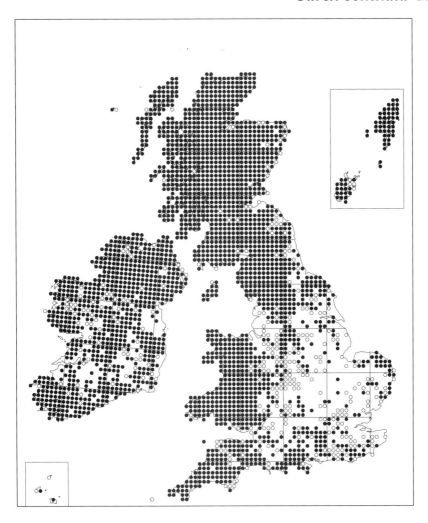

Carex echinata is abundant in the N and W of Britain and on wet, sandy heaths in the S, SE and E, but rarer in the Midlands owing to loss through drainage. Throughout Ireland, with some patchiness in the SE.

50 *Carex echinata* Murray

Star Sedge   Map 50

Rhizomes very short; shoots densely tufted; roots whitish; scales pale brown, persistent. *Stems* 10–40(–60) cm, slender, trigonous and ± striate to subterete. *Leaves* up to 30 cm × 1–2.5 mm, thick, keeled or becoming flat, gradually tapered to a trigonous rough tip, shiny, mid to dark green; hypostomous; sheaths often white with green veins, becoming pale brown, soon decaying, and inner face hyaline-green; apex ± straight; ligule *c.* 1 mm, rounded, tubular. *Inflorescence* 1–3 cm; bracts glumaceous or rarely setaceous and equalling the inflorescence, occasionally greatly exceeding it. *Spikes* 2–5, ± distant, 3–6 mm, sessile, stellate when mature, the terminal spike female at top, male below, lower spikes all female. *Male glumes* 2.5–3 mm, broadly lanceolate, pale brown with broad hyaline margin; apex obtuse. *Female glumes* 2–2.5 mm, broadly ovate, embracing lower part of utricle, pale red-brown, with green midrib and broad, hyaline margin; apex acute. *Utricles* 3–4 mm, ovoid, plano-convex, faintly ribbed, green becoming yellow-brown, divaricate at maturity; beak *c.* 1 mm, broad, serrate, bifid; stigmas 2; nut obovoid or orbicular-compressed.   *Fr.* 6–8.

Carex echinata is widespread in mire communities usually within the pH range of 4.5–5.7, e.g. *Carex echinata–Sphagnum fallax–S. denticulatum* associations (**M6**) or with *C. nigra*, *C. panicea* and *C. viridula* subsp. *oedocarpa*, *Eriophorum angustifolium*, *Sphagnum papillosum* and *S. russowii* (**M7**). Found on mesotrophic soils that are seasonally or permanently waterlogged, e.g. in heath reverting to bog with *Erica tetralix*, *Trichophorum germanicum* and *Eriophorum vaginatum* (**M15**). In more eutrophic mires with *C. dioica* (**M10**), where soils are silty, but absent from dystrophic bogs and base-rich fens. Lowland to alpine, reaching 1100 m in Central Highlands.

Easily distinguished by the squarrose mature utricles which form a characteristic star-shaped spike; in young stages the few-flowered spikes are the best distinction. The glossy, thick, dark green leaves and whitish sheaths with green veins, help to separate it from other *Carex* spp. of its habitat.

A hybrid with *C. canescens* (**54 × 50** *C.* × *biharica* Simonk.) is recorded from Scotland and one with *C. dioica* (**50 × 51** *C.* × *gaudiniana* Guthnick) from Denbighshire (v.c. 50), Co. Westmeath (v.c. H23) and West Mayo (v.c. H27). Hybrids with *C. paniculata* and *C. spicata* are said to occur but have not been reported from the British Isles.

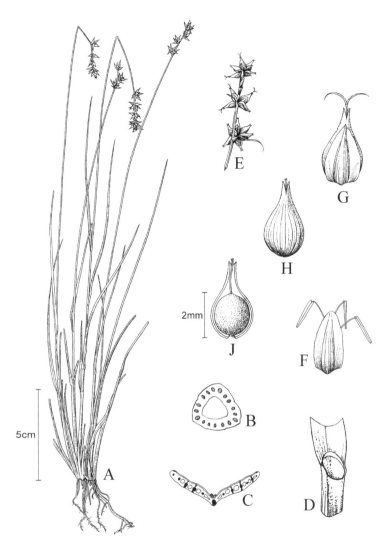

A Fertile shoot; **B** T.S. stem (culm); **C** T.S. leaf; **D** Inner face of leaf-sheath and ligule; **E** Upper spikes; **F** Male floret; **G** Female floret; **H** Utricle; **J** Section through utricle, showing nut.

M50 × 51 Carex × gaudiniana (*Carex echinata × C. dioica*)

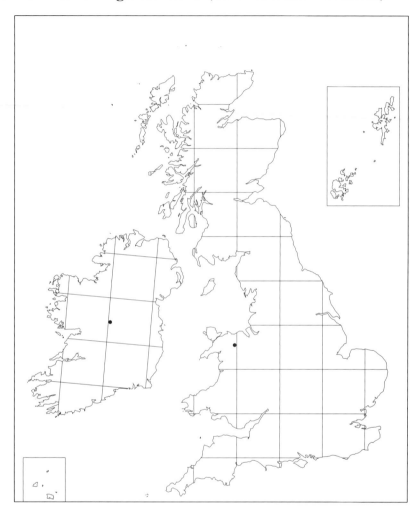

Carex × gaudiniana is known, growing with both parents, only at Hiraethog, Denbighshire (v.c. 50), and in Ireland at Bog Lake, Co. Westmeath (v.c. H23), and Louisburgh, West Mayo (v.c. H.27).

Carex × *gaudiniana* Guthnick

Carex echinata × *C. dioica*   *Map 50 × 51*

This densely tufted hybrid can be distinguished from *C. echinata* by its noticeably overtopping inflorescence, filiform stem, strongly inrolled, deep green leaves and contiguous spikes, and from *C. dioica* by its monoecious inflorescence, broader but more inrolled, tapering leaves and strongly divaricate, sessile female spikes. It differs from both in the golden sheen of its inflorescence, especially when fresh, and the presence of empty, wrinkled utricles. Seen in the field, the small and rather cruciform inflorescence is very striking and is diagnostic: see p. 283.

Carex echinata	*Carex* × *gaudiniana*	*Carex dioica*
Plants monoecious.	**Plants monoecious.**	Plants dioecious.
Stems 10–40(–60) cm, overtopping the leaves.	Stems 22–31 cm, much overtopping the leaves.	Stems 5–30cm, slightly overtopping the leaves.
Leaves to 30 cm × 1–2.5 mm, mid to dark green, shiny, gradually tapering to trigonous tip.	**Leaves** to 23 cm × 2–2.5 mm, deep green, shiny above, **strongly inrolled**, tapering to fine tip.	Leaves 5–20 cm × 0.3–1 mm, dark green, incurved, with rounded apex.
Inflorescence 10–30 mm; spikes 2–5, ± distant, 3–6 mm long, sessile; terminal spike ♀ above, ♂ below.	**Inflorescence (10–)15–20 mm, cruciform with a golden sheen; terminal spike mostly ♂, often ♀ at top, narrowly cylindrical.**	Inflorescence a single terminal ♂ or ♀ spike; ♂ spike 8–20 mm long, narrowly cylindrical.
♀ part of spikes subglobose; lower ♂ flowers appressed to rachis.	**♀ spikes 2–3, 5–6 mm long, narrowly ovoid, contiguous, strongly divaricate, sessile.**	♀ spike 1, 5–20 mm long, subglobose to cylindrical.
♀ glumes broadly ovate, pale red-brown with green midrib and a broad, hyaline margin.	**♀ glumes** ± ovate, acute, medium brown, often **with** a green midrib and **a golden sheen.**	♀ glumes ± ovate, acute, red- to purple-brown; midrib pale, with a ± hyaline margin.
Utricles 3–4 mm, ovoid, plano-convex, green to yellow-brown.	**Utricles** 2.5–3.2 mm, ovoid, plano-convex, green, **sterile.**	Utricles 2.5–3.5 mm, ovoid, compressed, pale red-purple-brown.

51   *Carex dioica* L.

Dioecious Sedge   Map 51

Plants dioecious. **Rhizomes** shortly creeping; shoots loosely tufted, often decumbent; roots often as thick as rhizome, pale purple-brown; scales pale purple- or orange-brown, soon decaying. *Stems* 5–30 cm, erect, terete, striate. *Leaves* 5–20 cm × 0.3–1 mm, rigid, ± erect, channelled or semicircular in transverse section, with 3 main veins and rounded apex, dark green, dying to a dull red-brown; hypostomous; sheaths becoming pale orange-brown, persistent, with inner face hyaline; apex straight but soon split; ligule 0.5 mm, rounded, tubular. *Inflorescence* a single terminal, usually unisexual, spike; bracts glumaceous or 0. *Male spike* 8–20 mm; *male glumes* 3–4 mm, ovate-oblong, red-brown with hyaline margin; apex obtuse or acute. *Female spike* 5–20 mm, subglobose to cylindric; *female glumes* 2.5–3.5 mm, red- to purple-brown, with pale midrib, dark nerve and ± hyaline margin, persistent; apex obtuse or acute; glume of lowest floret often enlarged, with acuminate apex. *Utricles* 2.5–3.5 mm, patent, rarely deflexed when ripe, broadly ovoid, compressed, pale red-purple-brown with darker ribs; beak 0.5–0.75 mm, serrulate, notched; stigmas 2; nut subglobose, compressed.   *Fr.* 7–8.

Carex dioica is a species of mesotrophic to eutrophic (calcareous) mires in wet, silty muds, rarely in pure peat, in pH range 5.5–6.5, at altitudes of 0 to *c.* 1000 m. Characteristic, with *Pinguicula vulgaris* and several other sedges, in **M10** communities; also in **M11**, **M12**, **M13**, **M15**, **M34**, **M37** and **M38** and in *Narthecium–Sphagnum* valley mires (**M21**) with *Rhynchospora alba*.

Variable in size of female spike, utricle and whole plant. The narrow leaf with three veins is a useful vegetative character. Occasionally found with a few female flowers at the base of the male spike, when it may be mistaken for *C. pulicaris.*

Hybrids with *C. echinata* (**50 × 51** *C.* × *gaudiniana* Guthnick) have been confirmed from Wales and Ireland. Hybrids with *C. canescens*, *C. lachenalii* and *C. maritima* are reported from Europe. *C. parallela* (Laest.) Sommerf., a North Scandinavian plant with narrower, smooth-beaked utricles (Fig. H_1), has been confused with forms of *C. dioica*; it could possibly occur here. Another dioecious species, the Central European *C. davalliana* Sm., with long-beaked, oblong-lanceoloid utricles (Fig. H_2), occurred in Somerset (see p. 516), but the site has completely changed and it is now considered extinct; other British records for this species have proved to be forms of *C. dioica*.

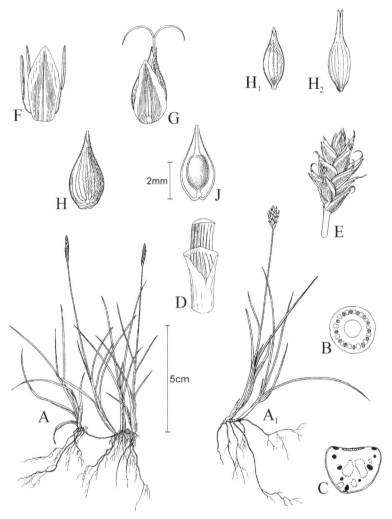

A Fertile male shoot; **A₁** Fertile female shoot; **B** T.S. stem (culm); **C** T.S. leaf; **D** Inner face of leaf-sheath and ligule; **E** Female spike; **F** Male floret; **G** Female floret; **H** Utricle (**H₁** *C. parallela*; **H₂** *C. davalliana*); **J** Section through utricle, showing nut.

M51 *Carex dioica*

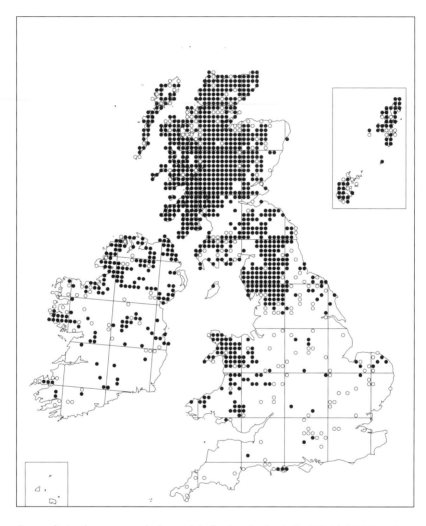

Carex dioica is common in base-rich flushes in the Lake District, N Pennines and N Wales; likewise in Scotland, especially on mica-schists and limestones of the N and W, rising to *c.* 1000 m in Breadalbanes (v.c. 88). Scattered in lowland Britain and Ireland. Rapidly diminishing in lowland areas owing to drainage.

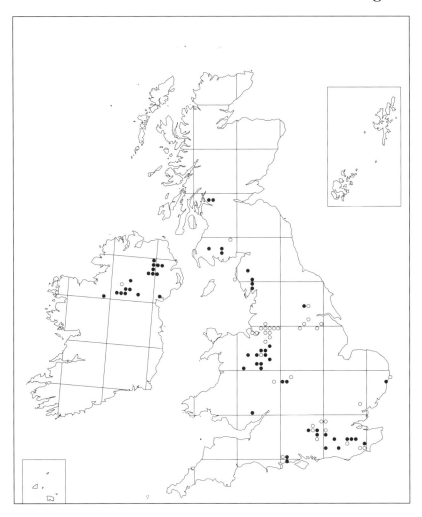

In Britain *Carex elongata* is found in the SE, as far west as the Hants–Dorset border, and in Warwickshire; scattered in Wales from Monmouth to Denbigh and then north from Cheshire to Cumberland and Stirlingshire. In Ireland it grows around Lough Neagh and from County Down south to Roscommon and Cavan. See also David (1978b).

273

52 *Carex elongata* L.

Elongated Sedge Map 52

Rhizomes short; shoots densely tufted, forming substantial tussocks in older populations; roots pale brown; scales grey-brown, usually persistent. *Stems* 30–80 cm, rough with upward-pointing teeth, trigonous. *Leaves* 25–90 cm × 2–5 mm, rough beneath, thin, ± flat or slightly keeled, tapering gradually to a very fine, flat tip, mid green, often red-brown and persistent on dying; hypostomous; sheaths forming short false stems, lower pale brown or pink-brown, shiny, persistent, with the inner face hyaline; apex concave; ligule 4–8 mm, acute, with little or no free margin. *Inflorescence* 3–7 cm, lax; lower bracts setaceous, upper glumaceous. *Spikes* 5–18, ± contiguous or lowest distant, 5–15 mm, ± erect, becoming divaricate on ripening, sessile, upper female at top, male at base, lower entirely female. *Male glumes* 2.5–3 mm, ovate-oblong, pale red-brown, with green midrib and broadly hyaline margin; apex rounded or obtuse, ± mucronate. *Female glumes* c. 2 mm, ovate-elliptic, red-brown, with green midrib; apex acute or obtuse. *Utricles* 3–4 mm, lanceoloid-ellipsoid, plano-convex, often curved, distinctly ribbed, green, with the ribs becoming dark red-brown; beak 0.5–0.75 mm, often minutely serrulate, truncate or indistinctly notched; stigmas 2; nut compressed-cylindric, stalked. *Fr.* 6–7.

C. *elongata* is a very local plant of damp soil in water-meadows, beside ditches, pools and lakes, and often with C. *paniculata* in boggy woodland, especially that dominated by alder (**W5**) or *Salix cinerea* and *Betula pubescens* (**W2**). It can withstand waterlogging where tussock growth is above the water level (David 1978b). Although C. *elongata* flowers quite freely, in England at least, reports suggest that the seed seldom appears to be viable and spread by that means is rare (R.W. David in Stewart *et al.* 1994).

This is a distinct species characterised by the long, divaricate, brownish spikes and the narrow, ellipsoid, ribbed utricle (with the ribs distinctively reddish at maturity); vegetatively the long ligule, pink-brown, persistent, non-fibrous sheaths and substantial tussocks separate it from **40–42** the C. *muricata* group.

Hybrids with C. *appropinquata*, C. *paniculata* and C. *remota* are recorded from mainland Europe but not from the British Isles.

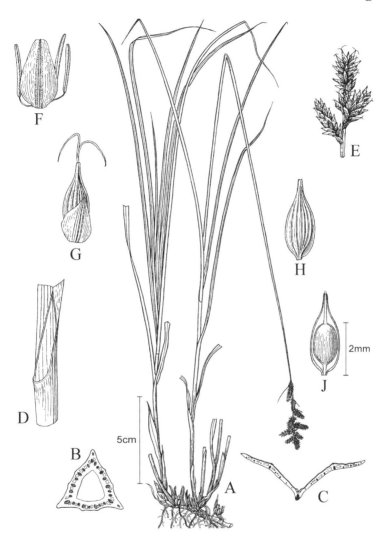

A Fertile shoot; **B** T.S. stem (culm); **C** T.S. leaf; **D** Inner face of leaf-sheath and ligule; **E** Upper spikes; **F** Male floret; **G** Female floret; **H** Utricle; **J** Section through utricle, showing nut.

53 *Carex lachenalii* Schkuhr

Hare's-foot Sedge   *Map 53*

Rhizomes shortly creeping; shoots closely tufted; roots brown; scales brown, soon fibrous. *Stems* up to 20(–30) cm, bluntly trigonous, striate. *Leaves* shorter than stems, 1–2 mm broad, flat, dark green; hypostomous; sheaths deep brown, becoming fibrous; ligule *c.* 1 mm, rounded. *Inflorescence* 2– 4 cm, red-brown. *Spikes* 2–5, closely contiguous, the upper at the apex of a triangle completed by the next two below, 5–8 mm, subclavate, female at top, male at base. *Male glumes* 2–3 mm, elliptic; apex obtuse, red-brown. *Female glumes c.* 2.5 mm, ovate, red-brown, with broad hyaline margin; apex obtuse. *Utricles* 2.5–4 mm, ovoid, markedly narrowed at base, usually green below and brown above; beak *c.* 0.5–0.8 mm, smooth, split at the back, with the halves overlapping; stigmas 2; nut obovoid, biconvex.   *Fr.* 7–9.

A very local but sometimes abundant plant of wet slopes and acid rock-ledges in the *Carex bigelowii–Alchemilla alpina–Sibbaldia procumbens* community (**U14**), between 750 and 1150 m and especially where late snow lies and then scattered in *Salix herbacea–Racomitrium heterosticum* (**U12**) or *Cryptogramma–Athyrium distentifolium* (**U18**) snow-bed communities; other sites on Geal-charn in the Alder Forest are in flushed areas, closest to **M6** association with *Carex echinata* and *C. canescens* or to *Anthelia julacea–Sphagnum denticulatum* springs (**M31**) (G. Rothero pers. comm.). On Ben Nevis it grows in very open vegetation on wet rock-ledges with *Alchemilla glabra*, *Cerastium arcticum*, *Deschampsia cespitosa*, *Juncus triglumis*, *Oxyria digyna*, *Saxifraga stellaris*, *Silene acaulis*, *Thymus polytrichus* subsp. *britannicus* and *Thalictrum alpinum*, with *Anthelia julacea*, *Marsupella emarginata* and *Philonotis fontana* (G. Rothero pers. comm.).

Closest in morphology to *C. leporina*, but in its British habitats this cannot be confused with any other sedge except its hybrid with *C. canescens* (**54** × **53** *C.* × *helvola* Blytt ex Fr.). The hybrid is completely sterile and is found with the parents in the Grampians (in some abundance on Lochnagar).

Carex lachenalii is a **Red Data List** species in Great Britain; *Status*: **Near threatened** (Cheffings & Farrell 2005).

276

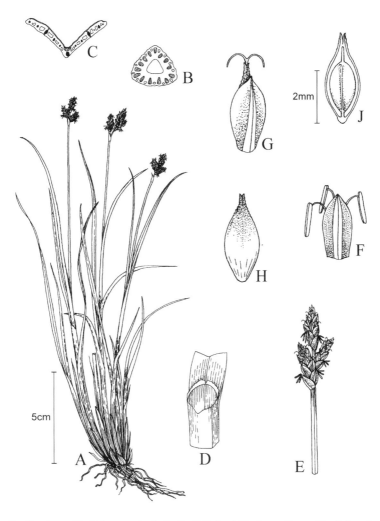

A   Fertile shoot; **B**   T.S. stem (culm); **C**   T.S. leaf; **D**   Inner face of leaf-sheath and ligule; **E**   Inflorescence; **F**   Male floret; **G**   Female floret; **H**   Utricle; **J**   Section through utricle, showing nut.

M53 *Carex lachenalii*

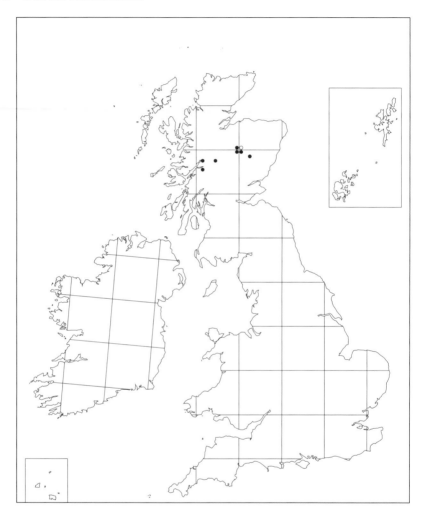

Carex lachenalii is found in the Cairngorms, Ben Alder Forest, Glencoe and the Ben Nevis range (Aonach Beag and, in 2002, on Ben Nevis itself). A record of this high-altitude sedge from Harris, v.c. 110 (J.W. Heslop Harrison 1945), has been shown to be an error (J.E. Raven in Preston 2004).

278

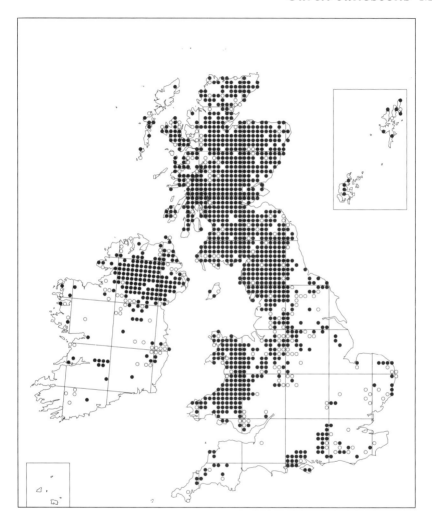

Carex canescens is found on wet sandy heaths in E England, Dorset etc. and becomes frequent in W and N Wales, N England and Scotland. In Ireland it is frequent in the NE but rare and scattered in the west and south.

54 *Carex canescens* L.[*]

White Sedge   *Map 54*

Rhizomes very shortly creeping; shoots loosely tufted; roots pale brown or whitish; scales pale or pink-brown, usually persistent. **Stems** 10–50 cm, rough above, slender, sharply trigonous, scarcely ribbed. **Leaves** 15–55 cm × 2–3 mm, soft, thin, flat or ± keeled, tapering gradually to a fine, rough, ± flat tip, pale green; amphistomous but with stomata mostly on underside; sheaths thin, forming short false stems only, lower pink-brown, soon decaying; inner face hyaline; apex ± straight; ligule 2–3 mm, acute. **Inflorescence** 3–5 cm; bracts glumaceous, lower sometimes setaceous. **Spikes** 4–8, contiguous or ± distant, 5–8 mm, female at top, male at base. **Male glumes** 2.5 mm, ovate or broadly elliptic, hyaline, with green midrib; apex obtuse. **Female glumes** *c.* 2 mm, ovate-oblong, hyaline, with green midrib; apex acute or apiculate. **Utricles** 2–3 mm, ovoid-ellipsoid, plano-convex, pale or blue-green to yellow, with yellowish ribs; beak 0.5–0.75 mm, minutely rough, notched; stigmas 2; nut obovoid or ellipsoid, biconvex.   **Fr.** 6–8.

   C. canescens is a component of the oligotrophic alpine *Carex–Sphagnum* mires (**M2**, **M4**) and of transitional zones with *C. echinata* and *S. fallax* (**M6**). A dominant sedge in high-altitude mires with *C. aquatilis*, *C. echinata* and *C. rariflora* (**M7**) to 1100 m (on Ben Alder: Foley & Porter 2002). Found also in lowland Britain in more mesotrophic mires (**M5**), e.g. those in the valley bogs of the New Forest, where it is usually associated with *C. rostrata*, *Eriophorum angustifolium* and *Sphagnum squarrosum*.

   The soft, pale green leaves and the acutely trigonous stems with pale fruiting heads distinguish this from any other sedge in Britain or Ireland. Hybrids with *C. paniculata* (**35** × **54** *C.* × *ludibunda* J. Gay), *C. echinata* (**54** × **50** *C.* × *biharica* Simonk.) and *C. lachenalii* (**54** × **53** *C.* × *helvola* Blytt ex Fr.) are found in Britain. Hybrids with *C. appropinquata*, *C. dioica*, *C. elongata* and *C. remota* are reported from elsewhere in Europe and Egorova (1999) lists a total of 13 species with which *C. canescens* hybridises in Eurasia.

---

[*]*Carex curta* Gooden. in previous editions

280

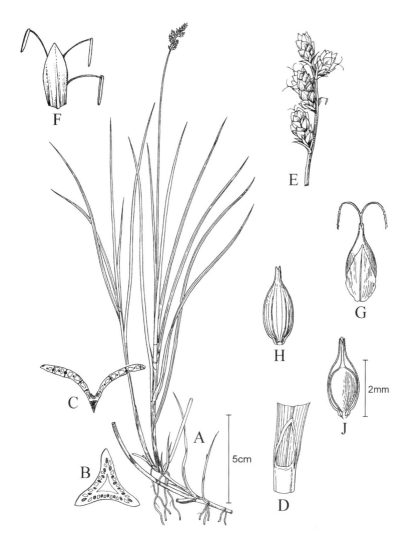

A Fertile shoot; **B** T.S. stem (culm); **C** T.S. leaf; **D** Inner face of leaf-sheath and ligule; **E** Inflorescence; **F** Male floret; **G** Female floret; **H** Utricle; **J** Section through utricle, showing nut.

54 × 50 *Carex* × *biharica* Simonk.

Carex canescens × *C. echinata*   (*not mapped*)

C. × *biharica* is intermediate between its parents in the number, distribution and shape of the spikes, length and shape of the ligule and length of the utricle. It resembles *C. echinata* in the distribution of leaf stomata and in the serrate utricle beak (distinguishable with lens), but it is closer to *C. canescens* in leaf breadth and in its contiguous spikes and appressed utricles; the anthers are unemergent and the utricles empty. It is best distinguished from **54** × **53** *C.* × *helvola* by wider-spaced spikes and longer utricles with a serrate beak.

This is a difficult hybrid to identify, but the most convincing records come from wet, acid substrates on higher ground in the mountains of Central Scotland (NN64, NO18, NO27). Similar plants from the same area with fusiform utricles and a non-serrate beak may be another form of this hybrid.

Carex canescens	*Carex* × *biharica*	*Carex echinata*
Stem 10–50 cm, slender, sharply trigonous, scarcely ribbed.	Stem 10–35 cm, slender, sharply trigonous, ± striate.	Stem 10–40(–60) cm, slender, trigonous, ± striate to subterete.
Leaves 15–55 cm × 2–3 mm.	Leaves 5–20 cm × 1–2.8 mm.	Leaves up to 30 cm × 1–2.5 mm.
Stomata on both leaf surfaces.	**Stomata on lower surface of leaf only.**	Stomata on lower surface of leaf only.
Ligule 2–3 mm, acute.	**Ligule** *c.* **2 mm, obtuse, tubular.**	Ligule *c.* 1 mm, rounded, tubular.
Inflorescence 3–5 cm.	Inflorescence 1.5–2.5 cm	Inflorescence 1–3 cm.
Spikes 4–8, contiguous or ± distant, cylindrical/ovoid.	**Spikes 4–6, usually contiguous but sometimes spaced below, ellipsoid; utricles all appressed.**	Spikes 2–5, ± distant, stellate when mature.
♀ glumes hyaline with green midrib; apex acute to apiculate.	♀ glumes pale brown; hyaline margin broad; apex acute to apiculate.	♀ glumes pale red-brown; hyaline margin broad; apex acute.
Utricles 2–3 mm, ovoid-ellipsoid; beak not serrate.	**Utricles** *c.* **3 mm, ovoid-ellipsoid, empty; beak serrate.**	Utricles 3–4 mm, ovoid; beak serrate.

Carex × gaudiniana (*Carex echinata × C. dioica*) **50 × 51**
Carex × biharica (*Carex canescens × C. echinata*) **54 × 50**
Carex × helvola (*Carex canescens × C. lachenalii*) **54 × 53**

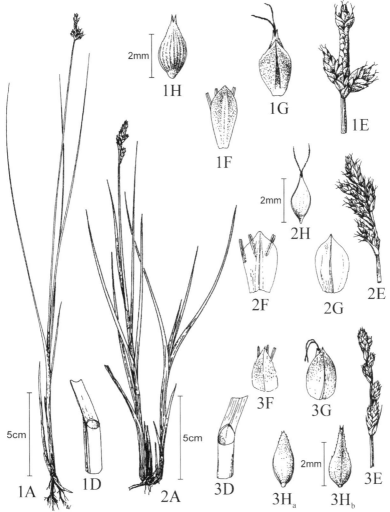

1 *Carex × gaudiniana* **2** *C. × helvola* **3** *C. × biharica*
A Fertile shoot; **D** Inner face of leaf-sheath and ligule; **E** Inflorescence; **F** Male floret; **G** Female floret; **H**, **H$_a$** Utricles, front view; **H$_b$** Utricle, side view.

54 × 53 *Carex* × *helvola* Blytt ex Fr.

Carex canescens × *C. lachenalii*   (*not mapped*)

C. × *helvola* is intermediate between the parents in distribution of stomata, ligule length and shape, and number and distribution of spikes. It differs from both in the ginger colour of the inflorescence, in the spikes clustered below the larger terminal spike and in its unemergent anthers and empty utricles.

Known with certainty only from Cairn Toul (NN99) and Lochnagar (NO28), both in v.c. 92, where it grows in the vicinity of both parents on gently sloping areas of soligenous sedge-mires (**M6**), among peat-hags and runnels, above 950 m. Records from the mountains of Perthshire appear to refer to **54 × 50** *C.* × *biharica*, but a recent atypical collection from the Ben Alder area may be *C.* × *helvola*.

Carex canescens	*Carex* × *helvola*	*Carex lachenalii*
Stem 10–50 cm, sharply trigonous, scarcely ribbed.	**Stem** 15–30 cm, **trigonous, distinctly ribbed.**	Stem up to 20(–30) cm, bluntly trigonous, strongly ribbed.
Leaves 2–3 mm broad, pale green.	**Leaves** 2–2.7 mm broad, pale **mid green, slightly glaucous.**	Leaves 1–2 mm broad, dark green.
Stomata on both surfaces of leaf.	**Stomata** on both leaf surfaces, **sparser above.**	Stomata on underside of leaf only.
Ligule 2–3 mm, acute.	**Ligule 1.5–2 mm, rounded to acute.**	Ligule 1 mm, rounded.
Spikes 4–8, cylindrical/ovoid, contiguous or ± distant.	**Spikes 5–7(–11); closely contiguous spikes below larger terminal spike, others ± spaced below; terminal subclavate, others ovoid.**	Spikes 2–5, closely contiguous, terminal subclavate, lower long-ovoid.
♀ glumes *c.* 2 mm, ovate-oblong, hyaline with green midrib; apex acute or apiculate.	♀ **glumes** 2–2.2 mm, broadly ovate, **ginger** with narrow hyaline margin; apex obtuse to acute.	♀ glumes *c.* 2.5 mm, ovate, red-brown with broad hyaline margin; apex obtuse.
Utricles 2–3 mm, pale or blue-green to yellow, with prominent ribs.	**Utricles** 2.2–2.4 mm, **ginger above,** pale to mid green, faintly ribbed below, **empty.**	Utricles 2.5–4 mm, brown above, green and faintly ribbed below.

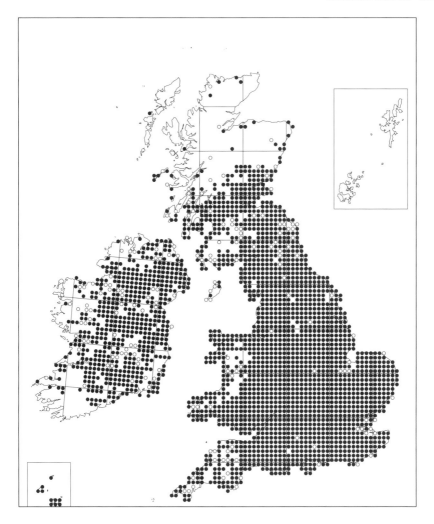

Carex hirta is found throughout most of Britain, reaching 470 m on Hartside, v.c. 70 (Porter & Foley 2002), becoming less common in Scotland and very rare north of the Great Glen; markedly scarcer or absent in areas with a rainfall over 1000 mm (40 inches) per year. Scattered throughout Ireland except in blanket mire areas.

55 *Carex hirta* L.

Rhizomes often far-creeping; shoots tufted; roots often much branched, pale brown; scales brown or red-brown, eventually becoming fibrous. *Stems* 15–70 cm, trigonous with rounded faces. *Leaves* 10–50 cm × 2–5(–8) mm, ± hairy on both surfaces, flat or ± keeled, gradually tapering to a fine point, mid green, often overwintering; hypostomous; sheaths hairy, those of sterile shoots forming a rigid false stem, with inner face hyaline, often densely hairy, and apex ± straight; ligule 1–2 mm, obtuse, fringed with hairs on free margin. *Inflorescence* up to 3/4 length of stem; lower bracts leaf-like, longer than spike but not exceeding inflorescence, upper bracts setaceous. *Male spikes* 2–3, 10–30 mm; *male glumes* 4–5 mm, obovate-oblanceolate, ± hairy, red-brown with pale midrib or often ± hyaline throughout; apex mucronate. *Female spikes* 2–3, contiguous or ± distant, 10–45 mm, cylindric, erect; peduncles smooth, up to twice as long as spike, half-ensheathed; *female glumes* 6–8 mm, ovate-oblong, green-hyaline; apex acute or midrib excurrent as a green ciliate awn. *Utricles* 5–7 mm, ovoid, many-ribbed, hairy, green; beak 2 mm, hispid, deeply bifid; stigmas 3; nut obovoid, trigonous, stalked. *Fr.* 6–9.

C. hirta is a plant of various soils, usually in grassy associations such as hedge-banks, meadows (even heavily trodden verges), including rich fen-meadow with *Juncus* spp., *Deschampsia cespitosa*, *Cirsium palustre* etc. (**M22**); also in consolidated sand-dunes (**SD9, SD12**), usually in hollows or channels where soil moisture accumulates; occasionally in damp woods.

This species can be confused with little else and is distinctive with its hairy utricles, male glumes and leaves. In specimens growing in damp shady situations the pubescence is lost from the leaves and sheaths, except near the apex of the hyaline inner face; the utricles and glumes are always hairy. This form has been called *C. hirta* var. *sublaevis* Hornem. but is hardly worthy of taxonomic recognition.

C. hirta hybridises with *C. vesicaria* (**55** × **61** *C.* × *grossii* Fiek) and with *C. rostrata*, but the latter hybrid has not been recorded in the British Isles.

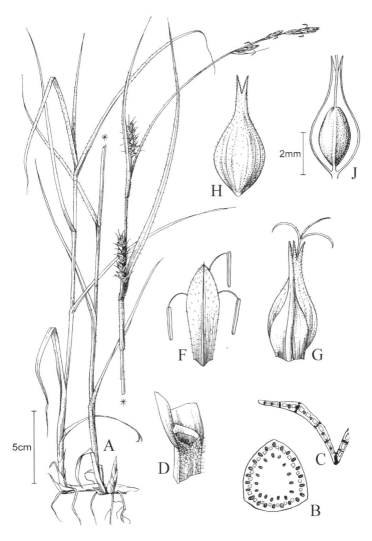

A Fertile shoot; **B** T.S. stem (culm); **C** T.S. leaf; **D** Inner face of leaf-sheath and ligule; **F** Male floret; **G** Female floret; **H** Utricle; **J** Section through utricle, showing nut.

55 × 61 *Carex* × *grossii* Fiek

Carex hirta × *C. vesicaria*   (*not mapped*)

A sterile hybrid with unemergent anthers and empty utricles, resembling
C. hirta in habit but much less hairy overall, especially in relation to the
leaves, male glumes and utricles. Additionally, the hairs are much shorter
than in *C. hirta,* the ligule is acute, the lower bracts are longer and the utricles
are more narrowly ovoid with less developed shoulders, whilst the female
glumes are lanceolate rather than ovate-oblong. From *C. vesicaria* it is most
readily distinguished by the hairs on the leaves, glumes and utricles.

Known from only a single site in Ireland at Magherabeg (T38), Co.
Wicklow (v.c. H20), where it was found in 1944 growing in a coastal marsh
amongst sand-dunes and where, by the mid-1960s, it had spread to form a
large population over 5 m across. However, despite numerous later searches,
neither the hybrid nor its parents have been seen at the site in recent years
(C. Brady pers. comm.) and it should perhaps be presumed extinct.

For a detailed description of this hybrid see Nelmes (1947).

Carex hirta	*Carex* × *grossii*	*Carex vesicaria*
Leaves hairy.	**Leaves very sparsely hairy.**	Leaves glabrous.
Ligule obtuse.	Ligule acute.	Ligule acute.
Lower bracts longer than spike but not than inflorescence.	**Lower bracts ± equalling inflorescence.**	Lower bracts exceeding inflorescence.
♂ glumes hairy.	♂ glumes glabrous or very sparsely hairy.	♂ glumes glabrous.
♀ glumes ovate-oblong; midrib excurrent.	♀ glumes lanceolate; apex acute, sometimes with an incipient, excurrent midrib.	♀ glumes narrowly lanceolate; apex acute or acuminate.
Utricles 5–7 mm, markedly ribbed, dull, ovoid with shoulders, densely hairy; hairs to 0.4 mm long.	**Utricles 5–6 mm, narrowly ovoid with incipient shoulders, shrunken, markedly ribbed, dull, empty and sterile, sparsely but distinctly hairy; hairs short (to 0.2 mm).**	Utricles 6–8 mm, ovoid-ellipsoid, lacking shoulders, glabrous, slightly ribbed, shiny.

Carex × *grossii* (*Carex hirta* × *C. vesicaria*)   **55 × 61**
Carex × *evoluta* (*Carex lasiocarpa* × *C. riparia*)   **56 × 58**

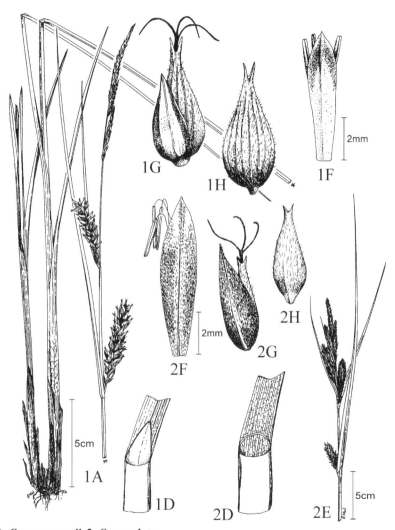

1 *Carex* × *grossii* **2** *C.* × *evoluta*
A Fertile shoot; **D** Inner face of leaf-sheath and ligule; **E** Inflorescence; **F** Male floret; **G** Female floret; **H** Utricle.

56 × 58 *Carex* × *evoluta* Hartm.

Carex lasiocarpa × *C. riparia*   *Map 56 × 58*

This hybrid is readily distinguished from *C. lasiocarpa* by its broader, flatter leaves, more robust female spikes, longer female glumes and less tomentose utricles. From *C. riparia* it is best distinguished by its narrower, more gradually tapering leaves, its fewer, narrowly cylindrical male spikes, its shorter more lanceolate but more acuminate female glumes and its tomentose utricles. On specimens examined most of the anthers had emerged and at least some of the utricles were filled, indicating partial fertility.

The earliest record is from Grunty Fen (v.c. 29), where it was found in 1833 (**CGE**) but not identified till much later. The second record was from disused peat-cuttings at Sharpham Peat Moor (v.c. 6), where it was first found by H.S. Thompson in 1915.

Carex lasiocarpa	*Carex* × *evoluta*	*Carex riparia*
A tall, slender plant with a narrow inflorescence.	A medium, robust plant with a fairly stout inflorescence.	A robust plant with a markedly broad, stout inflorescence.
Leaves 1–2 mm wide, inrolled, tapering gradually to a fine whip-like apex.	**Leaves 3–5 mm wide, plicate, tapering gradually to a fine point.**	Leaves 6–20(–24) mm wide, plicate, tapering abruptly to an acute apex.
♂ spikes 1–3, ± contiguous, cylindric, 2–3 mm wide.	**♂ spikes 3–4, loosely clustered,** cylindric, up to 3.5 mm wide.	♂ spikes 3–6, tightly clustered, broadly fusiform, 3.5–7 mm wide.
♀ spikes 1–3 cm × 4–6 mm, contiguous or ± distant, narrowly cylindric-oblong.	♀ spikes (2.5–)3–4 cm × 8–10 mm, contiguous or ± distant, broadly cylindric-oblong.	♀ spikes 3–10 cm × 10–15 mm, ± contiguous, broadly cylindric-fusiform.
♀ glumes 3.5–5 mm long, lanceolate, apex acute or acuminate.	**♀ glumes 5.5–6.5 mm long,** ± lanceolate, distinctly acuminate.	♀ glumes 7–10 mm long, oblong-lanceolate or narrowly ovate acuminate.
Utricles 3.5–4.5 mm long, ovoid, distinctly tomentose.	**Utricles 4–5.5 mm long, ovoid, sparsely tomentose.**	Utricles 5–8 mm long, ovoid, ± inflated, glabrous.

290

Carex × *evoluta* (*Carex lasiocarpa* × *C. riparia*)   *M56 × 58*

Carex × *evoluta* has been recorded from Redgrave and Lopham Fens (v.c. 25), Grunty Fen (v.c. 29), Woodwalton Fen (v.c. 31) and Sharpham Peat Moor (v.c. 6), where it was first found in 1915; although lost from this site by 1955, it was refound nearby at Street Heath, where it still exists.

56 *Carex lasiocarpa* Ehrh.

Slender Sedge   *Map 56*

Rhizomes far-creeping, forming large stands; shoots loosely tufted, slender; roots pale yellow-brown; scales pale or yellow-brown, occasionally wine-red. **Stems** 45–120 cm, slender, stiff, smooth or slightly rough above, trigonous, striate. **Leaves** 30–100 cm × 1–2 mm, flat or more usually inrolled, long-attenuate into a fine acicular, stiff, whip-like point which lies flat when en masse giving a characteristic striate texture to the mire community, grey-green; hypostomous; sheaths dark purple-brown to pale red-brown, soon decaying, with inner face membranous, purple- or pale brown, persistent or often fibrillose, and apex straight, dark purplish; ligule 2–3 mm, obtuse. **Inflorescence** 1/8–1/6 length of stem; bracts leaf-like, very slender, lower often exceeding inflorescence. **Male spikes** 1–3, ± contiguous, 20–70 mm; **male glumes** 4–6 mm, lanceolate, purple-brown, with a green or pale midrib; apex acute. **Female spikes** 1–3, contiguous or ± distant, 10–30 mm, cylindric-oblong, erect, ± sessile; **female glumes** 3.5–5 mm, lanceolate, chestnut-brown, with a pale midrib; apex acute or acuminate. **Utricles** 3.5–4.5 mm, ovoid, tomentose, grey-green; beak 0.5–1 mm, ± deeply bifid; stigmas 3; nut ovoid, trigonous.   **Fr.** 7–9.

C. lasiocarpa is an indicator species of mesotrophic to eutrophic mires and reed-swamp (*Phragmites–Peucedanum palustre*, **S24**), on substrata ranging from sedge peats to sandy raw soils of exposed lake shores. It sometimes forms pure stands in submerged situations but is more often associated with *Myrica gale*, *C. rostrata* and *Sphagnum squarrosum* (**M5**); this association develops into a *C. lasiocarpa–Myrica* scrub vegetation with much *Sphagnum fallax*. Often associated with *Cladium* and hypnoid mosses (**M9** communities) in lowland Britain. In Ireland it is associated with *Phragmites*, *C. rostrata*, *C. limosa*, *Eriocaulon* etc.

The narrow grey-green leaves with whip-like tips and red- or purple-brown lower sheaths distinguish this species from any other in these habitats; in fruit it is easily recognisable by its tomentose utricles. For vegetative differences between *C. lasiocarpa* and **93** *C. buxbaumii*, see that species.

In England *C. lasiocarpa* forms a hybrid with *C. riparia* (**56 × 58** *C. × evoluta* Hartm.). Hybrids with *C. rostrata* and *C. vesicaria* are reported from mainland Europe but not from the British Isles.

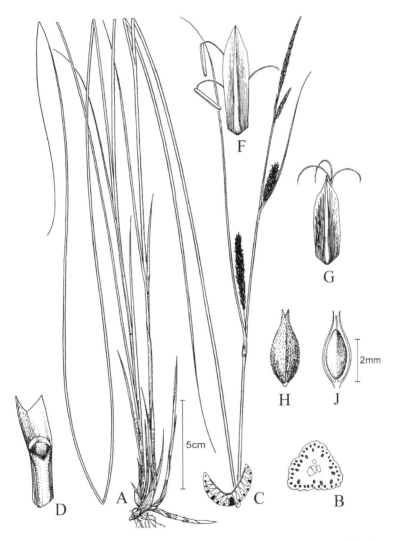

A Fertile shoot; **B** T.S. stem (culm); **C** T.S. leaf; **D** Inner face of leaf-sheath and ligule; **F** Male floret; **G** Female floret; **H** Utricle; **J** Section through utricle, showing nut.

M56 *Carex lasiocarpa*

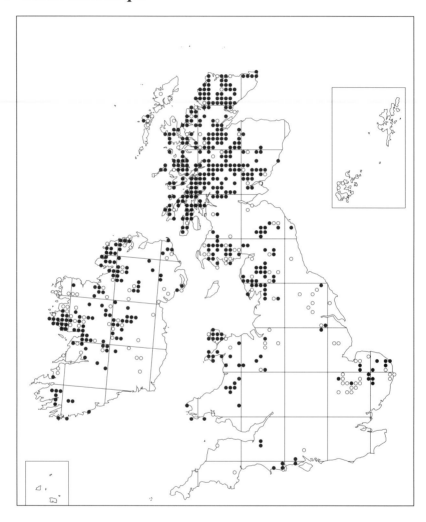

Carex lasiocarpa is widespread in much of Scotland and the far NW of England; also in Wales and on old peat-cuttings in East Anglia; now rare or decreasing elsewhere in England. In Ireland, mainly central and western.

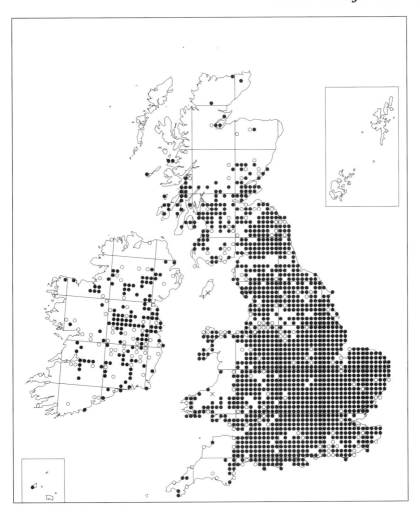

Carex acutiformis is similar in distribution to **58** *C. riparia*, but more frequent, though it is less prevalent in W and central Wales and the SW English counties; generally more common further north, but becoming rare in Scotland north of the Grampian Highlands. In Ireland surprisingly infrequent in view of the eutrophic habitats available.

57 *Carex acutiformis* Ehrh.

Lesser Pond-sedge   *Map 57*

Rhizomes far-creeping; shoots tufted; roots brown, often dark; scales grey-brown, soon fibrous. ***Stems*** 60–150 cm, solid, rough, often smooth below, sharply trigonous. ***Leaves*** up to 160 cm × 5–20(–26) mm, thin, keeled or plicate, arcuate, gradually tapering to apex, glaucous at first, becoming dull, often red-green above at apex; hypostomous; sheaths usually red-streaked, translucent, showing aerenchyma pattern below but not above ligule (see below), with inner face hyaline-brown, persistent, usually fibrillose on splitting; apex deeply concave to V-shaped; ligule 5–15 mm, acute, with free tissue *c.* 0.4 mm wide. ***Inflorescence*** 1/4–1/3 length of stem; bracts leaf-like, exceeding inflorescence. ***Male spikes*** 2–3, clustered, 1–5 cm; ***male glumes*** 5–6 mm, oblong to oblanceolate, dark purple-brown with pale midrib; apex obtuse to subacute. ***Female spikes*** 2–4, ± contiguous to distant, 2–6 cm, cylindric, erect, upper sessile and often male at top, lowest only shortly pedunculate; ***female glumes*** 4–5 mm, oblong-lanceolate, red- or purple-brown, with paler midrib; apex acute or with serrulate acumen. ***Utricles*** 3.5–5 mm, ellipsoid-ovoid, ribbed, finely mamillate, greyish-green; beak *c.* 0.5 mm, notched; stigmas 3; nut obovoid, trigonous, flat at apex. ***Fr.*** 7–9.

A characteristic species of sedge-swamps (**S7**) and, with *C. riparia* (and *C. elata*), in transition zones to **S6,** and there remaining in wet climax woodland (**W2, W5, W6,** "semi-swamp carr": Lambert 1951). In lakes, ponds, ditch/stream margins and wet meadows with *Juncus subnodulosus* (**M22**). *Carex acutiformis* is predominantly a lowland plant (to 370 m in Garrigill, v.c. 70: Foley & Porter 2002).

Carex acutiformis may be confused with **58** *C. riparia*. The fewer, less contiguous male spikelets and the obtuse or subacute male glumes usually distinguish it. The leaf aerenchyma pattern ('cells' > 5 mm) is usually obscure just above the acute ligule, whereas in *C. riparia* it is easily seen above and below the rounded ligule, with 'cells' 1.5–2 mm. Both **98** *C. acuta* and **101** *C. elata* have two stigmas and *C. elata* lacks rhizomes; *C. acuta* is less distinct, but the brown, persistent, inner faces to the sheaths lack fibrillae.

C. acutiformis hybridises with *C. riparia* (**57** × **58** *C.* × *sooi* Jákucs), *C. vesicaria* (**57** × **61** *C.* × *ducellieri* Beauverd) and *C. acuta* (**57** × **98** *C.* × *subgracilis* Druce); hybrids with species **56, 61, 67** and **101** occur in Europe.

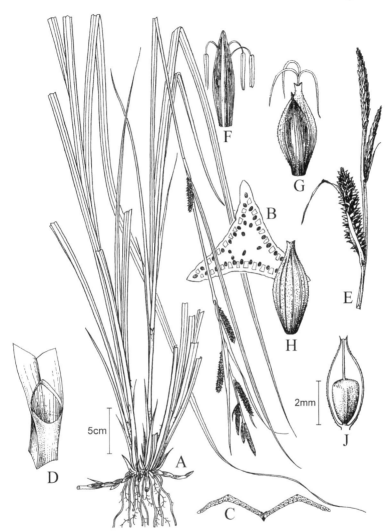

A Fertile shoot; **B** T.S. stem (culm); **C** T.S. leaf; **D** Inner face of leaf-sheath and ligule; **E** Upper spikes; **F** Male floret; **G** Female floret; **H** Utricle; **J** Section through utricle, showing nut.

57 × 58 *Carex* × *sooi* Jákucs

Carex acutiformis × *C. riparia*   Map 57 × 58

Although closer to *C. acutiformis* in shape and number of male spikes, in utricle length and ribbing and in ligule length, this variable, partially fertile hybrid possesses the more abruptly tapered leaves, the longer, often stouter, female spikes, the more tapered utricles and the acuminate male glumes of *C. riparia*. However, a clonal patch of plants from Ulverscroft (v.c. 55) also appears to be this hybrid but is closer to *C. riparia*, with fusiform male spikes and a short, rounded ligule, although the utricles are similar in length and ribbing to those of *C. acutiformis*. The aerenchyma pattern is intermediate, being clearly visible above the ligule as in *C. riparia* but with longer 'cells' (up to 3.5 mm) than is usual in that species.

Carex × *sooi* was not accepted by Wallace (1975, p. 525), but there is convincing material from v.cc. 25, 27, 28, 29, 41 and 66. It occurs in similar wet areas to the parents and usually in the presence of both.

Carex acutiformis	*Carex* × *sooi*	*Carex riparia*
Leaves tapering gradually.	**Leaves tapering ± abruptly.**	Leaves tapering abruptly.
Ligule 5–15 mm, acute.	Ligule to 17 mm, ± acute.	Ligule 5–10 mm, obtuse.
♂ spikes 2–3, 1–5 cm long, cylindric.	♂ **spikes 2–3, 2.5–5 cm long**, cylindric.	♂ spikes 3–6, 2–6 cm long, fusiform.
♂ glumes 5–6 mm; apex obtuse-subacute.	♂ **glumes 5.5–6 mm; apex ± acuminate.**	♂ glumes 7–9 mm; apex acuminate.
♀ spikes 2–6 cm × 7–8 mm, lowest only shortly pedunculate.	♀ **spikes 5–7.5 cm × 7–12 mm, lowest sometimes long-pedunculate.**	♀ spikes 3–10 cm × 10–15 mm, lower often long-pedunculate.
♀ glumes 4–5 mm.	♀ glumes 4–7 mm.	♀ glumes 7–10 mm.
Utricles 3.5–5 mm, ellipsoid-ovoid, ribbed, greyish-green; beak *c.* 0.5 mm, notched.	**Utricles 4–5.5 mm, ellipsoid-ovoid, ribbed, brown, distorted; beak 0.5–0.7 mm, notched.**	Utricles 5–8 mm, ovoid, obscurely ribbed, green or yellowish-brown; beak 1.5 mm, bifid.

Carex × sooi (*Carex acutiformis* × *C. riparia*)   **57 × 58**
Carex × ducellieri (*Carex acutiformis* × *C. vesicaria*)   **57 × 61**
Carex × subgracilis (*Carex acutiformis* × *C. acuta*)   **57 × 98**

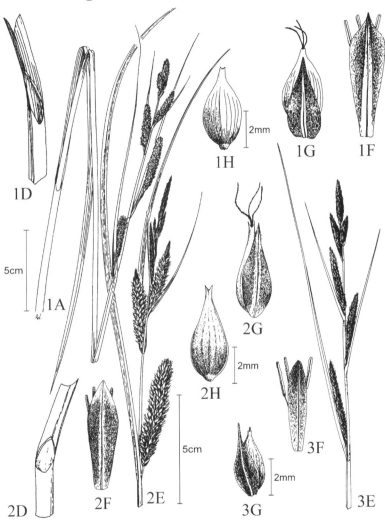

1 ***Carex* × *sooi*** **2** ***C.* × *ducellieri*** **3** ***C.* × *subgracilis***
A Fertile shoot; **D** Inner face of leaf-sheath and ligule; **E** Inflorescence; **F** Male floret; **G** Female floret; **H** Utricle.

M57 × 58 *Carex* × *sooi* Jákucs (*Carex acutiformis* × *C. riparia*)

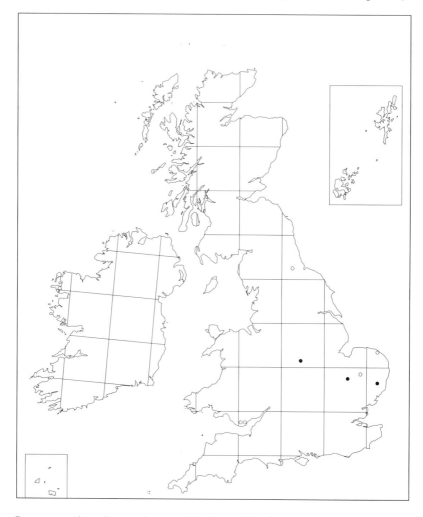

Carex × *sooi* is perhaps under-recorded; it should be looked for wherever clones of the parents intermingle in lowland marshy areas.

Carex × *ducellieri* Beauverd

57 × 61

Carex acutiformis × *C. vesicaria*   (*not mapped*)

In general appearance this plant resembles *C. acutiformis* in the shape of its male spikes and *C. vesicaria* in the shape of its female spikes, in leaf width and in the length of the lowest bract. Additionally, as in *C. acutiformis*, the female spikes are positioned close to the male spikes, not distant as in *C. vesicaria*. In utricle size and beak length it is intermediate between its parents. Utricles are also often empty and shrivelled.

Known only from acidic wet carr near Ebblake (SU10), S. Hants (v.c. 11), in the presence of both parents, where it was found in 1986 and seen again in 2002 and 2005.

Carex acutiformis	*Carex* × *ducellieri*	*Carex vesicaria*
Leaves 7–10(–18) mm wide, glaucous becoming dull.	Leaves 4.5–6 mm wide, pale mid green.	Leaves 4–8 mm wide, mid green or yellow-green.
Lowest bract slightly exceeding the inflorescence.	**Lowest bract far exceeding the inflorescence.**	Lowest bract appreciably exceeding the inflorescence.
♂ spikes relatively broad.	**♂ spikes relatively broad.**	♂ spikes very narrow.
♀ spikes all often ♂ at the top, close to the ♂ spikes, ± contiguous to distant, cylindric, erect, the upper sessile, the lowest only shortly pedunculate.	♀ **spikes** often ♂ at the top, **close to the** ♂ **spikes,** contiguous above, the lowest distant, **cylindric but tapering above,** erect, ± **sessile.**	♀ spikes distant from the ♂ spikes, oblong-cylindric, erect, subsessile or lowest with peduncle as long as the spike.
Utricles 3.5–5 mm, ellipsoid-ovoid, not inflated, greyish-green, ± patent; beak *c.* 0.5 mm, notched.	**Utricles 5–6 mm,** ellipsoid to narrowly ellipsoid, ± inflated, greenish-brown, **patent, often empty;** beak *c.* **1–1.5 mm, usually bifid.**	Utricles 6–8 mm, ovoid-ellipsoid, inflated, ± shiny, olive green to yellow-green, ascending; beak *c.* 2 mm, smooth, bifid.

M57 × 98 Carex × subgracilis (*Carex acutiformis* × *C. acuta*)

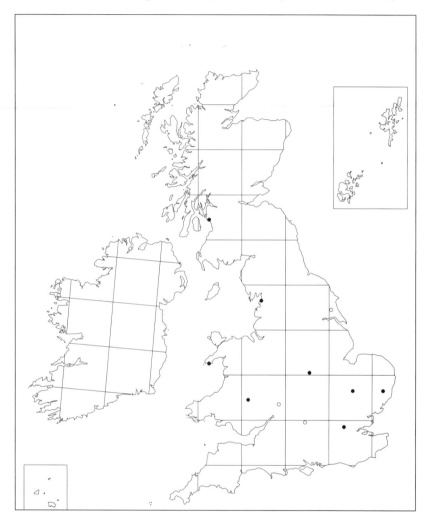

There are confirmed records of *Carex × subgracilis* from sites scattered throughout England and Wales, with an isolated site at Ardrossan (v.c. 75). Various other records which are unsupported by voucher specimens await confirmation.

302

Carex × *subgracilis* Druce

57 × 98

Carex acutiformis × *C. acuta*

Map 57 × 98

Carex × *subgracilis* is intermediate between the parents in the length and shape of the female glumes, in leaf width and in the size of the flat, sterile utricle. This hybrid is closer to *C. acuta* in spike length and to *C. acutiformis* in ligule shape and in inflorescence and beak length. Anthers do not emerge and the empty utricles have usually two but occasionally three stigmas on the same spike.

Found in marshes and mires and along river, lake and reservoir margins, usually in the presence of both parents.

Carex acutiformis	*Carex* × *subgracilis*	*Carex acuta*
Leaves 5–20(–26) mm wide.	**Leaves 5–10 mm wide.**	Leaves 3–10 mm wide.
Ligule 5–15 mm, acute.	Ligule 4–7 mm, acute, sometimes with spare hyaline material.	Ligule 4–6 mm, obtuse, truncate.
Inflorescence 1/4–1/3 length of stem; lowest bract exceeding inflorescence.	**Inflorescence 1/3 length of stem;** lowest bract just exceeding inflorescence.	Inflorescence 1/6 to 1/4 length of stem; lowest bract well exceeding inflorescence.
♂ spikes 2–3, 10–50 mm.	♂ spikes 2–3, 35–60 mm.	♂ spikes 2–4, 20–60 mm.
♂ glumes 5–6 mm, oblong-oblanceolate.	♂ glumes 3.5–4.5 mm, ± lanceolate.	♂ glumes 4.5–5.5 mm, elliptic- to obovate-oblong.
♀ spikes 2–4, 2–6 cm, cylindric.	**♀ spikes 3–4, 4–10 cm,** narrowly cylindric.	♀ spikes 2–4, 3–10 cm, cylindric.
♀ glumes 4–5 mm, oblong-lanceolate; apex acute or with serrulate acumen.	**♀ glumes 3–4 mm,** lanceolate, markedly narrower than the utricle; **apex** ± acute, **not serrulate.**	♀ glumes 2.5–4 mm, oblong-obovate; apex obtuse or margin inrolled and forming a cusp, not serrulate.
Utricles 3.5–5 mm; beak 0.5 mm; stigmas 3.	**Utricles 3–4 mm, flat, sterile; beak 0.5 mm; stigmas 2(–3).**	Utricles 2–3.5 mm; beak almost 0; stigmas 2.

58 *Carex riparia* Curtis

Greater Pond-sedge *Map 58*

Rhizomes far-creeping; shoots tufted; roots thick, pale brown; scales grey-brown, soon fibrous. **Stems** 60–130 cm, solid, rough, sharply trigonous. **Leaves** up to 160 cm × 6–20(–24) mm, rigid, erect, thin, sharply keeled or plicate, ± abruptly attenuate to a short trigonous apex, glaucous on both sides, persisting as pale brown litter; hypostomous but with a few scattered stomata on upper surface; sheaths grey-brown or often red-tinged, with aerenchyma pattern equally easily seen both above and below ligule, with inner face hyaline, becoming brown and persisting; apex concave; ligule 5–10 mm, obtuse (rounded like the top of a thumb when pressed flat). **Inflorescence** *c.* 1/3 length of stem; lower bracts leaf-like, exceeding inflorescence, upper setaceous. **Male spikes** 3–6, fusiform, tightly clustered, 2–6 cm; **male glumes** 7–9 mm, oblong-lanceolate, dark brown with midrib and margins paler; apex acuminate. **Female spikes** 1–5, ± contiguous, 3–10 cm, cylindric-fusiform, upper erect, ± sessile and often male at top, lower pedunculate; peduncles rough, often as long as spike, shortly ensheathed; **female glumes** 7–10 mm, oblong-lanceolate or narrowly ovate, dark, often purple-brown, with paler or green midrib; apex acuminate. **Utricles** 5–8 mm, ovoid, ± inflated, green or yellowish-brown; apex tapered; beak 1.5 mm, strongly bifid; stigmas 3; nut oblong-ovoid, trigonous, stalked. **Fr.** 6–9.

A plant often forming large stands by slow-flowing rivers, in ditches and around ponds, sometimes with *C. acutiformis*, *C. acuta*, *C. pseudocyperus* etc. Found in tall-herb fens (**S24, S25, S26**), sometimes with *C. acutiformis*. The ecological preferences of the two species are not clear-cut. *C. riparia* may be dominant (**S6**) or present (**S3, S4, S5**) in swamp, especially where water stands in spring, and can remain in deep shade in wet carr of East Anglia (**W1, W5, W6**).

The colour and erect habit of the wider leaves is sufficient to distinguish this species from **98** *C. acuta* (which has 2, not 3 stigmas). See **57** *Carex acutiformis* for the differences from that species.

In Britain *C. riparia* hybridises with *C. acutiformis* (**57** × **58** *C.* × *sooi* Jákucs), *C. lasiocarpa* (**56** × **58** *C.* × *evoluta* Hartm.), *C. rostrata* (**58** × **60** *C.* × *beckmanniana* Figert) and *C. vesicaria* (**58** × **61** *C.* × *csomadensis* Simonk.). None of these hybrids has been recorded from Ireland. Hybrids with *C. elata* and *C. flacca* are recorded for mainland Europe.

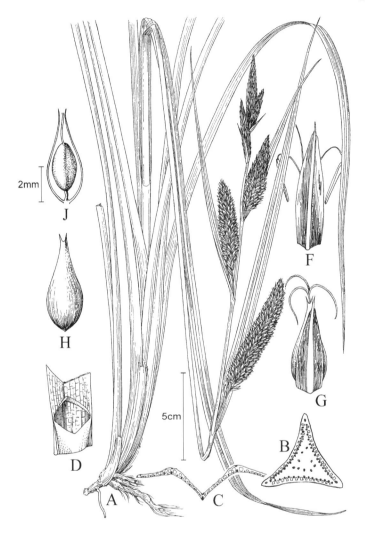

A Fertile shoot; **B** T.S. stem (culm); **C** T.S. leaf; **D** Inner face of leaf-sheath and ligule; **F** Male floret; **G** Female floret; **H** Utricle; **J** Section through utricle, showing nut.

M58 *Carex riparia*

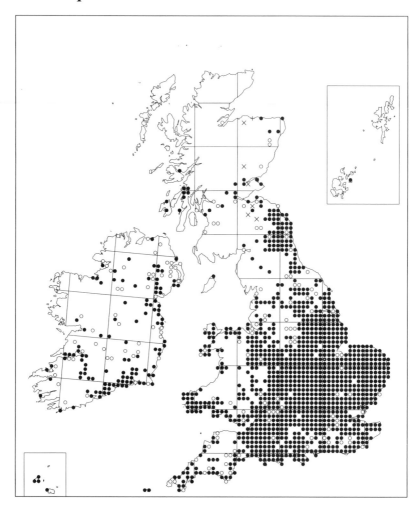

Carex riparia is a lowland plant, most frequent in S and E England, rare in NW England; in Wales mainly near the coast; in Scotland as far N as Morven (v.c. 97) and N Aberdeenshire. In Ireland mainly in the E and SW.

306

Carex × *beckmanniana* Figert

58 × 60

Carex riparia × *C. rostrata*   (*not mapped*)

Although *Carex* × *beckmanniana* superficially resembles *C. riparia*, close examination shows it to be intermediate between its parents, especially in stature, leaf width, distribution of stomata and length of ligule, male glume, and utricle. However, it is closer to *C. riparia* in stem section and in having an aerenchyma pattern that is clearly discernible in proximity to the ligule. In its spongy stem-sheaths, its sometimes distant lowermost female spike and its longer acicular leaf-point it approaches *C. rostrata*. A variable proportion of the anthers does not emerge and all utricles appear empty.

It was first recorded in 1992 at Birsay (HY32), Orkney (v.c. 111), and was still present in 2005, growing in a *Carex rostrata* mire beside a ditch containing *C. riparia*.

Carex riparia	*C.* × *beckmanniana*	*Carex rostrata*
Stem 60–130 cm, sharply trigonous; sheaths not spongy; aerenchyma pattern clear above ligule.	Stem 80–100 cm, triquetrous; **sheaths spongy; aerenchyma pattern clear** above ligule.	Stem 20–100 cm, trigonous to subterete below; sheaths spongy; aerenchyma pattern unclear above ligule.
Leaves 6–20(–24) mm wide, with an abruptly tapered apex, mainly hypostomous.	**Leaves 7–10 mm wide**, with a long acicular point, **amphistomous.**	Leaves 2–7 mm wide, with a long acicular point, mainly epistomous.
Ligule 5–10 mm.	Ligule 2–5 mm.	Ligule 2–3 mm.
♂ spikes 3–6, 2–6 cm long, fusiform.	♂ spikes 1–3, 1.5–5.5 cm long, cylindric.	♂ spikes 2–4, 2–7 cm long, narrowly cylindric.
♂ glumes 7–9 mm, oblong-lanceolate.	♂ **glumes 6–7.5 mm,** lanceolate.	♂ glumes 5–6 mm, elliptic-oblanceolate.
♀ spikes 1–5, 3–10 cm, cylindric-fusiform, ± contiguous.	♀ **spikes 2–4, 4–7 cm,** cylindric, **contiguous or lowest distant.**	♀ spikes 2–5, 3–8 cm, cylindric, contiguous or lowest distant.
♀ glumes 7–10 mm.	♀ glumes 4–5 mm.	♀ glumes 3–5.5 mm.
Utricles 5–8 mm, ovoid, ± inflated; apex tapered.	**Utricles 5.5–6.5 mm, flat; apex tapered.**	Utricles 3.5–6.5 mm, ovoid, inflated.

58 × 61 *Carex* × *csomadensis* Simonk.

Carex riparia × *C. vesicaria*   *Map 58 × 61*

This variable hybrid, identifications of which have often been questioned, is generally closer to *C. riparia*, from which it differs in its narrower leaves, its fewer, shorter spikes and its much more slender male spikes; additionally, the female glumes and utricles are shorter and the latter more strongly ribbed. From *C. vesicaria* it differs in its glaucous rather than yellow-green leaves, its broader male spikes, the darker appearance of the female spikes, the darker, shorter utricles which are more concealed by the broader glumes, and its more splayed utricle beak. This hybrid can be distinguished from **57 × 61** *C.* × *ducellieri* by its longer spikes, its longer, broader and darker female glumes, the long peduncle of the lowest female spike and the generally darker colour of the female spikes.

The most convincing specimen of this hybrid, and the one on which the table and the illustration are based, is from Co. Wicklow (v.c. H20).

Carex riparia	*C.* × *csomadensis*	*Carex vesicaria*
Leaves 6–20(–24) mm broad, glaucous.	**Leaves (3–)4–6 mm broad**, glaucous.	Leaves 4–8 mm broad, mid green or yellow-green.
Ligule obtuse or rounded.	Ligule obtuse or rounded.	Ligule acute.
♂ spikes 2–6 cm × 4–10 mm, broad.	♂ **spikes 3–3.5 cm × 3–4 mm, slender.**	♂ spikes 1–4 cm × 1–2 mm, slender.
♀ spikes not distant from ♂ spikes, 3–10 cm long.	♀ spikes ± distant from ♂ spikes, 4.5–5.5 cm long.	♀ spikes distant from ♂ spikes, 2–4(–7) cm long.
♀ glumes 7–10 mm long, oblong-lanceolate or narrowly ovate, purple-brown, concealing much of utricle.	♀ **glumes 5–6.5 mm long**, ovate-lanceolate to lanceolate, rich brown, **often concealing much of utricle**, sometimes noticeably reflexed.	♀ glumes 4–6 mm long, narrowly lanceolate, purplish-brown, not greatly concealing utricle.
Utricles 5–8 mm long, obscurely ribbed, not shiny, green or yellowish-brown; beak widely bifid.	**Utricles 5–6 mm long, ribbed, empty, sterile**, ± shiny, brown**; beak widely bifid.**	Utricles 6–8 mm long, inflated, ribbed, ± shiny, olive green; beak broadly notched but not bifid.

Carex × *beckmanniana* (*Carex riparia* × *C. rostrata*) **58 × 60**
Carex × *csomadensis* (*Carex riparia* × *C. vesicaria*) **58 × 61**

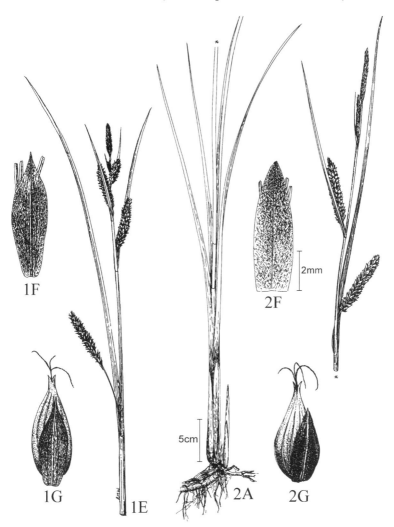

1 *Carex* × *beckmanniana* 2 *C.* × *csomadensis*
A Fertile shoot; **E** Inflorecence; **F** Male floret; **G** Female floret.

M58 × *61* **Carex** × **csomadensis** (*Carex riparia* × *C. vesicaria*)

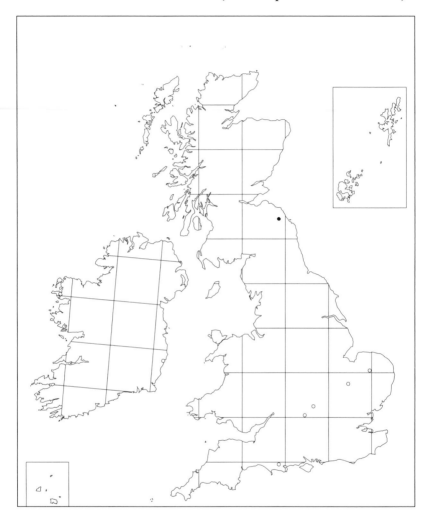

Accepted records of *Carex* × *csomadensis* (only one post-1970) are from riversides, fens and marshes in v.cc. 9, 22, 24, 28, 29 (where the specimen seems much closer to the *C. vesicaria* parent), 81 and H20.

Carex pseudocyperus M59

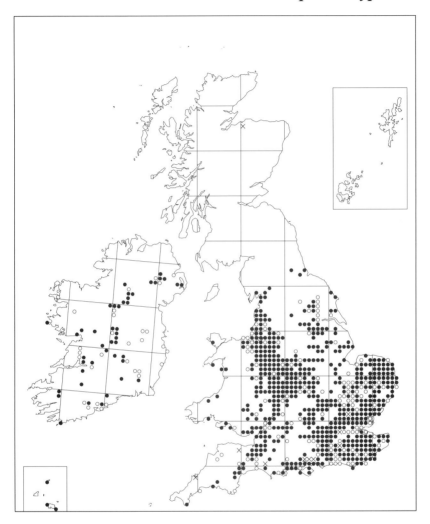

Carex pseudocyperus is predominantly a lowland plant. In England mainly in the SE and Midlands, extending as far north as N Lancs and Co. Durham; rare in Wales; scattered but less frequent than formerly in Ireland. Introduced in the isolated locality in NE Scotland (Moray), as in some sites in England.

311

59 *Carex pseudocyperus* L.

Map 59

Rhizomes short; shoots loosely tufted; roots thick (up to 1.5 mm), orange-brown, felted; scales dark brown or grey-brown, persistent. *Stems* 40–90 cm, solid, sharply trigonous; angles rough. *Leaves* up to 120 cm × 5–12 mm, rigid, erect, thin, plicate, very rough on keel and margins, tapered gradually to a fine point, bright yellow-green, passing through yellow to grey-brown on dying, persistent; hypostomous; sheaths becoming pink- or grey-brown, persistent, with inner face hyaline, forming fibrillae on splitting; apex straight or concave; ligule 10–15 mm, obtuse. *Inflorescence* 1/6–1/4 length of stem; bracts leaf-like, lowest 3–4 times longer than inflorescence. *Male spike* 1, 2–6 cm; *male glumes* 5–7 mm, elliptic-lanceolate, brown with a green or paler midrib; apex long-acuminate, ciliate. *Female spikes* 3–5, clustered at top and often exceeding male spike, 2–10 cm, cylindric, pendent; peduncles slender, rough, lowest only shortly ensheathed; *female glumes* 5–10 mm, ovate, brownish hyaline, with midrib green with few fine hairs, drawn out into a long, fine, ciliate arista. *Utricles* 4–5 mm, broader than glumes, ovoid-ellipsoid, patent, ribbed, green, soon falling when ripe; beak *c.* 2 mm, smooth, deeply bifid; stigmas 3; nut obovoid, trigonous. *Fr.* 7–8.

Carex pseudocyperus is a component of reed (*Phragmites*) swamp with *Galium palustre* (**S4b**) and in East Anglia of the *Cicuta virosa* sub-community of *Phragmites–Peucedanum* fen (**S24e**). Elsewhere it is mainly a plant of eutrophic or mesotrophic open-water swamps, often along sides of slow-flowing dykes and in ponds, oxbows and derelict canals, with *Juncus effusus* and *Sparganium erectum* (**S17**). It can tolerate some shade and is occasionally found in pools in woods.

This species is unmistakable and stands out amongst other riparian sedges by its yellow-green colour and pendulous, bristly female spikes that soon lose their utricles at maturity.

Carex pseudocyperus forms sterile hybrids with *C. rostrata* (**59** × **60** *C.* × *justi-schmidtii* Junge) and, in mainland Europe, with *C. vesicaria*.

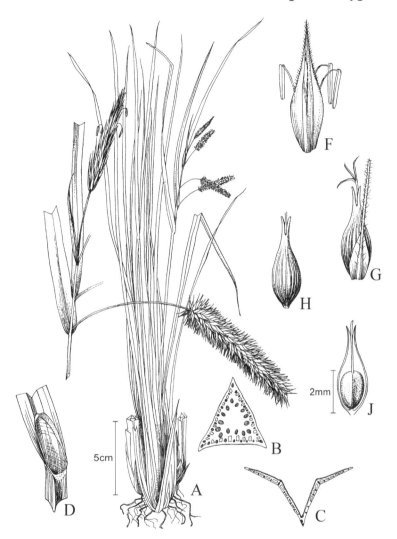

A   Fertile shoot; **B**   T.S. stem (culm); **C**   T.S. leaf; **D**   Inner face of leaf-sheath and ligule; **E**   Upper spikes; **F**   Male floret; **G**   Female floret; **H**   Utricle; **J**   Section through utricle, showing nut.

59 × 60 *Carex* × *justi-schmidtii* Junge

Carex pseudocyperus × *C. rostrata*   (*not mapped*)

A sterile hybrid that is best distinguished from *C. rostrata* by its longer, slightly drooping female spikes and by its leaves, glaucous beneath but otherwise appearing greener. From *C. pseudocyperus* it is distinguished by its slightly glaucous, mid green, rather than yellow-green, leaves and by its less pendulous, sessile or shortly pedunculate female spikes. In the hybrid the utricles feel empty and taper more gradually into the beak than in *C. rostrata*; they are less narrowly ovoid, shorter-beaked, less deeply bifid and less strongly ribbed than in *C. pseudocyperus*. Stomata occur on both leaf surfaces and the female glumes are intermediate between those of the parents in their size and in the shape of their apices.

In 1955 this hybrid was found at Cranberry Rough (TL99), W Norfolk (v.c. 28), where it was growing on peat in a drainage channel near alder carr (Petch & Swann 1956). It has disappeared from here but in 1988 was found in Ireland at Lough Asladee (H43), Fermanagh (v.c. H33).

C. pseudocyperus	*C.* × *justi-schmidtii*	*Carex rostrata*
Leaves to 12 mm wide, bright yellow-green.	**Leaves to 10 mm wide, bright green above, glaucous beneath.**	Leaves to 7 mm wide, glaucous above, dark green and shiny beneath.
Stomata on lower surface of leaf.	**Stomata on both leaf surfaces.**	Stomata on upper surface of leaf.
♀ spikes pendulous, 2–10 cm, borne on long peduncles.	**♀ spikes slightly drooping, 5–10 cm, ± sessile to shortly pedunculate on lowest spike.**	♀ spikes suberect, 3–8 cm, subsessile, or lowest spike shortly pedunculate.
♀ glumes < twice length of utricles, markedly aristate, ciliate.	**♀ glumes equal to or exceeding the utricles, ± aristate, ciliate.**	♀ glumes shorter than utricles, neither aristate nor ciliate.
Utricles 4–5 mm, strongly ribbed, ovoid-ellipsoid, tapering into deeply bifid beak, 2 mm.	**Utricles 4.5–5.5 mm, ribbed, ovoid, tapering ± gradually into slender bifid beak, 1–1.5 mm, empty, sterile.**	Utricles 3.5–6.5 mm, faintly ribbed, ovoid, inflated, abruptly contracted into very slender shortly bifid beak, 1–1.5 mm.

314

Carex × justi-schmidtii
(Carex pseudocyperus × C. rostrata)

59 × 60

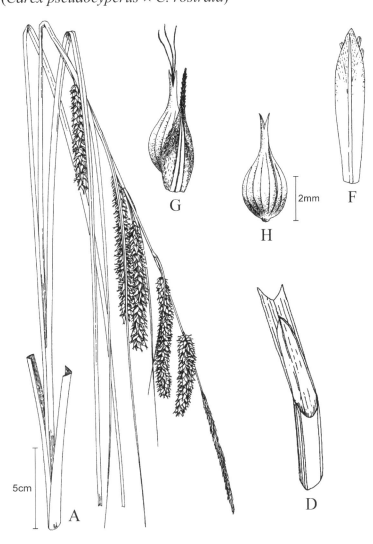

G

2mm F

H

D

5cm

A

A Fertile shoot; **D** Inner face of leaf-sheath and ligule; **F** Male floret; **G** Female floret; **H** Utricle.

60   *Carex rostrata* Stokes

Bottle Sedge   *Map 60*

Rhizomes far-creeping; shoots few in each tuft; roots thick, purple- or orange-brown; scales pale grey-brown, rarely red-tinged, soon decaying. ***Stems*** 20–100 cm, subterete and smooth below, trigonous and rough above. ***Leaves*** 30–120 cm × 2–7 mm, rough, rigid, keeled or plicate, or in some habitats inrolled (as in marram grass), tapering to a long (2–6 cm) acicular point, glaucous on upper surface, dark green and shiny beneath, over-wintering; mainly epistomous but occasionally with a few lines of stomata on lower surface; sheaths herbaceous, thick, spongy, dark brown, often streaked with red, the inner ones pink, with inner face hyaline, becoming brown and often fibrillose on splitting; apex straight; ligule 2–3 mm, rounded. ***Inflorescence*** up to 1/2 length of stem; bracts usually leaf-like, equalling or exceeding inflorescence. ***Male spikes*** 2–4, 2–7 cm, lower ones with setaceous bracts; ***male glumes*** 5–6 mm, elliptic-oblanceolate, brown with a paler midrib and narrow hyaline margin; apex acute or obtuse. ***Female spikes*** 2–5, contiguous or lowermost distant, 3–8 cm, cylindric, suberect, subsessile or lowest shortly stalked; ***female glumes*** 3–5.5 mm, narrower than utricle, oblong-lanceolate, purplish-brown with pale midrib; apex acute. ***Utricles*** 3.5–6.5 mm, ovoid, inflated, faintly ribbed, yellow-green, patent; beak 1–1.5 mm, smooth, bifid; stigmas 3; nut subglobose-trigonous.   ***Fr.*** 7–9.

A plant of swamps and mesotrophic lake-margins where the pH is 4.5–6.5 (e.g. **A22**); also found with *Menyanthes trifoliata*, *Potentilla palustris* and *Equisetum fluviatile* (**S9**, **S27**), with other sedges and mosses, e.g. *Sphagnum* spp. (**M4**, **M5**) and *Aulacomnium* and *Calliergonella cuspidata* (**M8**, **M9**), and in *Salix pentandra* woodland (**W3**).

Carex rostrata shows some variation in leaf width. In Ireland a robust form with larger utricles has been recorded in error as the closely allied Scandinavian species *C. rhynchophysa* Fisch., C.A. Mey. & Avé-Lall.

This species can be confused with **61** *C. vesicaria* (see that species), but *C. rostrata* has glaucous and dark green leaves with stomata on upper surface and a shorter ligule, spongy leaf-sheaths and shorter, more tapered utricle.

C. rostrata forms hybrids with *C. pseudocyperus* (**59** × **60** *C.* × *justischmidtii* Junge) and *C. vesicaria* (**60** × **61** *C.* × *involuta* (Bab.) Syme), the latter often forming large stands. Further hybrids with *C. acutiformis*, *C. hirta*, *C. lasiocarpa* and *C. riparia* are reported from mainland Europe.

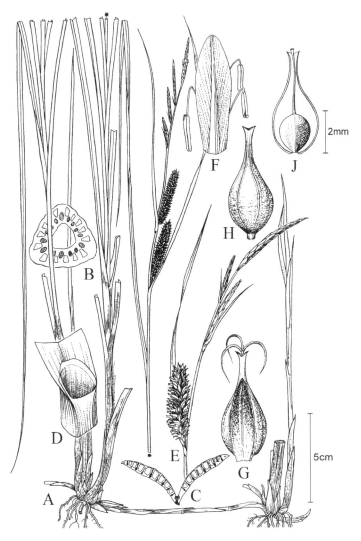

A Fertile shoot; **B** T.S. stem (culm); **C** T.S. leaf; **D** Inner face of leaf-sheath and ligule; **E** Upper spikes; **F** Male floret; **G** Female floret; **H** Utricle; **J** Section through utricle, showing nut.

M60 Carex rostrata

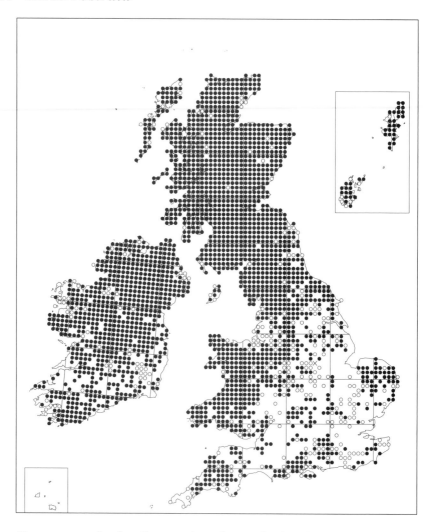

Carex rostrata is often frequent throughout upland Wales, northern England
and Scotland. More scattered in the lowlands, being lost through drainage.
Similarly frequent in Ireland but disappearing as peatlands are removed.

Carex × *involuta* (*Carex rostrata* × *C. vesicaria*)   *M60 × 61*

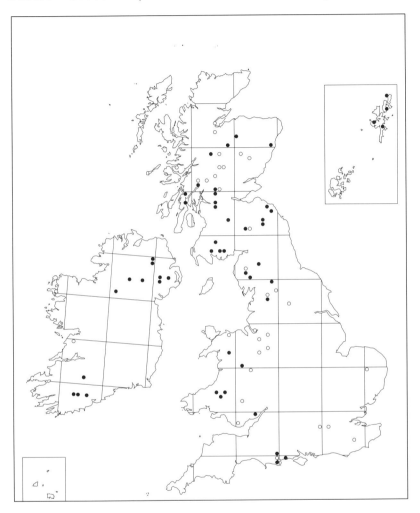

Carex × *involuta*, one of the more common sedge hybrids, occurs throughout much of the British Isles but is absent from large areas of eastern England and the far south-west.

60 × 61 *Carex* × *involuta* (Bab.) Syme

Carex rostrata × *C. vesicaria*   *Map 60 × 61*

This variable hybrid differs from *Carex rostrata* in the yellowish-green colour of its flatter leaves, its shorter inflorescence and its shorter female spikes, in which the utricles are longer but less tightly packed, less patent and also less abruptly contracted into the beak. From *Carex vesicaria* it is distinguished by its longer female spikes with less tapering, less ascending but somewhat more closely packed utricles. It differs from both parents in the stomata, which occur on both sides of the leaf, and in being at least partially sterile. On some plants none of the anthers emerge and all utricles are empty. It should be noted that the inflated utricles of the parents often *appear* empty.

Carex × *involuta* may be found in open wet places, especially by lakes and pools, e.g. in *C. rostrata–Potentilla palustris* tall-herb fen (**S27**) where *C. vesicaria* occurs also.

Carex rostrata	*Carex* × *involuta*	*Carex vesicaria*
Leaves 2–7 mm wide, glaucous on upper surface, dark green and shiny beneath, keeled or sometimes inrolled.	**Leaves** variable, **3–5(–6) mm wide, yellowish-green, plicate or often almost flat.**	Leaves 4–8 mm wide, mid green or yellow-green, plicate.
Sheaths spongy.	Sheaths spongy.	Sheaths not spongy.
Stomata mainly on upper surface of leaf.	**Stomata in variable quantity on both surfaces of leaf.**	Stomata on lower surface of leaf only.
Ligule 2–3 mm, rounded.	Ligule *c.* 4 mm, rounded.	Ligule 6–12 mm, acute.
Inflorescence up to 1/2 length of stem.	Inflorescence up to 1/4 length of stem.	Inflorescence up to 1/3 length of stem.
♀ spikes 2–5, 3–8 cm in length.	**♀ spikes 2–3, 3–6 cm in length.**	♀ spikes 2–3, 2–4(–7) cm in length.
Utricles 3.5–6.5 mm, ovoid, inflated, abruptly constricted, patent, tightly compact.	**Utricles 6–7 mm, broadly ellipsoid, inflated, erecto-patent, compact, usually empty.**	Utricles 6–8 mm, ovoid-ellipsoid, inflated, tapering, ascending, not tightly compact.

320

Carex × *involuta* (*Carex rostrata* × *C. vesicaria*)   **60 × 61**

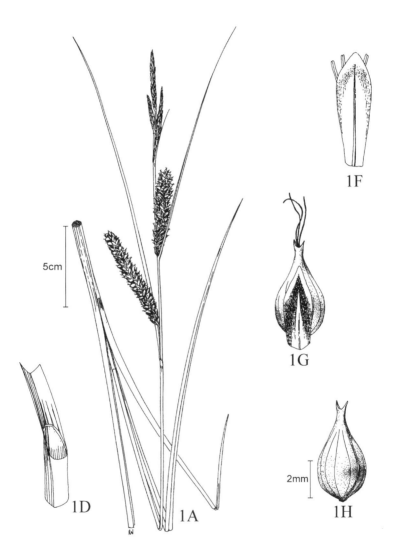

A Fertile shoot; **D** Inner face of leaf-sheath and ligule; **F** Male floret; **G** Female floret; **H** Utricle.

61 *Carex vesicaria* L.

Bladder Sedge   *Map 61*

Rhizomes shortly creeping; shoots slender, markedly trigonous, 2–3 in each tuft; roots thick, pale yellow-brown; scales brown- or purple-red, usually persistent. *Stems* 30–120 cm, trigonous, but with a sharp, low ridge on the angles rough above, smooth below. *Leaves* up to 150 cm × 4–8 mm, serrulate at least towards tip, thin, rigid, plicate, gradually tapered to a fine point, mid green or yellow-green, quickly decaying; hypostomous; sheaths becoming purple-red, persistent, inner face hyaline, fibrillose on splitting, apex straight or concave; ligule 6–12 mm, acute. *Inflorescence* 1/4–1/3 length of stem; bracts leaf-like, lower exceeding inflorescence *Male spikes* 2–4, 10–40 mm, the lower often with setaceous bracts; *male glumes* 4–6 mm, elliptic or oblanceolate, purplish-brown with green or paler midrib and hyaline margins; apex ± acute. *Female spikes* 2–3, ± contiguous but distant from the male spikes, 2–4(–7) cm, oblong-cylindric, erect, the lowest often pendent; *female glumes* 4–6 mm, narrowly lanceolate, purplish-brown with paler or green midrib; apex acute or acuminate, hyaline. *Utricles* 6–8 mm, ovoid-ellipsoid, inflated, ribbed, ± shiny, olive green to yellow-green, ascending; beak *c.* 2 mm, smooth, broadly notched; stigmas 3; nut obovoid, trigonous. *Fr.* 7–8.

A plant of mesotrophic mires forming a characteristic community around Scottish lowland lakes with *C. aquatilis, C. nigra, C. rostrata, Juncus effusus* etc. (**S11**). Also in more open situations with *C. rostrata–Potentilla palustris* tall-herb fen (**S27**) and on inorganic soils (e.g. in *Filipendula–Angelica* mires, **M27**), at edges of streams, dykes and canals. Often persisting when colonisation to *Alnus–Salix–Betula* carr (**W1, W2, W3, W7**) takes place.

Variable in size of utricle and female glume and in leaf structure. Differences from **60** *C. rostrata* are given under that species; when sterile the red fibrillose leaf-sheaths of the angled, slender shoots and the yellow-green leaves with stomata on the lower surface, the longer, acute ligule and the longer, more tapered utricle of *C. vesicaria* are sufficient to distinguish it.

Carex vesicaria hybridises with *C. hirta* (**55** × **61** *C.* × *grossii* Fiek), *C. riparia* (**58** × **61** *C.* × *csomadensis* Simonk.) and *C. rostrata* (**60** × **61** *C.* × *involuta* (Bab.) Syme). For a discussion on hybrids with **62** *C. saxatilis* see that species. A hybrid with *C. pseudocyperus* is recorded for mainland Europe.

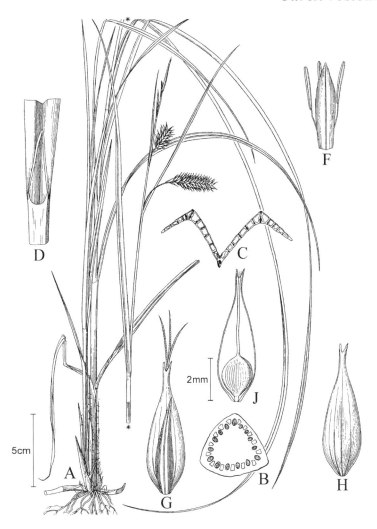

A Fertile shoot; **B** T.S. stem (culm); **C** T.S. leaf; **D** Inner face of leaf-sheath and ligule; **F** Male floret; **G** Female floret; **H** Utricle; **J** Section through utricle, showing nut.

M61 Carex vesicaria

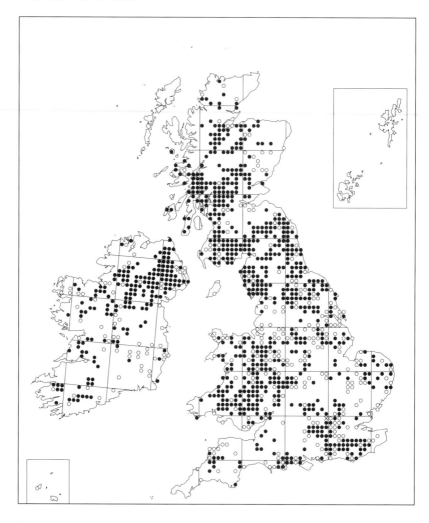

Carex *vesicaria* is scattered throughout Britain, becoming less common in
C and SW England; in Scotland uncommon N of the Great Glen and absent
from the Hebrides. Scattered in Ireland; probably better recorded in the north,
but decreasing in the SE owing to loss of habitat.

Carex × *grahamii* (*Carex vesicaria* × *C. saxatilis*)   *M61 × 62*

Carex × *grahamii* is found in montane flushes on steep slopes above 750 m, occasionally amongst *C. saxatilis*, on the schists of the Breadalbanes; the Clova plants, although found in similar habitat, are more robust. It occurs in v.cc. 88, 90, 97 and 98.

61 × 62 *Carex × grahamii* Boott

Carex vesicaria × *C. saxatilis*   Map 61 × 62

C. × *grahamii* differs from *C. vesicaria* in its lesser stature, its shorter male spikes, its more ovoid and shorter female spikes, its shorter female glumes and its smaller, rounder utricles. It differs from *C. saxatilis*, to which it shows the greater affinity, in its taller stature, its longer male spikes and glumes, its often longer, ovoid-cylindric female spikes, its rather longer greenish-brown utricles and its three stigmas. The anthers emerge and dehisce but the utricles remain unfilled.

C. × *grahamii* was originally described from a single population, still extant, in Corrie Sharroch, Glen Clova. It is sterile and generally regarded as a hybrid of *C. vesicaria*, a lowland species, and *C. saxatilis*, a plant of mires above 750 m, rare in the Grampians but more common further west. Some records may prove to be hybrids between *C. saxatilis* and *C. rostrata*.

Carex vesicaria	*Carex × grahamii*	*Carex saxatilis*
Stems 30–120 cm.	**Stems 20–60 cm.**	Stems 15–40 cm.
Ligule 6–12 mm, acute.	**Ligule 2–6 mm, subacute.**	Ligule 2–4 mm, rounded.
Bracts exceeding inflorescence.	**Bracts ± equalling inflorescence.**	Bracts ± equalling inflorescence.
♂ spikes 2–4, 10–40 mm.	**♂ spikes 1(–2), 15–25 mm.**	♂ spike 1 (rarely 2), 10–15 mm.
♂ glumes 4–6 mm, purplish-brown.	**♂ glumes 4–5.5 mm,** rich brown.	♂ glumes 3–4 mm, purple-black.
♀ spikes 2–3, 20–40(–70) mm, oblong-cylindric.	**♀ spikes 2–3, 10–20(–30) mm, ovoid to cylindric.**	♀ spikes 1–3, 5–20 mm, ovoid or subglobose.
♀ glumes 4–6 mm, narrowly lanceolate, purplish brown.	**♀ glumes 2–3 mm,** ovate, rich brown.	♀ glumes 2–3 mm, ovate, purple- to dark red-brown.
Utricles 6–8 mm, ribbed, ± shiny, olive-green; beak *c.* 2 mm; stigmas 3.	**Utricles 3–6 mm, greenish-brown, empty;** beak up to 1 mm; **stigmas 3.**	Utricles 3–3.5 mm, often dark purple-green; beak 0.5 mm; stigmas 2.

Carex × *grahamii* (*Carex vesicaria* × *C. saxatilis*)   **61 × 62**

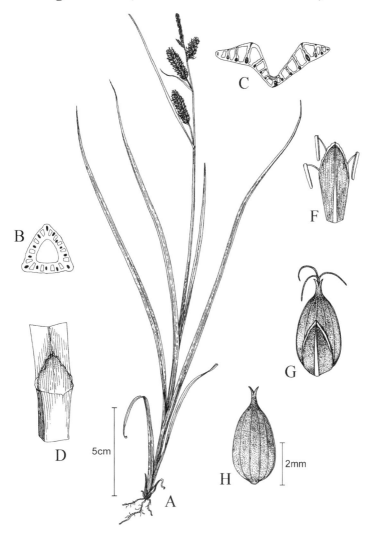

A Fertile shoot; **B** T.S. stem (culm); **C** T.S. leaf; **D** Inner face of leaf-sheath and ligule; **F** Male floret; **G** Female floret; **H** Utricle; **J** Section through utricle, showing nut.

62 *Carex saxatilis* L.

Russet Sedge   *Map 62*

Rhizomes far-creeping, producing tufts of 1–3 shoots at frequent, ± regular intervals; roots pale yellow-brown; scales grey-brown, often tinged wine-red, soon becoming fibrous. **Stems** 15–40 cm, ± rough above, trigonous, often curved. **Leaves** 12–40 cm × 2–4 mm, often curved, thick, bluntly keeled or channelled, gradually tapering to a trigonous point up to 5 cm long, mid-green, ± shiny, becoming straw-coloured; hypostomous; sheaths thick, white, tinged with wine-red, persistent, with inner face hyaline; apex straight; ligule 2–4 mm, rounded, slightly tubular. **Inflorescence** 1/5–1/4 length of stem; lower bracts leaf-like, shorter than or equalling the inflorescence, upper usually glume-like. **Male spike** 1, rarely 2, 10–15 mm; **male glumes** 3–4 mm, oblanceolate, purple-black with hyaline margin; apex ± acute. **Female spikes** 1–3, ± contiguous, 5–20 mm, ovoid or subglobose, erect, only the lowest rarely shortly pedunculate; **female glumes** 2–3 mm, ovate, purple- to dark red-brown with a paler midrib and hyaline margin; apex ± acute. **Utricles** 3–3.5 mm, ovoid, ± inflated, often dark purple-green on exposed faces, shiny; beak 0.5 mm, ± notched; stigmas 2 (or 3?); nut subglobose.   **Fr.** 8–9.

A plant of mires where the water movement is not great; tolerant of a wide range of pH and Ca^{++} content, especially on saddles or slightly sloping hillsides with *C. vaginata*, *C. viridula* subsp. *oedocarpa*, *Eriophorum angustifolium*, *Juncus triglumis*, *Persicaria vivipara*, *Thalictrum alpinum* and associated bryophytes (*Aneura pinguis*, *Scapania undulata*, *Scorpidium revolvens* etc.) (**M12**).

A variable plant, especially in size, colour and texture of the utricles. Forms with lax-flowered, more or less pendulous spikes can be confused with **88** *C. atrofusca*. *C. saxatilis* has been reported as having two or three stigmas on the same spike; all such plants should be investigated for possible sterility (i.e. hybridity with **60** *C. rostrata* or **61** *C. vesicaria*). **61** × **62** *C.* × *grahamii* Boott is thought to have the latter origin: see that entry. Though *C. saxatilis* and *C. rostrata* often grow in the same area, no hybrid between the two has yet been confirmed for Britain.

Wallace (1975) discusses a further hybrid with '*C. flava*' (called *C.* × *marshallii* by A. Bennett but not described and therefore invalidly named: Bennett 1925; Druce 1926). Specimens in **BM** and **OXF** may be one of the parents, but collections from v.c. 97 are believed to be the hybrid with **78a** *C. viridula* subsp. *brachyrrhyncha* and this is described on p. 397.

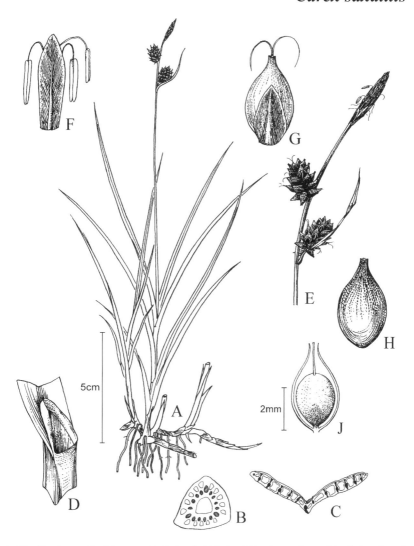

A Fertile shoot; **B** T.S. stem (culm); **C** T.S. leaf; **D** Inner face of leaf-sheath and ligule; **E** Inflorescence; **F** Male floret; **G** Female floret; **H** Utricle; **J** Section through utricle, showing nut.

M62 Carex saxatilis

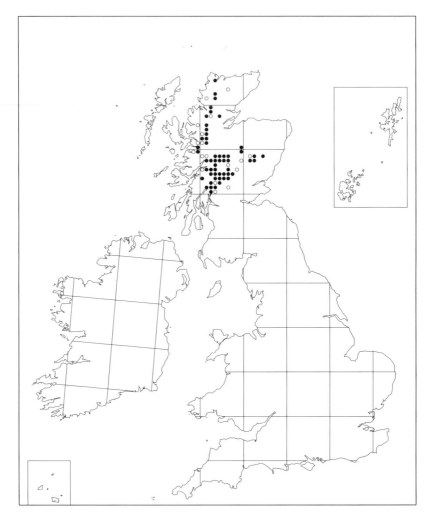

Carex saxatilis is confined to the Scottish mountains, mainly in the high rainfall areas of the west and usually in places where snow lies late, at between 460 and 1125 m; very local in the Cairngorms and Clova mountains.

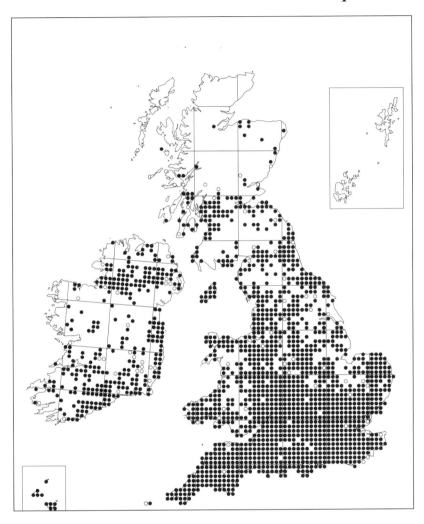

Carex pendula is predominantly a lowland species in England and Wales, absent from many of the uplands but reaching 410 m at Alston, v.c. 70 (Foley & Porter 2002); mainly coastal in Scotland, rare north of the Great Glen. Widespread but generally scarce throughout Ireland.

63 *Carex pendula* Huds.

Pendulous Sedge   Map 63

Rhizomes short; shoots in tufts often up to 70 cm across; roots up to 3 mm thick, red-brown; scales red-brown, persistent or becoming fibrous. **Stems** 60–230(–300) cm, trigonous. **Leaves** 20–120 cm × 12–20 mm, rigid, thin, keeled, ± flat, abruptly tapering to a blunt point, with margins rough, yellow-green above, matt-glaucous beneath, with up to 69 thin, close-packed, inconspicuous veins (T. O'Mahony pers. comm.), red-brown on dying, often overwintering; hypostomous; sheaths red-brown, persistent, with inner face hyaline only at concave apex; ligule 40–80 mm long, acute, with free margin < 1 mm wide. **Inflorescence** *c*. 1/3 to 1/2 length of stem; bracts leaf-like, ± equalling or slightly shorter than inflorescence. **Male spikes** 1–2, 6–10 cm; **male glumes** 6–8 mm, lanceolate, brownish-hyaline; apex acuminate. **Female spikes** 4–5, ± contiguous, lowest often distant, 7–16 cm, cylindric, erect at first, becoming pendent; peduncles rough, ensheathed, with lower half as long as spike; **female glumes** 2–2.5 mm, ovate, red-brown with pale midrib; apex acute or acuminate. **Utricles** 3–3.5 mm, broadly ellipsoid or ovoid, trigonous, ± glaucous-green, becoming brown; beak *c*. 0.3 mm, truncate; stigmas 3; nut obovoid, trigonous.   **Fr.** 6–7.

C. pendula is a species preferring acid but base-rich, heavy soils and is frequent in alder–ash–*Lysimachia nemorum* woods (**W7**), especially where there is a constant water supply, e.g. in runnels and beside wet ditches, with *C. remota* and *C. laevigata* in the *Carex remota–Cirsium palustre* sub-community. Also in hazel–ash–sycamore woodland, with *Mercurialis perennis* (**W8**) and in more open stages of these woodlands, on Wealden and Oxford clays, often with *C. strigosa*. Also found where seepage water occurs, along roadsides and edges and rides of planted or rough woodland.

A species easily recognisable by its large size. Young plants can be confused with **7** *Scirpus sylvaticus* or with **66** *C. strigosa*, but the red-brown sheaths, long ligule and the more glaucous colour are sufficient to separate *C. pendula*. Widely grown, and so frequently an accidental introduction. However, as reproduction by seed can be prolific, it is difficult to be certain about the status of some populations and we follow the policy adopted in the *New Atlas* (Preston *et al.* 2002) and show all records as native.

No hybrids are known.

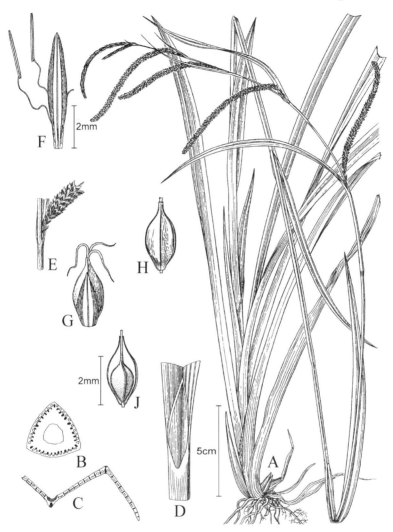

A Fertile shoot; **B** T.S. stem (culm); **C** T.S. leaf; **D** Inner face of leaf-sheath and ligule; **E** Base of upper spike; **F** Male floret; **G** Female floret; **H** Utricle; **J** Section through utricle, showing nut.

64 *Carex sylvatica* Huds.

Wood-sedge   *Map 64*

Rhizomes very short; shoots often densely tufted; roots grey-brown; scales brown, soon fibrous. **Stems** 15–60(–150) cm, spreading or nodding, slender, trigonous. **Leaves** 5–60 cm × 3–7(–11) mm, with *c.* 17–31(–37) veins, soft, slightly keeled or plicate, slightly tapered towards base, abruptly tapered to a sharp apex, mid green to yellow-green, becoming brown and then bleached on dying, overwintering; hypostomous; sheaths hyaline, becoming chestnut-brown, with inner face splitting and persisting as brown membrane; apex concave; ligule 2–4 mm long, obtuse, with free portion *c.* 0.25–0.4 mm wide. **Inflorescence** 1/3–1/2 length of stem; lowermost bracts leaf-like, sometimes longer than inflorescence, upper setaceous and shorter than spike. **Male spike** usually 1, 1–4 cm, very slender; **male glumes** 4–5 mm, oblong-oblanceolate, brown-hyaline; apex acute or obtuse and mucronate. **Female spikes** 3–5, ± distant, 2–6.5 cm, lax-flowered, often pendent; peduncles rough, filiform, up to three times the length of the spike, with base ensheathed; **female glumes** 3–5 mm, ovate-lanceolate, hyaline, straw-coloured or brown, with green midrib; apex acute or acuminate. **Utricles** 3–5 mm, ellipsoid- or obovoid-trigonous, green, with two prominent lateral nerves; beak 1–1.5 mm, bifid; stigmas 3; nut oblong, trigonous.   **Fr.** 4–8.

A plant of heavy, often wet soils with *Mercurialis perennis* in ash–maple (**W8**) and ash–rowan (**W9**) woods and in oak (*Quercus robur*) woods with *Rubus fruticosus* and *Pteridium* (**W10**), although sometimes on chalky soils with little clay (beech woodlands, **W12**, **W14**); occasionally in open scrub and grassland but then more likely a relic of woodland.

Carex sylvatica can be confused with little else in its habitat except **66** *C. strigosa*, which has utricles with a very short beak (*c.* 0.3 mm). Non-fruiting plants can be distinguished by the ligule, which in *C. sylvatica* is 2–4 mm long, obtuse and with a very narrow (< 0.5 mm) free portion; in *C. strigosa* the ligule is 5–8 mm, acute and with at least 0.6 mm of free tissue.

A hybrid with *C. strigosa* has been recorded in France and one with *C. hirta* in Austria.

A Fertile shoot; **B** T.S. stem (culm); **C** T.S. leaf; **D** Inner face of leaf-sheath and ligule; **E** Upper spikes; **F** Male floret; **G** Female floret; **H** Utricle; **J** Section through utricle, showing nut.

M64 *Carex sylvatica*

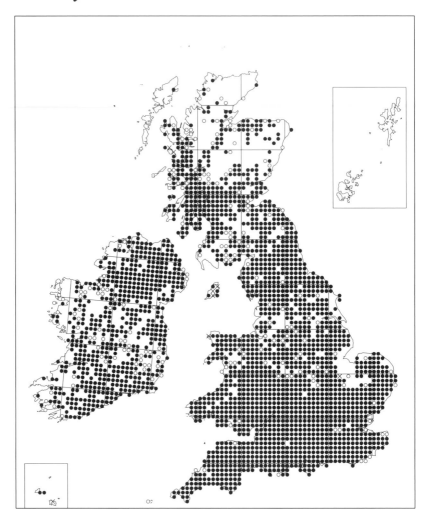

Carex sylvatica is frequent throughout the British Isles, but in Scotland uncommon in the main Grampian massif and rare or absent in the north. Generally lowland but reportedly reaching 640 m in the Scottish Highlands (Porter & Foley 2002).

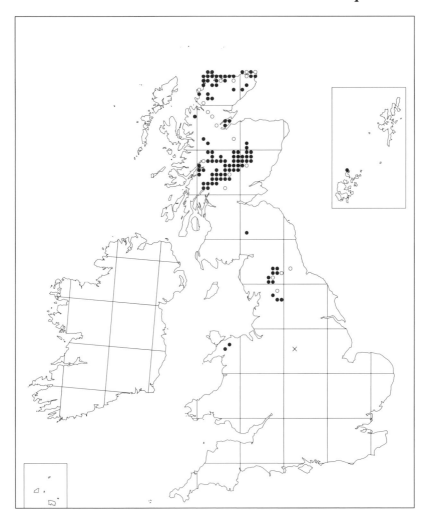

Carex capillaris is rare in Snowdonia, local in the North Pennines and Southern Uplands and frequent in the Grampians and in limestone areas of N Scotland, where it descends to sea level. It is not found in Ireland.

65 *Carex capillaris* L.

Hair Sedge   *Map 65*

Rhizomes short; shoots in ± open tufts; roots slender, purple-brown; scales dark brown or red-brown, soon becoming fibrous. ***Stems*** 10–60 cm, bluntly trigonous to subterete. ***Leaves*** 5–10 cm × 0.5–2.5 mm, stiff, sometimes arcuate, flat or ± channelled, gradually tapered to a short subulate tip, mid green, changing to red- and then grey-brown on dying, usually overwintering; sheaths red-brown, soon becoming fibrous, with inner face hyaline; apex straight; ligule *c.* 1 mm, rounded. ***Inflorescence*** up to 1/2 length of stem but usually much less; bracts leaf-like, usually a single one subtending a cluster of spikes, ± exceeding inflorescence, but the bract of any distant spike shorter. ***Male spike*** 1, 5–10 mm, few-flowered, overtopped by female spikes; ***male glumes*** 2–3 mm, oblong-obovate, hyaline with a brown midrib; apex obtuse to rounded. ***Female spikes*** 2–4, 5–25 mm, rarely more than 10-flowered, clustered and usually appearing to arise from a single node, though lowest sometimes distant; peduncles up to 4 cm, hair-like, half ensheathed; ***female glumes*** 2–3 mm, caducous, broadly ovate, hyaline or straw-coloured; apex acute or mucronate. ***Utricles*** *c.* 3 mm, narrowly ovoid-ellipsoid, olive to dark brown, smooth, shiny; beak 0.5 mm, truncate; stigmas 3; nut ellipsoid, trigonous.   ***Fr.*** 6–8.

A plant of wet hillsides, mostly on base-rich soils or areas flushed by base-rich water, in *Festuca ovina–Agrostis capillaris–Thymus polytrichus* grassland (**CG10**); also in *Dryas octopetala–Carex flacca* heath (**CG13**), on ledges in the *Dryas–Silene acaulis* community (**CG14**) and on moist steep banks with *Saxifraga aizoides–Alchemilla glabra* (**U15**). Found on sugar limestone in a sub-community with *Kobresia simpliciuscula* (**CG9d**) and also in mineral-rich *Carex dioica–Pinguicula vulgaris* mires (**M10**), where specimens may become luxuriant. Usually found at moderate to high altitudes, reaching 1035 m on Ben Lawers, v.c. 88 (Porter & Foley 2002).

When flowering, *C. capillaris* is not likely to be confused with any other species, but in the vegetative state it can be difficult to separate from **87** *C. pilulifera*, which may grow in adjacent grassland not flushed with base-rich water. The latter tends to form larger tufts with wider leaves that have a longer acicular point and are often appressed to the ground.

No hybrids are known.

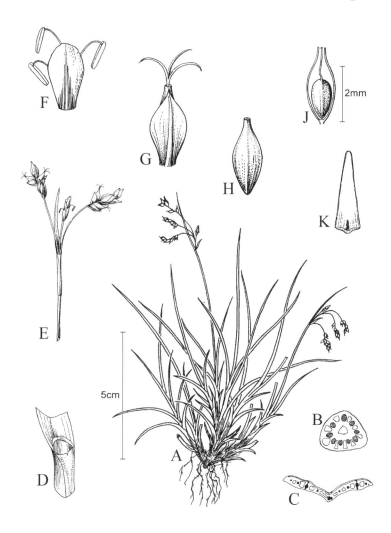

A Fertile shoot; **B** T.S. stem (culm); **C** T.S. leaf; **D** Inner face of leaf-sheath and ligule; **E** Upper spikes; **F** Male floret; **G** Female floret; **H** Utricle; **J** Section through utricle, showing nut; **K** Leaf-tip, enlarged.

66   *Carex strigosa* Huds.

Thin-spiked Wood-sedge   *Map 66*

Rhizomes usually short; shoots tufted with short stolons; roots pale brown; scales orange- or red-brown, becoming fibrous. **Stems** 35–70 cm, trigonous-subterete, often spreading. **Leaves** 15–40 cm × 6–15 mm, thin, ± arcuate, plicate, 37–45-veined with two lateral veins prominent on upper surface, abruptly tapered to a sharp point, mid-green, pinkish-brown to pale greyish-brown distally on dying, with darker, chocolate-brown blotches; sheaths thin, brown, occasionally red-tinged, persistent, with inner face hyaline, finely striate, quickly becoming fibrillose; apex truncate to convex, often erose-denticulate (T. O'Mahony pers. comm.); ligule 5–8 mm long, acute, often shortly tubular, with free portion *c.* 0.6–1 mm wide. **Inflorescence** 1/2–3/4 length of stem; bracts leaf-like, longer than spikes, not exceeding inflorescence. **Male spike** 1, 3–4 cm; **male glumes** 4.5–5.5 mm, narrowly obovate, brown, with green midrib; apex acuminate. **Female spikes** 3–6, distant, lowest often remote, 2.5–8 cm, lax-flowered, not pendent; peduncles smooth, half ensheathed; **female glumes** *c.* 2.5 mm, ovate or ovate-lanceolate, green becoming brown; apex acute. **Utricles** 3–4 mm, oblong-ellipsoid or narrowly ellipsoid, often curved, green; beak *c.* 0.3 mm, truncate; stigmas 3; nut subglobose-oblong, trigonous, shortly stalked.   *Fr.* 6–9.

C. strigosa is a plant of base-rich loamy or, less frequently, heavy soils especially near streams or in damp hollows; usually in open glades in ash–maple woods (**W8**) with *Mercurialis perennis*, *Anemone nemorosa* etc. White & Doyle (1982) list *C. strigosa* in Ireland as one of six diagnostic species for the *Carici remotae–Fraxinetum*, a community of species-rich ash–alder woods (*cf.* **W7**).

C. strigosa grows in similar situations to **64** *C. sylvatica* and is most often confused with that species when sterile; the rounded utricle with a very short beak easily distinguishes it when in fruit. The leaves of *C. strigosa* are usually wider and not so soft as those of *C. sylvatica*, and the ligule in the latter is shorter (2–4 mm) and obtuse and cannot be described as tubular; the free portion is less than 0.5 mm wide. Small **63** *C. pendula* has red-brown scales, leaf-sheaths tinged with wine-red and a longer ligule than *C. strigosa*.

A hybrid with *C. sylvatica* has been recorded in France.

340

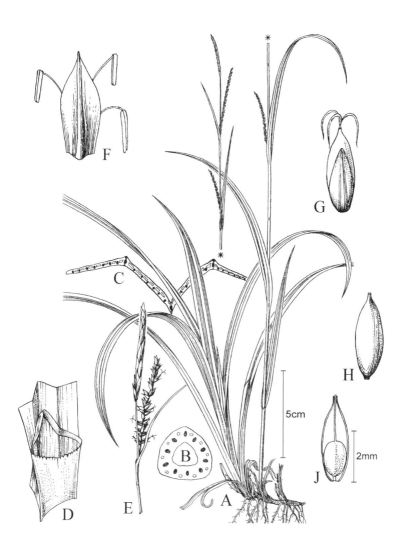

A Fertile shoot; **B** T.S. stem (culm); **C** T.S. leaf; **D** Inner face of leaf-sheath and ligule; **E** Upper spikes; **F** Male floret; **G** Female floret; **H** Utricle; **J** Section through utricle, showing nut.

M66 *Carex strigosa*

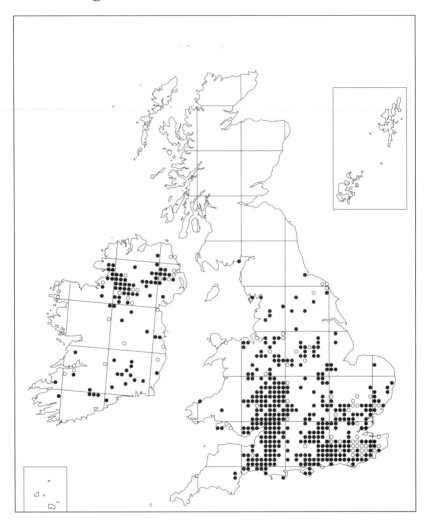

Carex strigosa is most frequent in lowland areas of the Weald, Somerset and Severn valley, otherwise scattered through England, rare in the E and in Wales and absent in the SW peninsula and N of the extreme S of Co. Durham (v.c. 66); in Scotland only in the S of Dumfries (v.c. 72). In Ireland, in scattered localities mainly in the E; more frequent on the limestone of Co. Leitrim (v.c. H29), Co. Cavan (v.c. H30) and Fermanagh (v.c. H33).

342

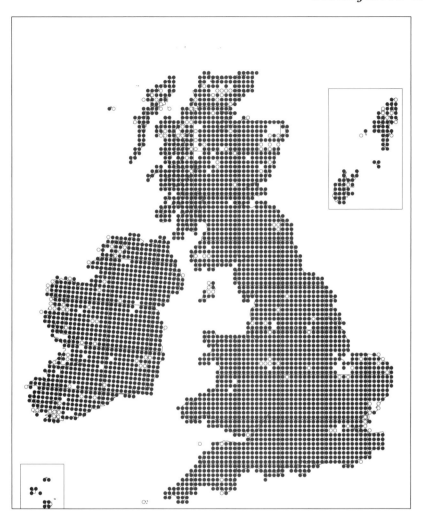

Carex flacca is possibly the most ubiquitous sedge in our flora and is found throughout the British Isles.

67   *Carex flacca* Schreb.

Glaucous Sedge   *Map 67*

Rhizomes often far-creeping, wiry; shoots loosely tufted; roots pale grey-brown; scales purplish-brown or red-brown, persistent. **Stems** 10–60 cm, rigid, trigonous-subterete. **Leaves** up to 50 cm × 1.5–4 mm, rigid, often arcuate, flat, gradually tapering to a fine point, glauco-pruinose above when young, becoming dull green, glaucous and densely mamillate beneath, with narrowly spaced veins on abaxial side, persisting as dark or rich brown litter; hypostomous; sheaths becoming dark brown, often flushed wine-red, persistent, entire, with inner face hyaline-brown, coarsely striate; apex straight or concave; ligule 2–3 mm long, rounded, tubular, with free portion *c.* 0.4–1 mm wide; apex notched. **Inflorescence** 1/5–1/3 length of stem; bracts leaf-like, lowest ± equal to inflorescence; sheath 0–3(–10) mm long. **Male spikes** (1–)2–3, 1–3.5 cm; **male glumes** 3–4 mm, oblanceolate, purple-brown, with pale midrib and hyaline margin; apex rounded or subacute. **Female spikes** 1–5, contiguous, 1.5–5.5 cm, cylindric, upper erect, subsessile, often 3 at top, lower ± nodding; peduncles up to as long as spike, rough, half ensheathed; **female glumes** 2–3 mm, oblong-ovate, purple-black, pruinose, with a wide, paler midrib and hyaline margin; apex obtuse to subacute. **Utricles** 2–3 mm, broadly ellipsoid to obovoid, often inflated on adaxial side, minutely papillose or scabrid, yellow-green, often turning deep purple-black; beak 0.2 mm, truncate; stigmas 3; nut ellipsoid, trigonous. *Fr.* 6–9.

C. *flacca* is found over a wide range of substrates and is tolerant of both dry and damp conditions. It is a common species of calcareous grasslands (**CG2–5, CG8–9, CG13**) and a component of flushes with C. *dioica* etc. (**M10**) and *Schoenus nigricans* (**M13**). Also in maritime communities, e.g. in saltmarshes with *Juncus gerardii* (**SM16**), sand-dune slacks with *Salix repens* (**SD14–15**) and maritime grasslands. It is not very tolerant of shade but can be found in open woods (e.g. **W19, W20**). Also in more acid conditions on heaths, e.g. *Erica vagans–Ulex europaeus* (**H6**) and with *Scilla verna* (**H7**). See also the Biological Flora account (Taylor 1956).

This is a variable species. It is often confused with **68** C. *panicea*, but that has leaves glaucous on both sides, with widely spaced veins and a distinctive subulate tip. Forms with dark glumes can be mistaken for **100** C. *nigra*, but that species has only two stigmas and a flattened, biconvex utricle.

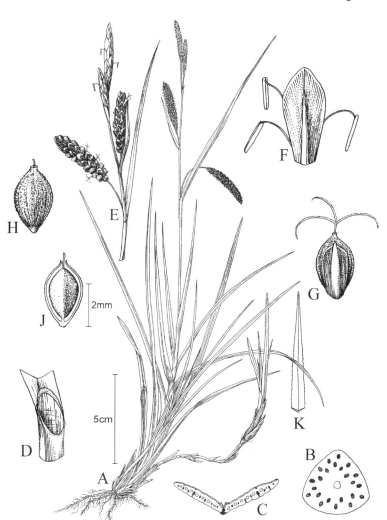

A Fertile shoot; **B** T.S. stem (culm); **C** T.S. leaf; **D** Inner face of leaf-sheath and ligule; **E** Upper spikes; **F** Male floret; **G** Female floret; **H** Utricle; **J** Section through utricle, showing nut; **K** Leaf-tip, enlarged.

68   *Carex panicea* L.

Carnation Sedge   *Map 68*

Rhizomes shortly creeping, fleshy; shoots loosely tufted; roots pale grey- or purple-brown; scales grey-brown or colourless, soon decaying. *Stems* 10–60 cm, often curved above, trigonous-subterete, striate, with basal leaves as long as the stem. *Leaves* up to 60 cm × 1.5–5 mm, rough at top, ± flat, tapering to a trigonous point, glaucous on both sides (in dense fen sometimes more yellow-green), with few, conspicuous, widely spaced veins on abaxial side, pale straw-coloured on dying; hypostomous; sheaths white or pale pink-brown, ribbed, not loose, persistent but fibrous on decay, with inner face hyaline, soon decaying; apex straight; ligule 1.5–2 mm, obtuse, with free portion 0.3–0.5 mm. *Inflorescence* 1/6–1/4(–1/3) length of stem; bracts leaf-like, shorter than inflorescence, tightly sheathed; sheaths 10–15 mm long. *Male spike* 1, 10–22 mm; *male glumes* 3–4.5 mm, ovate-oblong to elliptic, purple-brown, with pale midrib and hyaline margin; apex ± obtuse. *Female spikes* 1–3, 10–20 mm, ± distant, few and lax-flowered, with rachis usually visible; *female glumes* 3–4 mm, broadly ovate, clasping utricle, purple or red-brown, with pale green midrib and green-hyaline margin; apex acute. *Utricles* 3–4 mm, broadly obovoid, inflated on adaxial side so that the apex points outwards (see Figure **H₁**), olive-green or ± purple-tinged; beak less than 0.5 mm, truncate; stigmas 3; nut oblong-obovoid, trigonous.   *Fr.* 6–9.

   C. panicea is a common component of many wet or damp soil communities in grasslands, including hay and water meadows, with, e.g., *Juncus subnodulosus* (**M22**) and *Phragmites* (**S24**); also in upland calcareous grasslands with *C. pulicaris* (**CG9, CG10**), in grass-heath (**CG11**) and on alpine cliffs, to 1100 m in the Cairngorms, where it can grow with *C. vaginata*. In various mires on deep peat with *Erica tetralix* (**M15**), in mesotrophic to oligotrophic mires with *Sphagnum* and *Molinia* (**M24, M26**), with *C. echinata* and *C. viridula* (**M6**), in eutrophic sedge-mires (e.g. **M10, M11**) and in springs with *C. nigra* and mosses (**M38**). Also on upper parts of saltmarshes (e.g. **MC10**), especially in the N and W (Foley & Porter 2002).

   When sterile, *C. panicea* can be confused with **67** *C. flacca* (see that species) and **100** *C. nigra*, but the latter species lacks the trigonous leaf-tips and totally whitish sheaths. In fruit, the sheathing bracts, the fewer, laxer spikes and the obliquely truncated beak of *C. panicea* are diagnostic. Hybrids with *C. magellanica* and *C. vaginata* are recorded in Scandinavia but not in the British Isles.

346

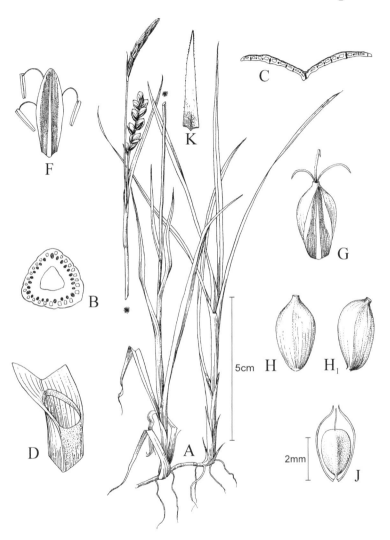

A Fertile shoot; **B** T.S. stem (culm); **C** T.S. leaf; **D** Inner face of leaf-sheath and ligule; **E** Upper spikes; **F** Male floret; **G** Female floret; **H** Utricle, abaxial view; **H₁** Utricle, view from side; **J** Section through utricle, showing nut; **K** Leaf-tip, enlarged.

M68 Carex panicea

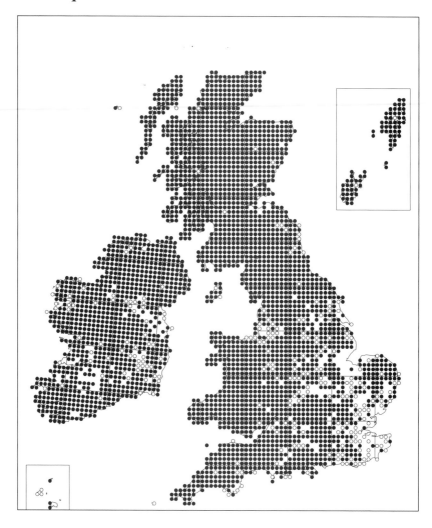

Carex panicea is found on soils of varying base content, being less frequent on those not receiving more or less continuous irrigation; it is thus common throughout our oceanic islands, being scarce only where suitable habitats are missing, e.g. in the Fens and on dry calcareous grasslands.

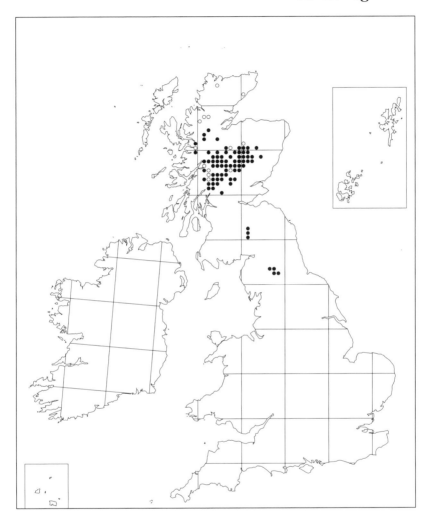

Carex vaginata is locally abundant in Highland Scotland but very local in the Southern Uplands (v.cc. 72, 78 and 79). In 2002 it was confirmed for Dufton Fell, v.c. 69 (Corner 2004), and further records between 2003 and 2005 extended the range to v.c. 70 and, most recently, to v.c. 65 (Corner *et al.* 2006).

69 *Carex vaginata* Tausch

Sheathed Sedge   *Map 69*

Rhizomes far-creeping; shoots tufted; roots brown; scales grey-brown, fibrous. *Stems* 15–40 cm, trigonous-subterete, striate. *Leaves* up to 60 cm × 3–6 mm, keeled, parallel-sided for much of their length and rather abruptly tapered to a flat point, yellow- to bronze-green, basal decumbent, those on the flowering stem subulate, at the very base only and 1–3 cm long; hypostomous; sheaths pale brown to dirty white, loose; ligule *c.* 2 mm, obtuse to subacute. *Inflorescence* 3/4 length of stem; lower bracts loosely sheathing (funnel-shaped) and shorter than spike. *Male spike* 1, 1–1.5 cm, ± clavate; *male glumes* more than 4.5 mm, orange-brown, with paler midrib. *Female spikes* 1–2(–3), 1–2 cm, ± distant, erect, few- and lax-flowered; *female glumes* 3 mm, broadly ovate, red-brown, with paler midrib; apex acute or mucronate. *Utricles* 3.8–5 mm, broadly obovoid, hardly inflated, ribbed; beak obliquely truncate, *c.* 1 mm; stigmas 3; nut ovoid-trigonous.
Fr. 7–9.

An alpine plant usually occurring above 700 m, although recorded at 370 m on Creag an Eirionnaich, v.c. 88 (Foley & Porter 2002). On wet rocky sills on often vertical cliffs with *Luzula sylvatica*, *Geum rivale*, *Angelica sylvestris* and other tall herbs (**U17**) and on rock outcrops with *Silene acaulis* and dwarf shrubs such as *Dryas octopetala* and several rare Arctic-Alpine willows (**CG14**). A component of *Carex saxatilis* mires (**M12**) in the Breadalbane mountains and along streams in sedge-dominated mires and on small (well-drained?) ledges in the Grampians, where it is often abundant but usually shy-flowering and therefore liable to be overlooked. In the Pennines it grows in damp grassland below limestone escarpments. Recent findings of *C. vaginata* in flower in England, probably as a result of cessation of grazing after sheep-culling during the foot and mouth epidemic, suggest that intensive grazing on hill communities is an important factor (*cf.* Robinson 2003). Work using DNA fingerprinting (French *et al.* 2005) suggests these plants must have been present in these sites for a considerable period of time.

Similar to **68** *C. panicea* in its few-flowered spike and utricle shape but distinguished by the yellow- or bronzy-green (not glaucous) colouring of the leaves with their flat, abruptly tapered tips. In fruit the apple-green utricles and the loose sheaths of both the bracts and the markedly short leaves at the base of the stem are distinctive. Potential hybrids may be found where the two species grow together but are so far unconfirmed.

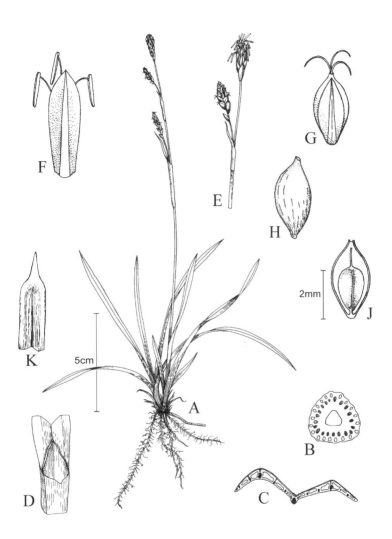

A Fertile shoot; **B** T.S. stem (culm); **C** T.S. leaf; **D** Inner face of leaf-sheath and ligule; **E** Upper spikes; **F** Male floret; **G** Female floret; **H** Utricle; **J** Section through utricle, showing nut; **K** Leaf-tip, enlarged.

70 *Carex depauperata* Curtis ex With.

Starved Wood-sedge   *Map 70*

Rhizomes shortly creeping; shoots few, loosely tufted or forming substantial tussocks if conditions are good; roots pale purple-brown; scales purple-brown, vermilion-flushed, glossy, persistent. *Stems* 30–100 cm, stout, trigonous-subterete. *Leaves* 20–60 cm × 2–4 mm, thin, flat, tapering from a broad base to a fine point, dull green and beset with numerous, stout, apically-directed aculeolae above, glossy, pale green with conspicuously dark green veins below, dying to a pale straw colour; hypostomous; sheaths purplish- or red-brown, shiny, persistent, with inner face hyaline, flecked with red, becoming brown; apex straight or concave; ligule 2–3 mm, obtuse, with margin of free tissue ciliolate. *Inflorescence* 1/4 length of stem; bracts leaf-like, longer than spikes, upper sometimes exceeding inflorescence. *Male spike* 1, 18–30 mm; *male glumes* 5–6.5 mm, elliptic, pale or red-brown, with a paler or green midrib and hyaline margins, lowest on spike up to 10 mm, bract-like; apex ± acute. *Female spikes* 2–4, distant, 2–6-flowered, 10–20 mm, erect; peduncles rough, half-ensheathed; *female glumes* 4.5–6 mm, broadly lanceolate to obovate, brown with a green midrib and broad hyaline margins; apex acute or mucronate. *Utricles* 7–9 mm, rhomboid-obovoid, narrowed into a solid base, distinctly ribbed, shiny, brownish-green; beak 3 mm, smooth or scabrid, obliquely truncate, split in front; stigmas 3; nut obovoid, trigonous.   *Fr.* 6–10.

This is a very rare plant of dry, relatively open deciduous woods, e.g. *Fraxinus–Acer campestre–Mercurialis perennis* (**W8**) and *Fraxinus–Sorbus aucuparia* (**W9**) woodland, and on wood-margins and hedge-banks on chalky or limestone soils (Birkinshaw 1990, 1991). Apparently not confined to such calcareous / high pH soils in mainland Europe (T. O'Mahony pers. comm.).

C. depauperata is easily recognisable by its large utricles and few-flowered spikes. Vegetatively similar to **84** *C. filiformis*, which, although of restricted range, could occur in similar habitats, but the glossy, vermilion-flushed scales and leaf-sheaths and red-flecked inner leaf-sheath face are absolutely diagnostic for *C. depauperata*.

No hybrids are known.

C. depauperata is a **Red Data List** species in Great Britain; *Status*: **Endangered** (Cheffings & Farrell 2005). It is protected under the Flora (Protection) Order 1999 in the Republic of Ireland.

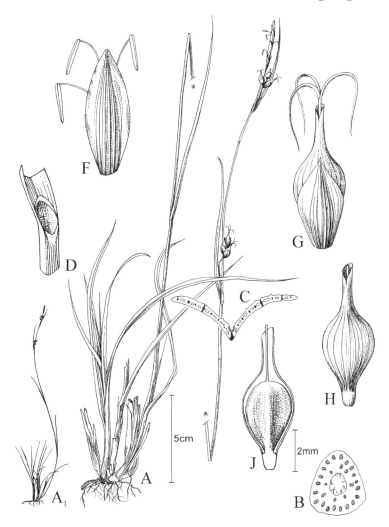

A Fertile shoot; **A₁** Same (much reduced); **B** T.S. stem (culm); **C** T.S. leaf; **D** Inner face of leaf-sheath and ligule; **E** Upper spikes; **F** Male floret; **G** Female floret; **H** Utricle; **J** Section through utricle, showing nut.

M70 Carex depauperata

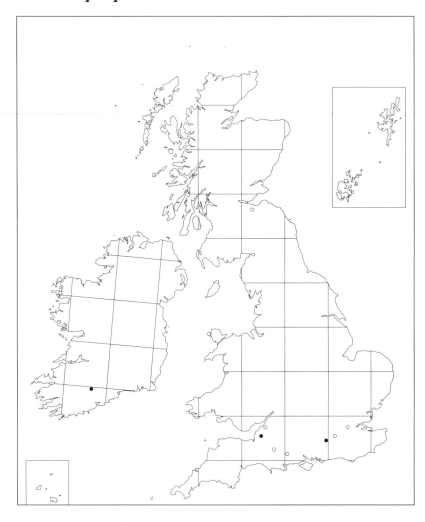

Carex depauperata has been found in Surrey, N Somerset, East Cork and Anglesey, but not recently seen in the last (v.c. 52). Formerly recorded in an area of v.c. 16, now part of Greater London, near Wimborne, v.c. 9, and from a wood in Bonelly, v.c. 83 (**DBN**); see Rich & Birkinshaw (2001). The last, if the provenance is correct, was its northernmost site.

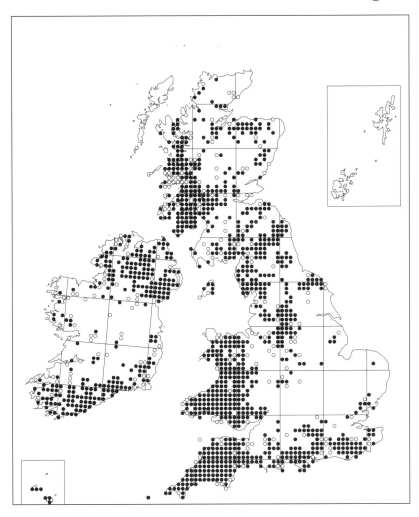

Carex laevigata is frequent in parts of the British Isles where annual rainfall is over 750 mm, e.g. in the Weald, SW and N England, Wales and mainly western Scotland. In Ireland it grows predominantly in the N and SW.

355

71 *Carex laevigata* Sm.

Smooth-stalked Sedge   *Map 71*

Rhizomes short; shoots forming dense tufts up to 30 cm across; roots yellow-brown, felty; scales brown or reddish, rarely becoming fibrous. *Stems* 30–120 cm, stout, trigonous with slightly rounded faces. *Leaves* 15–60 cm × 5–12 mm, thin, shallowly keeled, plicate, abruptly tapered, smooth but with fine teeth on edges and midrib below, bright green, brown and persisting when dead; hypostomous; sheaths persistent, distinctly veined, with hyaline areas between them when young, brown on aging, with inner face hyaline, flecked pink; apex convex or lingulate; ligule 7–15 mm, acute or obtuse. *Inflorescence* 1/4–2/3 length of stem; bracts leaf-like, longer than spike but not exceeding inflorescence. *Male spikes* 1 or 2, 2–6 cm; *male glumes* 5–6 mm, oblong-oblanceolate, pale orange-brown with red-brown flecks; margins and base hyaline; apex obtuse and mucronate or rarely long-acute. *Female spikes* 2–4, distant, 2–5 cm, ovoid-cylindric, ± erect, lowest usually pendent; peduncles to 80 mm, ensheathed; *female glumes* 3–5 mm, ovate or ovate-lanceolate, brown-hyaline, often with red-brown flecks; midrib green; apex acuminate, often rough at tip. *Utricles* 4–6 mm, ovoid or subglobose, partially inflated, ± strongly ribbed, green with fine reddish dots; beak 1.5 mm, ± scabrid, deeply bifid; stigmas 3; nut trigonous-globose.   *Fr.* 7–8.

C. laevigata is predominantly a plant of lowland shady, moist situations, more rarely in open habitats; most common in *Alnus–Fraxinus* woodlands (**W7**) on acid but base-rich clay soils, but also on peat (e.g. **W3**).

This species could be confused initially and in marginal habitats with **72** *C. binervis* or **73** *C. distans*, but the fine red dots on the utricles (and often on the male and female glumes) and acuminate female glumes lacking a hyaline edge are distinctive. Also the male glumes of *C. binervis* and *C. distans* are purplish, not gingery-brown. Vegetatively the differences are not so obvious: the dark green leaves of *C. binervis* have splotches of wine-red on dying, which are never seen on *C. laevigata*, and the much shorter ligule and usually narrower leaf of *C. distans* are sufficient to distinguish that species.

Hybrids between this species and *C. binervis* (**72** × **71** *C.* × *deserta* Merino) and **78b** *C. viridula* subsp. *oedocarpa* have been recorded in Britain, but the latter was not available for examination by the authors. A putative hybrid with **79** *Carex pallescens* (David 1974) has been redetermined as *C. laevigata*; see that species.

356

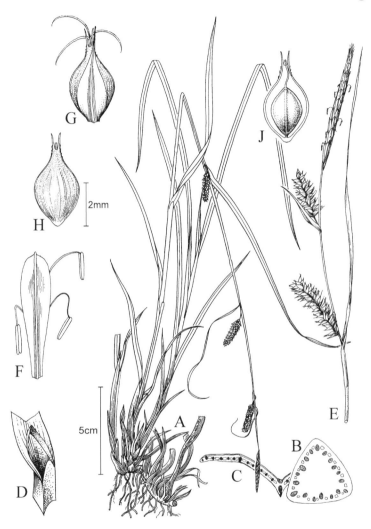

A Fertile shoot; **B** T.S. stem (culm); **C** T.S. leaf; **D** Inner face of leaf-sheath and ligule; **E** Upper spikes; **F** Male floret; **G** Female floret; **H** Utricle; **J** Section through utricle, showing nut.

72 *Carex binervis* Sm.

Green-ribbed Sedge   *Map 72*

Rhizomes shortly creeping; shoots tufted; roots thick, grey-brown; scales orange-brown, persistent, ***Stems*** 15–150 cm, trigonous-terete, often with a single furrow. ***Leaves*** 7–30 cm × 2–6(–8) mm, rigid, often arcuate in dwarf plants, keeled or ± flat, ± abruptly tapering to a fine point, matt dark green above, glossy light green with dark green veins below, later with wine-red splotches and persisting as pink- or orange-brown litter, often overwintering; hypostomous; sheaths dull, red-brown, persistent; apex convex or straight on lower leaves (Figure **D**), lingulate on stem leaves (Figure **D₁**); ligule 1–2 mm, rounded, with free tissue *c.* 0.5 mm wide, cartilaginous, involute, with margin minutely papillate. ***Inflorescence*** up to 1/2 length of stem; lower bracts leaf-like, 2–4 times as long as spike, upper glume-like. ***Male spike*** 1, 20–45 mm; ***male glumes*** 4–4.5 mm, oblong-obovate, purplish with paler midrib; apex obtuse or rounded and mucronate, scarious. ***Female spikes*** 2–4, distant, 15–45 mm, cylindric, rigid, lowermost usually nodding; peduncles half-ensheathed, lowest up to 10 cm; ***female glumes*** 3–4 mm, ovate, dark purple-brown to black, with green or pale brown midrib; apex obtuse, mucronate. ***Utricles*** 3.5–4.5 mm, purple-brown or partly green, broadly elliptic, with two prominent green lateral nerves (continuing into beak); beak 1–1.5 mm, rough, widely notched; stigmas 3; nut obovoid, trigonous, olive-brown.   ***Fr.*** 6–8.

A plant of acid, siliceous soils most commonly found in lowland sandy heaths, rough pastures and rocky coastal cliffs, to *c.* 950 m on wet alpine cliff-ledges (**U17**). Also in mountain grasslands of *Nardus stricta* (**U5**), the *Pteridium–Galium saxatile* community (**U20**), *Festuca–Agrostis* grassland (**CG10**) and at higher altitudes with *Alchemilla alpina* (**CG11**).

It is difficult to distinguish in the vegetative state from **102** *C. bigelowii*, but it lacks the purplish-brown scales and the glaucous leaves of that species; also *C. bigelowii* never has the wine-red splotches on the dying leaves. In maritime situations *C. binervis* may be confused with **73** *C. distans* (see that species).

C. binervis has been found hybridising with *C. laevigata* (**72** × **71** *C.* × *deserta* Merino), with **74** *C. punctata* and with *C. viridula* subsp. *oedocarpa* (**78b** × **72** *C.* × *corstorphinei* Druce) in Britain. None of these hybrids has been recorded in Ireland. Hybrids with *C. flava* and *C. viridula* subsp. *brachyrrhyncha* are recorded from mainland Europe.

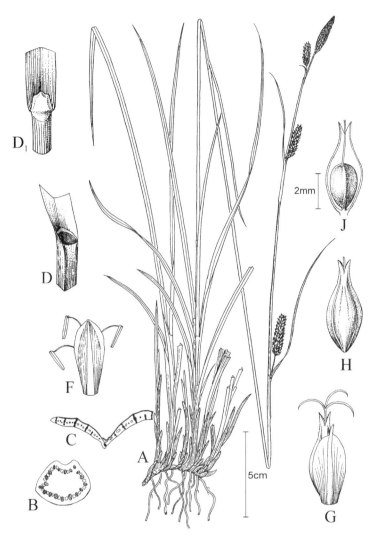

A Fertile shoot; **B** T.S. stem (culm); **C** T.S. leaf; **D** Inner face of leaf-sheath and ligule on lower leaves; **D₁** Inner face of leaf-sheath on upper stem leaves; **F** Male floret; **G** Female floret; **H** Utricle; **J** Section through utricle, showing nut.

M72 Carex binervis

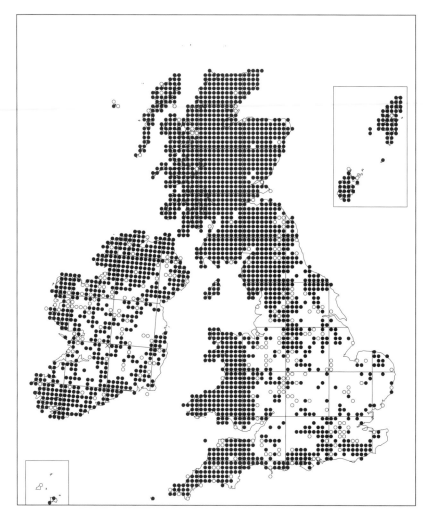

Carex binervis is frequent throughout Britain except in the arable-dominated, drier S Midlands and East Anglia and is similarly frequent throughout most of Ireland.

Carex × deserta (*Carex binervis × C. laevigata*)   *M72 × 71*

The only two collections of *Carex × deserta* are from a damp low cliff by the roadside east of Llyn Du, Tremadoc (v.c. 49), in 1961, and from a small patch in a wet area of Dunkery Hill, Exmoor (v.c. 5), first found in 1998 and again in 2004.

72 × 71 *Carex* × *deserta* Merino

Carex binervis × *C. laevigata*   *Map 72 × 71*

There are only two collections of this hybrid known, from Tremadoc and Dunkery Hill. These are intermediate between the parents in stem height, in leaf dimensions, in ligule length and in female glume and utricle length but, whilst still intermediate, differ substantially from each other in their female glumes and the shape and coloration of their utricles. The female glumes vary from ovate to lanceolate with an acuminate or mucronate apex and the utricles are plano-convex, varying between ovoid and elongate; they are pale green in colour and unmarked or dotted or blotched deep red. The Tremadoc plants appear to be wholly sterile, those from Dunkery Hill partially so.

Carex binervis	*Carex* × *deserta*	*Carex laevigata*
Stems 15–150 cm, trigonous to terete, often with a single furrow.	Stems 50–70 cm, ± trigonous.	Stems 30–120 cm, trigonous with slightly rounded faces.
Leaves 7–30 cm × 2–6(–8) mm, matt dark green above, glossy light green below.	**Leaves 20–30 cm × 3.5–6 mm, bright green.**	Leaves 15–60 cm × 5–12 mm, bright green.
Ligule 1–2 mm, rounded.	**Ligule 4–6 mm**, obtuse, sometimes with raised edge.	Ligule 7–15 mm, acute or obtuse, with raised edge.
♀ glumes 3–4 mm, ovate, dark purplish-brown with a green or pale midrib; apex obtuse, mucronate.	♀ glumes 4–4.5 mm, very variable in shape, ovate to lanceolate, mid brown with a pale midrib; apex scabrid, elongate-acuminate or with a mucronate tip.	♀ glumes 3–5 mm, ovate or ovate-lanceolate, brown-hyaline with a green midrib; apex scabrid, acuminate.
Utricles 3.5–4.5 mm, with 2 prominent green lateral nerves, purple-brown or partly green, broadly ellipsoid.	**Utricles** 4.2–5.2 mm, variably ribbed, **pale green**, sometimes dotted and/or blotched deep red, ovoid to elongate, plano-convex.	Utricles 4–6 mm, ± strongly ribbed, green with fine reddish dots, ovoid or subglobose.

Carex × deserta (*Carex binervis × C. laevigata*)   **72 × 71**
Carex binervis × C. punctata   **72 × 74**

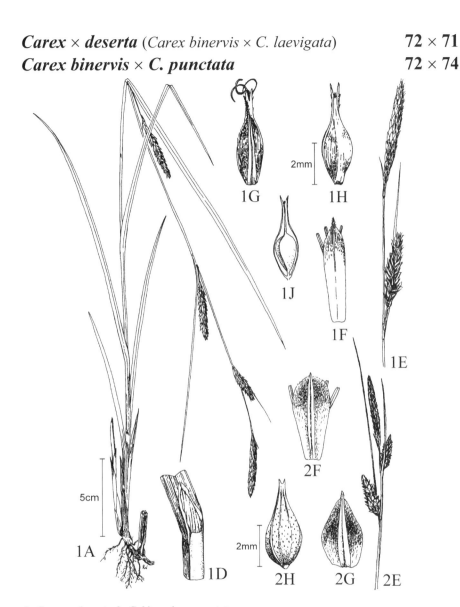

1 *Carex* × *deserta* 2 *C. binervis* × *punctata*
A Fertile shoot; **D** Inner face of leaf-sheath and ligule; **E** Upper spikes; **F** Male floret; **G** Female floret; **H** Utricle; **J** Section through utricle, showing nut.

363

72 × 74 *Carex binervis* × *C. punctata*

(not mapped)

Whilst clearly distinguishable from *Carex punctata*, this sterile hybrid closely resembles its other parent, *C. binervis*, in general appearance, in the shape of both male and female spikes and in the angle at which the utricles are set on the spike axis. However, the utricle of the hybrid resembles that of *C. punctata* in being pale and dotted with red-brown and in its beak which has only a shallow notch and scarcely divergent tips.

This is known only from one locality near Barmouth (SH61), Merioneth (v.c. 48), where a single plant was discovered in June 1954 by P.M. Benoit, growing on a wet, heathy rock near the sea-shore in the presence of both parents (Benoit 1958). Subsequently two plants were found in 1959. It has not been recorded there or elsewhere in the British Isles since 1960.

Carex binervis	*Carex binervis* × *C. punctata*	*Carex punctata*
Stems up to 150 cm.	Stems up to 150 cm.	Stems up to 100 cm.
Bracts exceeding spike but not inflorescence.	Bracts usually shorter than inflorescence but sometimes exceeding it.	At least one bract usually exceeding inflorescence.
♂ spike *c.* 0.4 × 2–4.5 cm.	**♂ spike *c.* 0.3–0.35 × 3 cm.**	♂ spike *c.* 0.2 × 1–3 cm.
♀ spikes all distant, gradually tapering above.	♀ spikes all distant, gradually tapering above.	Upper ♀ spikes contiguous, lower distant, not or scarcely tapering above.
♀ glumes dark purple-brown to black.	**♀ glumes pale purple-brown.**	♀ glumes yellowish or pale brown.
Utricles ovoid, at *c.* 45° to spike axis, gradually narrowing into beak, purple-brown or partly green.	**Utricles** ovoid, at *c.* 45° to spike axis, gradually narrowing into beak, pale yellow-green, **minutely dotted with red-brown, sterile.**	Utricles obovoid to ellipsoid, at up to 90° to spike axis, abruptly narrowing into beak, pale green, minutely dotted with red-brown.
Beak widely notched.	Beak with shallow, inconspicuous notch; tips scarcely divergent.	Beak with shallow, inconspicuous notch.

Carex distans M73

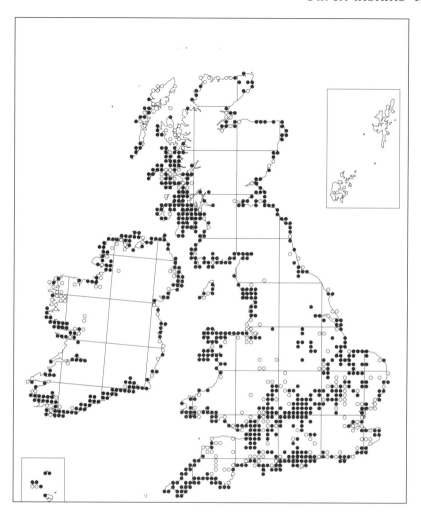

Carex distans is found throughout Britain but has not been recorded for Shetland nor recently in Orkney. North of the Severn–Humber line it is a coastal plant, but in S and E England it is found also inland. Frequent in Ireland but rarely far from the coast.

73 *Carex distans* L.

Distant Sedge   *Map 73*

Rhizomes short; shoots ± densely tufted; roots red-brown; scales dark brown or black, rarely wine-red. *Stems* 15–100 cm, smooth, trigonous-terete. *Leaves* 10–15(–25) cm × 2–6 mm, rigid, ± erect, flat, tapered to a fine point, grey-green (young leaves may be yellow-green) rapidly becoming brown, then ash-grey and persisting on dying; hypostomous; sheaths persisting, becoming fibrous, dark to mid brown, the younger ones orange-brown, with inner face herbaceous, hyaline towards top with a brown margin; apex convex or straight (Figure **D**) or on stem leaves lingulate (Figure **D₁**); ligule 2–3 mm, obtuse. *Inflorescence* compact at flowering, elongating on fruiting to at least 2/3 length of stem; bracts leaf-like, the lower shorter than adjacent internode, the upper longer but not exceeding inflorescence. *Male spike* usually 1, 15–30 mm; *male glumes* 3–4 mm, obovate, pale to purplish-brown; apex subacute to obtuse-mucronate. *Female spikes* 2–4, 10–20 mm, oblong-cylindric, erect; peduncles < 40 mm, ensheathed; *female glumes* 2.5–3.5 mm, ovate-oblong, pale brown or pale reddish-brown, with greenish midrib; apex acute to obtuse with hyaline margins, mucronate. *Utricles* 3.5–4.5 mm, trigonous-ellipsoid, rounded at base, tapered at apex, greenish to brown, distinctly nerved, inserted at an angle of 45–60° to stem axis; beak 0.75 mm, ± rough, bifid; stigmas 3; nut trigonous-ellipsoid, yellow-brown. *Fr.* 6–7.

  C. distans is a plant of rocky or sandy places (with *Festuca–Armeria*, **MC8**, often in the spray zone) and in brackish marshes with *Juncus gerardii* and *J. maritimus* (**SM16** and **SM18**) and with *Festuca rubra* etc. in **MG11**. Also in inland wet meadows (e.g. with *Festuca arundinacea* and *Agrostis stolonifera*, **MG12**, and then less tufted).

  Resembling **72** *C. binervis*, but that has darker utricles, often mottled purplish, and male glumes that are usually purple-brown; also its rhizome scales are red-brown and the decaying leaves, blotched with wine-red, remain pink-brown, not grey as in *C. distans*. **76** *C. hostiana* has a trigonous blunt tip to the more yellow-green leaves and bracts. For the differences between *C. distans* and **74** *C. punctata*, with which it may grow, see that species.

  C. distans hybridises with *C. extensa* (**73** × **75** *C.* × *tornabenii* Chiov.), *C. hostiana* (**73** × **76** *C.* × *muelleriana* F.W. Schultz) and with all three subspecies of *C. viridula* (**73** × **78** *C.* × *luteola* Podp.). A hybrid with *C. flava* has been recorded for mainland Europe.

Carex distans 73

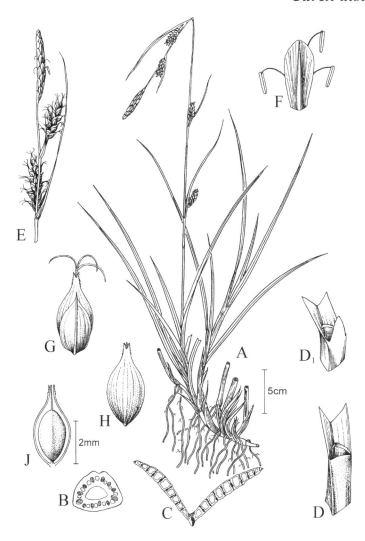

A Fertile shoot; **B** T.S. stem (culm); **C** T.S. leaf; **D** Inner face of leaf-sheath and ligule on lower leaves; **D₁** Inner face of leaf-sheath on upper stem leaves; **E** Upper spikes; **F** Male floret; **G** Female floret; **H** Utricle; **J** Section through utricle, showing nut.

367

M73 × *75* *Carex* × *tornabenii* Chiov. (*C. distans* × *C. extensa*)

Carex × *tornabenii* was first collected at Mochras in 1948 and seen again in 2004 and later at Morfa Dyffryn and Morfa Harlech (all v.c. 48). It has also been found in W Cornwall (v.c. 1) at Harbour Cove, Padstow, and Kemyel Crease and was confirmed at a site in Kirkcudbrightshire (v.c. 73) in 1987.

Carex × *tornabenii* Chiov.

73 × 75

Carex distans × *C. extensa*

Map 73 × 75

This hybrid can be distinguished from *C. distans* by its lowest bract which appreciably exceeds the inflorescence, its more closely spaced female spikes and its shorter utricles. From *C. extensa* it differs in its greater height, its longer male spike and its much less clustered, and less globose, female spikes. From both it differs in its unemergent anthers and empty utricles.

Plants known are found in open saltmarsh areas (e.g. *Juncus maritimus* communities **SM15, SM18**) and on low, wet cliffs. At all localities the parents occur within the same general area.

Carex distans	*Carex* × *tornabenii*	*Carex extensa*
Stems 15 –100 cm.	Stems to 80 cm.	Stems to 40 cm.
Leaves flat, up to 6 mm wide.	Leaves slightly keeled, up to 3 mm wide.	Leaves ± keeled, up to 3 mm wide.
Female spikes oblong-cylindric, 10–20 mm, distant.	**Female spikes ellipsoid-cylindric, often tapered, 8–17 mm, well separated along upper part of stem.**	Female spikes subglobose to cylindric, 5–20 mm, ± contiguous at top of stem.
Bracts not exceeding inflorescence, all ± erect.	**Bracts exceeding inflorescence, not deflexed.**	Bracts far exceeding inflorescence, often deflexed.
♂ spike 15–30 mm, separated from closest female spikes by up to 1–2 times its own length.	**♂ spike 20–30 mm, separated from closest female spike by 0.5–1.5 times its own length.**	♂ spike 5–25 mm, separated from closest female spike by up to 1/3 of its own length.
♀ glumes brown with greenish midrib.	♀ glumes pale brown with pale midrib.	♀ glumes red-brown with grey-green midrib.
Utricles 3.5–4.5 mm, trigonous-ellipsoid, rounded at base; beak bifid.	**Utricles 3.25–3.5 mm, ± ellipsoid, empty, sterile;** beak notched.	Utricles 3–4 mm, ovoid or ellipsoid; beak notched.

73 × 76 *Carex* × *muelleriana* F.W. Schultz

Carex distans × *C. hostiana*   (*not mapped*)

This hybrid differs from *Carex distans* in its proportionately longer, pale green leaves that are abruptly contracted to a point, its greyer basal sheaths and the hyaline margin of the male and female glumes. From *C. hostiana* it differs in the non-trigonous leaf-tips, the longer male spike and the longer bracts. From both it may be distinguished by the unemergent anthers, the often tapered, compressible female spikes and the wrinkled, empty utricles. It could occur with *C.* × *fulva*, from which it might best be separated by its longer spikes (male to 30 mm, female to 20 mm) and shorter lowest bracts (exceeding spike but distinctly shorter than inflorescence).

Carex × *muelleriana* has been recorded only from a meadow near Sherfield upon Loddon (v.c. 12) and a damp meadow at Holton-le-Moor (v.c. 54). It has not been possible to trace a record from Co. Dublin (v.c. H21).

Carex distans	*Carex* × *muelleriana*	*Carex hostiana*
Stems 15–100 cm.	Stems 30–40 cm.	Stems 15–60 cm.
Leaves 10–15(–25) cm × 2–6 mm; apex tapered to a fine point, grey-green.	**Leaves 18–25 cm × 1.5–3.5 mm; apex often abruptly contracted to a fine point, light green.**	Leaves 5–30 cm × 2–5 mm, abruptly contracted into a parallel-sided tip, light to yellow-green.
Lowest bract much longer than spike.	**Lowest bract much longer than spike.**	Lowest bract little longer than spike.
♂ spike 15–30 mm.	**♂ spike to 30 mm.**	♂spike(s) 10–20 mm.
♂ glumes pale to purplish-brown.	**♂ glumes pale brown, with narrow hyaline margin.**	♂ glumes brown, with broad hyaline margin.
♀ spikes 2–4, oblong-cylindric.	**♀ spikes 2–3, ovoid-cylindric, often tapering above.**	♀ spikes 1–3, ovoid-cylindric.
♀ glumes brown with greenish midrib and a narrow hyaline margin towards apex.	**♀ glumes light brown, usually with a hyaline margin from apex to base.**	♀ glumes dark brown with green midrib and broad hyaline margin from apex to base.
Utricles green-brown to dark brown.	**Utricles pale yellow-brown, wrinkled, empty.**	Utricles yellow-green.

370

Carex × tornabenii (*Carex distans × C. extensa*)   73 × 75
Carex × muelleriana (*Carex distans × C. hostiana*)   73 × 76
Carex × luteola (*C. distans × C. viridula* subsp. *viridula*) 73 × 78c

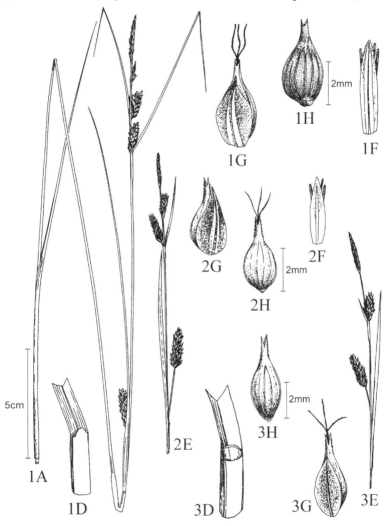

1 *Carex × tornabenii* **2** *C. × luteola* **3** *C. × muelleriana*
A Fertile shoot; **D** Inner face of leaf-sheath and ligule; **E** Inflorescence; **F** Male floret; **G** Female floret; **H** Utricle.

371

M73 × 78 **Carex × luteola** (*Carex distans × C. viridula*)

Carex × luteola with *C. viridula* subsp. *brachyrrhyncha* as a parent has been recorded from both inland and coastal sites, near Tottenhoe (v.c. 30), Island of Danna (v.c. 101) and near Bangor (v.c. H38), that with subsp. *oedocarpa* from a coastal site near Tobermory, Isle of Mull (v.c. 103), and that with subsp. *viridula* from a coastal site near Bangor (v.c. H38) only.

Carex × luteola Sendtn. 73 × 78

Carex distans × C. viridula **Map 73 × 78**

Carex distans hybridises in our area with all subspecies of *C. viridula*, producing appreciably differing offspring. In all specimens examined utricles are empty and anthers unemergent. The hybrid with subsp. *brachyrrhyncha*, on which the table below is based, has been recorded from both inland and coastal sites (v.cc. 30, 101 and H38). It differs from *C. distans* in its longer leaves and bracts and the more abruptly contracted, longer-beaked utricles. The hybrid with subsp. *oedocarpa*, recorded from a coastal site in v.c. 103, resembles *C. distans* in its long stems (to 30 cm) which far overtop the rather short leaves (< 15 cm) but differs from it in its rounder, more clustered, tapering female spikes. Utricles (4.0–4.5 mm) are intermediate, tapering more or less evenly into a long beak (*c.* 1.5 mm). The subsp. *viridula* hybrid, from a coastal site in v.c. H38 only, is a much smaller plant (to 20 cm) with the long bracts of subsp. *viridula* but with longer (to 13 mm), tapering, distant female spikes. The utricles are intermediate in size between those of the parents (3.5–4 mm) but taper abruptly to a distinct beak.

Carex distans	*Carex × luteola*	*Carex viridula* subsp. *brachyrrhyncha*
Leaves 10–15(–25) cm × 2–6 mm, flat, grey-green.	**Leaves 25–40 cm × 2.5–4.5 mm, keeled, pale green.**	Leaves 10–40 cm × 1.2–3.5(–5.4) mm, keeled, mid green to yellow-green.
Lowest bract shorter than adjacent internode, erect.	**Lowest bract erect, appreciably exceeding adjacent internode but not inflorescence.**	Lowest bract exceeding inflorescence, sometimes reflexed.
♀ spikes 10–20 mm, oblong-cylindric, distant, lowest with peduncle to 40 mm.	**♀ spikes** 10–20 mm, cylindric, **tapering above**, upper ± contiguous, lowest distant and with long peduncle.	♀ spikes 8–15 mm, ovoid to cylindrical, upper densely clustered, lower often distant and with short peduncle.
Utricles 3.5–4.5 mm, trigonous-ellipsoid, tapered at apex, greenish to brown; beak 0.75 mm long, rough.	**Utricles 3.5–4 mm, ovoid, pale, distorted, empty**, narrowing abruptly into prominent beak, 1.5–1.7 mm long.	Utricles 3–5.5 mm, obovoid-trigonous, yellow-green, patent, lower deflexed; beak 1.5–2 mm long.

373

74 *Carex punctata* Gaudin

Dotted Sedge   *Map 74*

Rhizomes shortly creeping; shoots tufted; roots orange-brown to black, not felty; scales brown, rarely red, becoming fibrous. *Stems* 15–100 cm, trigonous. *Leaves* 10–50 cm × 2–7 mm, usually as long as the stem, but variable, flat or shallowly keeled, abruptly tapered to a fine tip, pale or yellow-green, persisting on dying as a grey-brown litter, doubtfully overwintering; hypostomous; sheaths persistent, orange- or pink-brown, with inner face hyaline, dark brown and concave at apex; ligule 3 mm, obtuse, tubular at least on culm. *Inflorescence* about 1/2 length of stem; bracts leaf-like, at least one usually, but not invariably, exceeding the inflorescence. *Male spike* 1, 10–30 mm; *male glumes* 3–4 mm, oblong-obovate, orange-brown; apex mucronate, often fimbriate. *Female spikes* 2–4, upper ± contiguous, lower distant, 5–25 mm, ovoid-cylindric; peduncles ensheathed; *female glumes* 2.5–3.5 mm, obovate, yellowish or pale brown, with green midrib and hyaline margin; apex acuminate or obtuse and mucronate. *Utricles* 3–4 mm, obovoid-ellipsoid, shiny, yellowish-green, minutely dotted with red-brown, ± inflated, prominently ribbed when dry, with lateral nerves prominent, inserted at an angle of 75–90° to stem axis and therefore strongly patent, narrowing abruptly into a beak 0.75 mm, notched; stigmas 3; nut obovoid, trigonous, dark brown, shortly stalked.   *Fr.* 7–8.

A plant of maritime habitats, preferring sandy well-drained soils, on raised beaches and at bases of cliffs, in non-brackish associations but with high base status, e.g. *Festuca rubra–Armeria/Plantago* spp. (**MC8, MC10**), and invariably in freshwater seepage zones but usually within reach of the salt spray (but apparently not dependent on salt if brought into cultivation: R. Murphy pers. comm.).

C. punctata is frequently confused with **73** *C. distans* (although the species rarely grow together) but is usually more erect and rigid, with broader and more yellow leaves. In *C. distans* none of the bracts exceeds the inflorescence, the ligule is not tubular, the male glumes are purple-brown and the more evenly tapered utricles are invariably inserted more obliquely on the axis of the spike. These points also differentiate **72** *C. binervis*, with which *C. punctata* has been found to form a sterile hybrid (see p. 364).

Hybrids with *C. viridula* subsp. *oedocarpa* and *C. pallescens* have been recorded from mainland Europe.

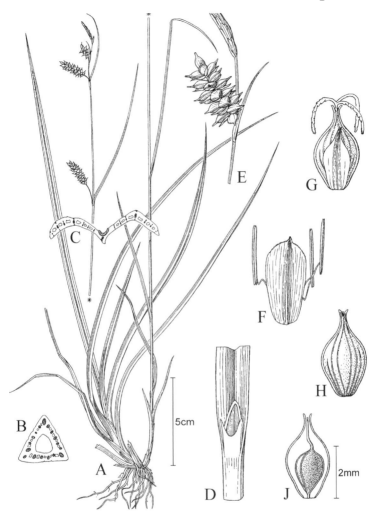

A Fertile shoot; **B** T.S. stem (culm); **C** T.S. leaf; **D** Inner face of leaf-sheath and ligule; **E** Upper spikes; **F** Male floret; **G** Female floret; **H** Utricle; **J** Section through utricle, showing nut.

M74 Carex punctata

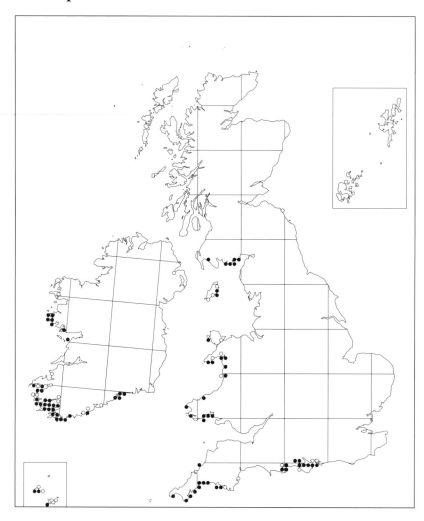

Carex punctata is a maritime oceanic species with its main stations in the SW of Britain and Ireland. In Britain it reaches as far north as the N shore of the Solway Firth and as far east as S Hants and in Ireland as far north as West Galway. See also David (1981b).

Carex extensa M75

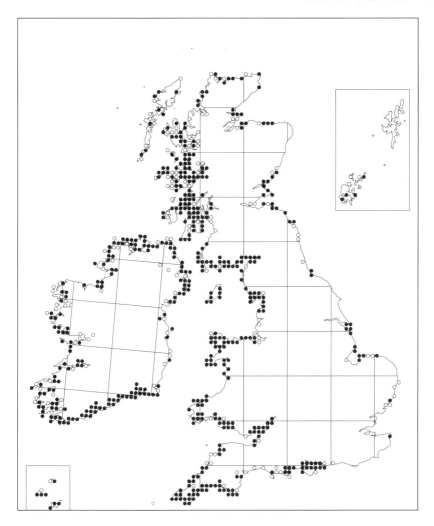

Carex extensa occurs around the coasts of the British Isles but is more local on the east side of both islands. Scottish plants are often very dwarf. The species is not recorded for Shetland.

377

75 *Carex extensa* Gooden.

Long-bracted Sedge   *Map 75*

Rhizomes short; shoots often forming large tufts; roots red-brown (often stained black); scales dark grey-brown, becoming ± fibrous. ***Stems*** 5–40 cm, rigid, bluntly trigonous, sometimes arcuate, tough. ***Leaves*** 5–35 cm × 2–3 mm, rigid, thick, ± keeled, deeply channelled and often inrolled, gradually tapered to a blunt apex, grey-green or glaucous, becoming on dying red-brown then grey, overwintering; hypostomous; sheaths orange-brown, occasionally red-tinged, darkening and often blackish and fibrous in decay; inner face narrow, hyaline; apex concave; ligule 2 mm, rounded, slightly tubular. ***Inflorescence*** 1/3–1/2 length of stem; bracts leaf-like, usually reflexed, far exceeding inflorescence. ***Male spike*** usually 1, rarely 2–3, 5–25 mm; ***male glumes*** 3–4 mm, obovate-elliptic, red-brown with paler midrib; apex obtuse. ***Female spikes*** 2–4, contiguous or lowest sometimes distant, 5–20 mm, subglobose to cylindric; peduncles ensheathed, lowest ± exserted; ***female glumes*** 1.5–2 mm, broadly ovate, red-brown with pale, often green, midrib, with ± hyaline margins; apex mucronate. ***Utricles*** 3–4 mm, ovoid or ellipsoid, grey-green or brownish with purplish blotches, weakly ribbed; beak 0.5–0.75 mm, smooth, notched; stigmas 3; nut broadly ovoid, trigonous.   ***Fr.*** 7–8.

A coastal plant, usually within reach of salt water or sea spray, on both muddy and sandy estuarine or littoral flats, in similar situations to *C. distans* and with *Blysmus rufus*, *Eleocharis uniglumis*, *Juncus gerardii*, *J. maritimus* and *Puccinellia* spp., in associations **SM15, SM18, SM19** and **SM20**.

There is no other plant in this habitat that could be easily mistaken for *C. extensa*, although very small non-flowering plants (often referred to as 'forma *minor*') on Scottish saltmarshes may be confused with forms of *C. viridula* subsp. *viridula*. The exceedingly long bracts, grey-green utricles and deeply channelled, glaucous leaves contrast with the yellow-green colours in *C. viridula* and are usually sufficient to identify *C. extensa*.

C. extensa forms a hybrid with *C. distans* (**73** × **75** *C.* × *tornabenii* Chiov.), which has been recorded in Britain; that with *C. viridula* subsp. *oedocarpa* is not recorded in the British Isles.

378

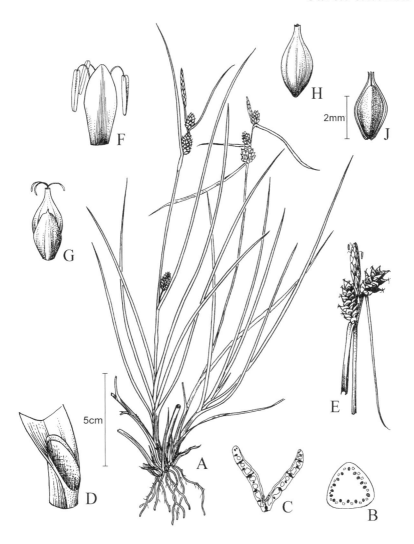

A Fertile shoot; **B** T.S. stem (culm); **C** T.S. leaf; **D** Inner face of leaf-sheath and ligule; **E** Upper spikes; **F** Male floret; **G** Female floret; **H** Utricle; **J** Section through utricle, showing nut.

76   *Carex hostiana* DC.

Rhizomes shortly creeping; shoots hardly tufted; roots of varying colours; scales pale brown, soon decaying and leaving robust fibres. *Stems* 15–60 cm, slightly rough, trigonous. *Leaves* 5–30 cm × 2–5 mm, ± flat or shallowly keeled, abruptly contracted into a parallel-sided, veinless tip several mm behind apex (Figure **K**), light green to yellow-green, grey-brown when dead, rarely overwintering; sheaths dark grey-brown, becoming fibrous, inner ones pale; inner face hyaline; apex convex or lingulate; ligule 1 mm, rounded. *Inflorescence* 1/4–1/2 length of stem; bracts leaf-like, longer than spike but not exceeding inflorescence, upper one sometimes very short. *Male spikes* 1 or 2, 10–20 mm; *male glumes* 3.5–4.5 mm, obovate-elliptic, brown with broad hyaline margin; apex obtuse. *Female spikes* 1–3, ± distant, 8–20 mm, ovoid-cylindric, erect; peduncles ensheathed for half their length; *female glumes* 2.5–3.5 mm, broadly ovate, dark brown with a conspicuous broad silvery (hyaline) margin and pale, often green, midrib; apex acute. *Utricles* 4–5 mm, obovoid, ribbed, yellow-green; beak 1 mm, ± deeply bifid, serrulate; stigmas 3, with style often shortly exserted and persistent; nut obovoid, trigonous, shortly stalked.   *Fr.* 7–8.

A plant of wet flushes and marshy ground where the water contains a fairly high proportion of bases and has a pH of 5.5–6.5, and so common on schistose and other igneous rock flushes (e.g. in **H5** *Erica vagans–Schoenus nigricans* heaths); often close to the shore in dune-slack communities with *Salix repens, Carex flacca* and *C. viridula* subsp. *viridula* (**SD14**). Common in hilly areas of N England and Scotland (e.g. in **M11**); more local along spring-lines and in valley mires in the S and E and in Wales with *Schoenus nigricans–Pinguicula vulgaris* (**M13b**). In Ireland it tolerates less base-rich mires (Webb & Scannell 1983) but probably gains base ions from salt-laden winds.

This species can be confused with **73** *C. distans*, but the longer beak and the contrast of the bright yellow-green utricle and dark brown female glume with broad silvery margins and the trigonous point to the leaf are sufficient to separate *C. hostiana* from it.

It hybridises with *C. distans* (**73** × **76** *C.* × *muelleriana* F.W. Schultz) and commonly with all subspecies of *C. viridula* (**76** × **78** *C.* × *fulva* Gooden.).

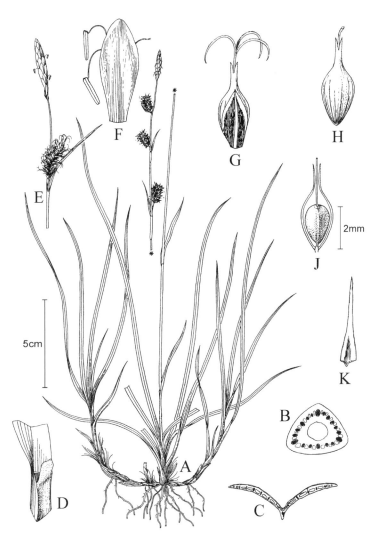

A Fertile shoot; **B** T.S. stem (culm); **C** T.S. leaf; **D** Inner face of leaf-sheath and ligule; **E** Upper spikes; **F** Male floret; **G** Female floret; **H** Utricle; **J** Section through utricle, showing nut; **K** Apex of leaf.

M76 Carex hostiana

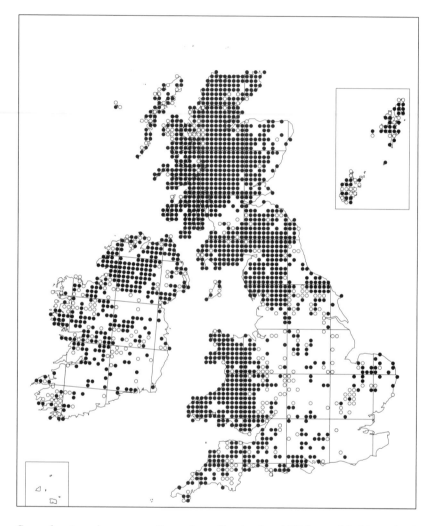

Carex hostiana is common throughout Scotland and Wales and in N England south to the Humber, thereafter more local and decreasing and quite uncommon in the SE. In Ireland it is less frequent in the south.

Carex × *fulva* (*Carex hostiana* × *C. viridula*)   *M76 × 78*

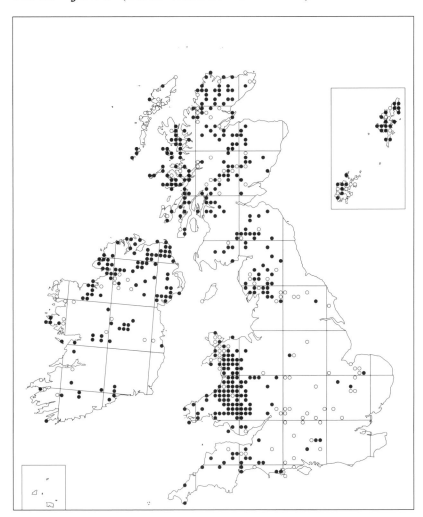

Carex × *fulva* sensu lato is mapped here to indicate frequency throughout the British Isles.

76 × 78 *Carex* × *fulva* Gooden.

Carex hostiana × *C. viridula*   Map 76 × 78

Carex hostiana hybridises with all three subspecies of *Carex viridula* to produce a highly sterile hybrid, perhaps the most common *Carex* hybrid in the British Isles. This hybrid differs from both parents in its pale, compressible female spikes which taper above (sometimes presenting a 'pineapple' shape), its unemerged anthers and its empty utricles. From *C. hostiana* it is further distinguished by its much longer bracts, and from *C. viridula* by its more fusiform male spikes, in which the glumes have a prominent hyaline margin, its more distant female spikes and by the whitish style bases which often protrude from the utricle apex. Details are given below for the hybrid involving subsp. *brachyrrhyncha*.   (*Cont. on p. 386.*)

Carex hostiana	*Carex* × *fulva*	*Carex viridula* ssp. *brachyrrhyncha*
Stems 15–60 cm.	Stems to 60 cm.	Stems 20–80 cm.
Bracts shortly exceeding spike.	**Bracts far exceeding spike**, often erect.	Bracts exceeding inflorescence.
♂ spike fusiform, to 20 mm long.	♂ spike fusiform, to 22 mm long.	♂ spike ± cylindric, to 20 mm long.
♂ glumes 3.5–4.5 mm, obovate-elliptic, brown with a broad hyaline margin; apex obtuse.	♂ **glumes** 3–4 mm, broadly lanceolate, mid-brown **with a broad hyaline margin**, especially so at the ± obtuse apex.	♂ glumes 3–3.5 mm, lanceolate-elliptic, orange- or red-brown with a green midrib; apex subacute.
♀ spikes < 20 mm long, ± distant, ovoid-cylindric, green-brown.	♀ **spikes** < 18 mm long, **pale, distant,** cylindric, **tapering above.**	♀ spikes < 15 mm long, upper contiguous, lower often distant, ovoid, green-brown.
♀ glumes broadly ovate, dark brown with broad hyaline margin.	♀ glumes broadly lanceolate, brown with a variable hyaline margin.	♀ glumes ovate-lanceolate, orange/red-brown with a narrow hyaline margin.
Utricles 4–5 mm, ± patent; beak 1 mm, straight, ± serrulate.	**Utricles** *c.* 4 mm, **empty;** beak 1–2 mm, **slightly deflexed,** ± serrulate.	Utricles 3–5.5 mm, lower deflexed; beak 1.5–2 mm, deflexed, smooth.

384

Carex × *fulva* s.l. (*Carex hostiana* × *C. viridula* subspp.) **76 × 78**
C. × *alsatica* Zahn (*C. flava* × *C. viridula* ssp. *oedocarpa*) **77 × 78b**

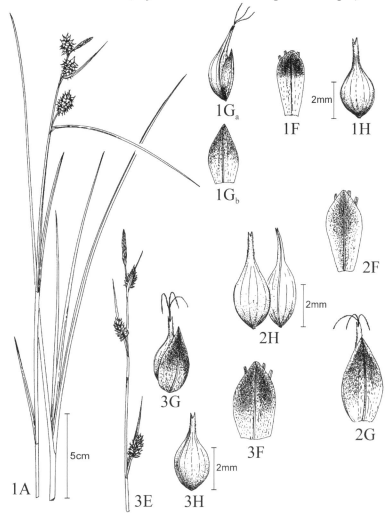

1 *Carex* × *alsatica* 2 *C. hostiana* × *viridula* subsp. *brachyrrhyncha*
3 *C. hostiana* × *viridula* subsp. *oedocarpa*
A Fertile shoot; E Inflorescence; F Male floret; G Female floret; G$_a$ Female floret
(side view); G$_b$ Female glume; H Utricle (abaxial view + side view for **2**).

76 × 78 *Carex* × *fulva* (continued)

Carex hostiana forms hybrids with all three subspecies of *C. viridula*, but on p. 384 we have given a detailed description of only one, that with subsp. *brachyrrhyncha*, found in base-rich flushes. This hybrid and that with subsp. *oedocarpa*, which is found in less base-rich soils, are both frequent, while that with subsp. *viridula* is extremely rare.

Many records do not distinguish the subspecies involved and it is often impossible to determine herbarium specimens; the decision as to which may be the parent is probably best made in the field, by identifying the subspecies present in the locality. Some additional pointers are given below. Since the three subspecies themselves intergrade, more precise details are not given.

C. hostiana × *C. viridula* subsp. *oedocarpa* differs only marginally from the *brachyrrhyncha* hybrid. This is mainly in its generally shorter flower-stems (usually less than 50 cm), which results in the inflorescences standing out above the leaves to a lesser extent, its slightly shorter male spikes (usually to 1.8 mm long), its shorter female spikes (usually to 15 mm long), its marginally smaller utricles (usually to 3.8 mm long) and in its preference for less base-rich habitats. It occurs sometimes in the absence of *C. hostiana*, although the subsp. *oedocarpa* parent is apparently always present.

C. hostiana × *C. viridula* subsp. *viridula* is distinguished by its small size (usually no more than 25 cm), its 1–2 short and slender female spikes (usually up to 10 mm long) and its small utricles (usually 2.5–3 mm, with beak up to 0.8 mm). The only confirmed records are from a fen, a lake-shore and a ditch in v.cc. 29, 88 and H16.

Nothosubspecies names in *Carex* × *fulva*

We have not attempted to find valid Latin names for the separate hybrids (technically nothosubspecies) between *C. hostiana* and the three subspecies of *C. viridula*. Goodenough, who first described *C. fulva*, considered it to be a full species and not a hybrid and based his description on specimens from various locations involving more than one subspecies of *C. viridula*. This means that we must examine all material that Goodenough would have seen and choose one specimen that can best represent his own concept of *C. fulva* to become *C. fulva* nothosubsp. *fulva*. Other specimens that have been attributed to hybrids within *C. viridula* in the broad sense (including *C. lepidocarpa*, *C. demissa* and *C. serotina*) will then need to be investigated in order to find legitimate names for the remaining two hybrids. As this work is not yet completed, names cannot be included here.

77   *C. flava* L.
78   *C. viridula* Michx.
78a   subsp. *brachyrrhyncha* (Čelak.) B. Schmid (including vars
     jemtlandica (Palmgr.) Blackstock & P.A. Ashton and *scotica*
     (E.W. Davies) B. Schmid); syn. *C. lepidocarpa* Tausch p.p.
78b   subsp. *oedocarpa* (Andersson) B. Schmid;
     syn. *C. demissa* Hornem.
78c   subsp. *viridula* (including vars *bergrothii* (Palmgr.) B. Schmid
     and *pulchella* (Lönnr.) B. Schmid); syn. *C. serotina* Mérat p.p.

The four main taxa listed above comprise one of the most difficult groups within our area. They are extremely variable, and that variation seems not to be correlated either with ecological factors or with general distribution. The characters traditionally used to distinguish the taxa are largely quantitative and tend to overlap a great deal; what qualitative characters there are tend to be difficult to recognise in dried material. Considerable gene exchange is presumed to take place between several of the taxa, since intermediate and at least partially fertile populations often occur. These intermediates have been explained as hybrids and have in some cases been synthesised (Davies 1956).

The treatment here is based on molecular studies (mainly on isoenzymes), backed up by a detailed morphometric analysis by Nigel Blackstock and Paul Ashton on British, Irish, Scandinavian and North American material. The results give data for an in-depth discussion on taxa relationships developed elsewhere (Blackstock 2007). We reiterate here the taxonomic conclusions based on the above and published in *British Wildlife* (Blackstock & Jermy 2001). This treatment agrees basically with the thorough studies of the group by B. Schmid (1980, 1983), by Crins & Ball (1989) and, in an account of Scandinavian material, by Pykala & Toivonen (1994). On molecular grounds *C. flava* sensu stricto is distinct enough to be considered a separate species (N. Blackstock pers. comm.) and we believe we should not follow Sell & Murrell (1996), who place all the yellow-sedges under that species, although we recognise the same taxa as they do but at different ranks. On the other hand, allozyme studies by Hedrén (2003) of a wide selection of Swedish and other material pointed to morphological differentiation at the species rather that the subspecies level. The relationships of the British taxa to plants elsewhere in Europe is still uncertain and we reserve judgement until more studies have been undertaken.

Hybrids

Much of the variation seen in *C. viridula* agg. may be due to hybridisation within the taxa where they grow together. They are rarely sterile and we have not attempted to describe such specimens as hybrids. On the other hand some hybrids within the group are obvious.

Within this group, **77** *Carex flava* hybridises with **78** *C. viridula*. The earliest available name for such a hybrid is *C.* × *alsatica* Zahn, originally given to the hybrid with **78b** *viridula* subsp. *oedocarpa*, and this epithet must be used for hybrids with other subspecies. As nothosubspecific names have not been formally made they cannot be used here.

77 × **78b** *C.* × *alsatica* is found in Britain where the two parents grow together in v.c. 69. Such plants are morphologically intermediate and wholly sterile. On the other hand, intermediate but fertile plants growing at Malham Tarn (v.c. 64), previously considered a possible hybrid between *C. flava* and **78a** *C. viridula* subsp. *brachyrrhyncha*, have been shown, on morphometric and molecular grounds (Blackstock & Ashton 2001; Blackstock 2007), to be not a hybrid but pure *C. flava*, though older herbarium material of similar morphology collected at Malham may be that hybrid.

However, in studies on plants from Greywell Fen (v.c. 12) that are morphometrically indistinguishable from *C. viridula* subsp. *brachyrrhyncha*, allozymes suggest a hybrid with *C. flava* back-crossing with *C. viridula* subsp. *brachyrrhyncha* and thus support the historic presence of *C. flava* in the population. Similar material from Coolagh Fen, Lough Corrib (v.c. H17), is, on the evidence of allozymes, pure subsp. *brachyrrhyncha* (N. Blackstock pers. comm.).

The following hybrids with species outside the complex are described in detail below, after one or other of the parents.

C. viridula hybridises with *C. hostiana* (also in this section) where the parents grow commonly together. Any of the subspecies can be involved, but the hybrid with subsp. *viridula* is the rarest. On morphological and locational grounds Goodenough's type specimen suggests subsp. *oedocarpa* as the parent. See **76** × **78a** *C.* × *fulva* Gooden.

C. viridula subsp. *oedocarpa* also hybridises with *C. binervis* (**78b** × **72** *C.* × *corstorphinei* Druce) and all three subspecies form hybrids with *C. distans* (**73** × **78** *C.* × *luteola* Sendtn.). A probable hybrid with *C. saxatilis* (**78a** × **62**), growing with subsp. *brachyrrhyncha* var. *scotica*, has been found in v.c. 97. A putative hybrid between **78b** and **71** *C. laevigata* has been recorded from Egryn Abbey in v.c. 48 (P.M. Benoit pers. comm.).

Carex flava is presently found in Britain only at Roudsea Wood NNR (v.c. 69) and Malham Tarn (v.c. 64). A confirmed herbarium specimen from an unlikely locality in Ennerdale (v.c. 70) is not mapped. Allozyme analysis of a population of *C. viridula* at Greywell Fen (v.c. 12) suggests the historic presence of *C. flava* also there (Blackstock & Ashton 2001; Blackstock 2007).

77 *Carex flava* L.

Large Yellow-sedge   Map 77

Rhizomes short; shoots 2–4, tufted; roots pale buff-brown; scales bleached, becoming fibrous. **Stems** 20–70 cm, trigonous, usually solid. **Leaves** 25–70 cm × 3–7(–10) mm, ± as long as stem, almost erect, flat, ± abruptly tapered to a rough tip, bright yellow-green rapidly becoming bleached to straw colour on dying; hypostomous; sheaths thin, ribbed, pale, becoming a bleached pink-brown and fibrous; inner face hyaline; apex ± straight; ligule 2–5 mm, obtuse, tubular. **Inflorescence** 1/5–1/6(–1/4) length of stem; bracts leaf-like, often patent or reflexed, far exceeding inflorescence. **Male spike** 1, 4–15(–22) mm; **male glumes** 3.5–4 mm, lanceolate-elliptic, orange-brown with pale midrib; apex subacute. **Female spikes** 2–3(–4), mostly clustered around male, 8–15(–20) mm, ovoid, ± sessile except for an occasional lowest distant spike which can have a partly ensheathed peduncle 4–5 cm long; **female glumes** 3.5–4.5 mm, ovate-lanceolate, orange-brown, with green midrib and ± hyaline margin; apex acute. **Utricles** (3.5–)4.4–6.5 mm, broadly ellipsoid, trigonous, ribbed, yellow-green to golden, patent, lower deflexed when ripe; beak 2–2.8 mm, conspicuously scabrous with 6–11 bristles on each side, notched, deflexed; stigmas 3; nut obovoid, trigonous.   **Fr.** 6–8.

C. flava prefers mineral-rich fens which are often slightly calcareous and where there is a regular through-flow of water. Although it is tolerant of competition and may grow in quite dense vegetation, it appears to need relatively open conditions for seedlings to become established. At Roudsea Wood it occurs in semi-shaded woodland (**W7** *Alnus glutinosa–Fraxinus excelsior–Lysimachia nemorum*) and on the margins of a **W5** *Alnus glutinosa–Carex paniculata* woodland (McKenna 2000). At Malham Tarn the site is much more open, with a very small population occurring in a **M26a** *Molinia caerulea–Crepis paludosa* mire, *Sanguisorba officinalis* sub-community (Blackstock & Ashton 2001).

C. flava is basically similar to **78a** *C. viridula* subsp. *brachyrrhyncha* but can be distinguished by the leaves being about as long as the stem, the compact inflorescence with the male spike sometimes partly hidden by the female spikes, the long bracts, the long utricle more gradually tapered into a beak 2–2.8 mm long and the longer ligule.

For hybrids in our area, see above, **77–78** *Carex flava* group. In mainland Europe *C. flava* hybridises with *C. binervis*, *C. distans* and *C. hostiana*.

C. flava is a **Red Data List** species in Great Britain; *Status*: **Vulnerable** (Cheffings & Farrell 2005).

390

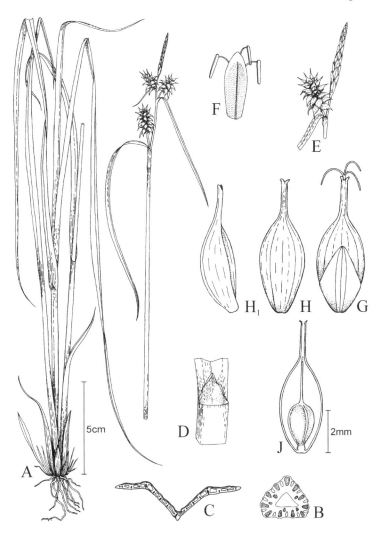

A Fertile shoot; **B** T.S. stem (culm); **C** T.S. leaf; **D** Inner face of leaf-sheath and ligule; **E** Upper spikes; **F** Male floret; **G** Female floret; **H** Utricle (abaxial view); **H₁** Utricle (side view); **J** Section through utricle, showing nut.

77 × 78b *Carex* × *alsatica* Zahn

Carex flava × *C. viridula* subsp. *oedocarpa*   (*not mapped*)

This hybrid is most readily distinguished from its parents by its overall blue-green appearance, its cylindrical to conical, readily compressible female spikes, its sterile utricles and its unemergent anthers. The female spikes, the utricles, the beak and the lowest bract are all intermediate in size between those of the parents.

C. × *alsatica* is known with certainty only from Roudsea Wood NNR (SD38) in Westmorland (v.c. 69), where it grows in some abundance in dappled shade in deciduous woodland over limestone. Both parents are present, with *C. flava* especially frequent. As noted above, morphometric and molecular studies (Blackstock & Ashton 2001; Blackstock 2007) support the historic presence of a hybrid between *C. flava* and *C. viridula* subsp. *brachyrrhyncha* at Greywell Fen (v.c. 12).

Carex flava	*Carex* × *alsatica*	*Carex viridula* subsp. *oedocarpa*
Leaves bright yellow-green, 3–7(–10) mm broad.	**Leaves bluish-green, 2.5–6 mm broad.**	Leaves dark yellow-green, 1.5–5 mm broad.
♀ spikes ovoid, relatively large, 8–15(–20) mm, clustered, lowest occasionally distant, sometimes to 2 cm, feeling hard when compressed.	**♀ spikes cylindrical or conical, intermediate in size between those of parents, 12–15 mm, clustered, lowest sometimes appreciably distant by 2–4(–8) cm, readily compressible.**	♀ spikes ovoid, relatively small, 7–13 mm, clustered, lowest usually remote, feeling hard when compressed.
Utricles (3.5–)4.4–6.5 mm, broadly ellipsoid, trigonous, lower deflexed when ripe.	**Utricles 4–5 mm, sterile, empty, arcuate,** usually erect but lower sometimes patent or deflexed.	Utricles 3–4 mm, lower deflexed when ripe.
Beak 1.8–2.8 mm long.	**Beak 1.5–2 mm long.**	Beak *c.* 1 mm long.

Carex viridula subsp. *brachyrrhyncha*   *M78a*

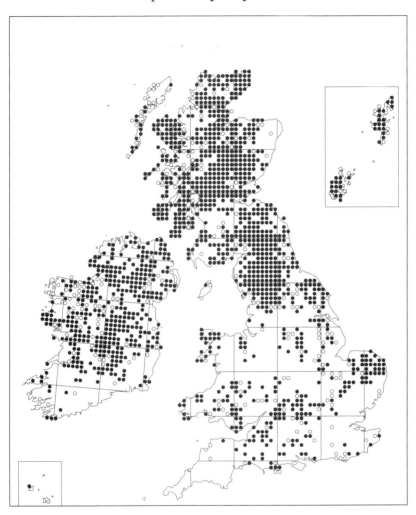

The distribution of *Carex viridula* subsp. *brachyrrhyncha* sensu lato follows that of base-rich strata, with sodium perhaps replacing calcium in coastal habitats. Var. *jemtlandica* has only been confirmed for Ireland, where it may be the more common variety on the turloughs of the west; fieldwork in W and N Scotland may reveal it there also. The upland var. *scotica* now needs to be recorded in detail.

78a *Carex viridula* Michx. subsp. *brachyrrhyncha* (Čelak.) B. Schmid
Carex lepidocarpa Tausch in previous editions

Long-stalked Yellow-sedge   *Map 78a*

Rhizomes short; shoots loosely tufted; roots pale buff-brown; scales grey-brown. **Stems** 20–80 cm, trigonous, solid, rough below spikes. **Leaves** 10–40 cm × 1.2–3.5(–5.4) mm, usually only 1/3–1/2 as long as stem, keeled, ± abruptly narrowed to a rough, blunt, trigonous point, mid- to yellow-green, becoming bleached straw colour, not overwintering; hypostomous; sheaths hyaline, ribbed, becoming pink-brown and fibrous; apex of inner face ± straight; ligule 1 mm, rounded, tubular. **Inflorescence** 1/10–1/4 length of stem; bracts leaf-like or the upper glumaceous, occasionally reflexed, exceeding inflorescence. **Male spike** 1, 10–20 mm, often on a conspicuous (up to 28 mm long) peduncle that is set at an angle to the flowering stem; **male glumes** 3–3.5 mm, lanceolate-elliptic, orange- or red-brown, with green midrib; apex subacute. **Female spikes** 1–3(–4), densely clustered to slightly distant, 8–15 mm, ovoid to cylindrical, sessile or lowermost with an ensheathed short peduncle; **female glumes** falling before the utricle, 2.5–4 mm, ovate-lanceolate, orange- or red-brown, with green midrib and often hyaline margin; apex acute. **Utricles** 3–5.5 mm, obovoid-trigonous, ribbed, yellow-green, patent, the lower deflexed; beak 1.5–2 mm, split, arcuate or deflexed in side view; stigmas 3; nut obovoid, trigonous. **Fr.** 7–8.

Carex viridula subsp. *brachyrrhyncha* probably has the most exacting ecological requirements of all the taxa in the *C. flava* group and is an indicator of good-quality base-rich habitats. It is a strong calcicole, as seedling growth is stunted by soluble aluminum ions released at low pH (Clymo 1960), and may be found occurring on base-rich fens and other wet areas that are regularly flushed with base-rich waters. *C. viridula* subsp. *brachyrrhyncha* has been recorded from the following NVC communities: *Carex rostrata–Sphagnum warnstorfii–Calliergonella cuspidata* mires (**M8, M9**), *Carex dioica–Pinguicula vulgaris* mire (**M10**), *Saxifraga aizoides* communities (**M11, U15**), *Schoenus nigricans–Juncus subnodulosus* mire (**M13**), *Juncus subnodulosus–Cirsium palustre* fen-meadow (**M22**) and springs dominated by *Palustriella commutata* (**M37, M38**); also in the *Cicuta virosa* sub-community of *Phragmites–Peucedanum palustre* tall-herb fen (**S24e**) and the *Blysmus rufus* saltmarsh community (**SM19**). See also Davies (1953b).

For hybrids see p. 388.   (*Continued on p. 396.*)

Carex viridula subsp. *brachyrrhyncha* 78a

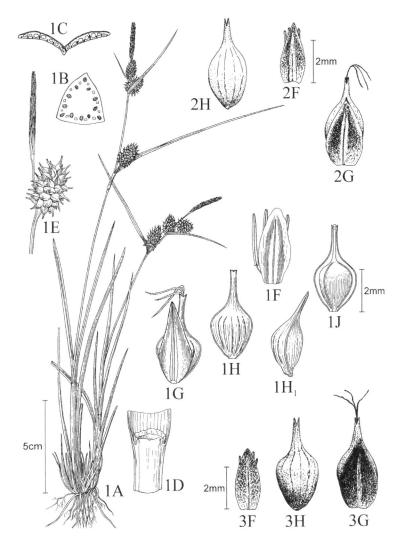

Carex viridula subsp. *brachyrrhyncha* **1** var. *brachyrrhyncha* **2** var. *jemtlandica*
3 var. *scotica*
A Fertile shoot; **B** T.S. stem (culm); **C** T.S. leaf; **D** Inner face of leaf-sheath and
ligule; **E** Upper spikes; **F** Male floret; **G** Female floret; **H** Utricle (abaxial view);
H₁ Utricle (side view); **J** Section through utricle, showing nut.

78a *Carex viridula* subsp. *brachyrrhyncha* (continued)

The characters and ecology described on p. 394 may be taken as those of var. *brachyrrhyncha*, but we recognise two further taxa at varietal rank. All these taxa grade into subsp. *oedocarpa*. Usually the ratio of leaf-length to stem-length is a good character to separate them. Additionally, the utricle in var. *brachyrrhyncha* has a more gradual transition to a longer, deflexed beak, compared to the distinct shoulder on that of subsp. *oedocarpa*, where the beak is usually straight (but see var. *jemtlandica* below).

Carex viridula subsp. *brachyrrhyncha* var. *jemtlandica* (Palmgr.) Blackstock & P.A. Ashton

This variety is most readily distinguished by examination of the female spikes and utricles. The female spikes are generally contiguous to approximate and often clustered close to the sessile or shortly stalked male spike. The straight-beaked utricles are much more loosely packed, and this gives the female spikes a much more globose to ovate appearance. Unlike in var. *brachyrrhyncha*, the lowermost female spikes of var. *jemtlandica* often have fewer utricles than the upper spikes, and this may also give the inflorescence an asymmetrical appearance. The part of the flowering stem just below the inflorescence of var. *jemtlandica* is smooth, as opposed to the rough flowering stem of the type variety.

Carex viridula subsp. *brachyrrhyncha* var. *scotica* (E.W. Davies) B. Schmid

Var. *scotica* can occur wherever there are suitable base-rich rocky ledges or flush-mire conditions in upland areas, possibly extending the altitudinal limit for the species to *c.* 1000 m. It is a characteristic component of the rich *Carex dioica–Pinguicula vulgaris* mire (**M10**) and *C. viridula* subsp. *oedocarpa–Saxifraga aizoides* mire communities (**M11**) in the Highlands of Scotland and a few outlying areas such as Upper Teesdale. It is generally shorter and stockier in stature than the other two segregates of subsp. *brachyrrhyncha*, being 10–20(–45) cm in height with very short (up to 10 cm), tough fibrous leaves (2.5–4 mm wide), and so is easily confused with subsp. *oedocarpa*. It should be separable from that taxon by the stout, straight, erect flowering stem and the larger utricles, which are (4–)4.25–4.5(–5) mm long. The female spikes are also characterised by the dark chestnut-brown, persistent glumes.

Carex viridula subsp. *brachyrrhyncha* (Čelak.) B. Schmid × *C. saxatilis* L.

78a × 62

C. × *marshallii* Benn., nomen nudum (*not mapped*)

This hybrid is intermediate between its parents in leaf length, in the variable number of stigmas and, most strikingly, in the chestnut colour of the inflorescence. It resembles subsp. *brachyrrhyncha* var. *scotica* in its lowest bracts that exceed the inflorescence, in the shape and length of the female glumes, in utricle size and in its long arcuate beak. It is closer to *C. saxatilis* in its ± sessile male spike and its larger, ± contiguous female spikes.

It is known only from collections made in 2002 and 2005 from flushed ledges and wet mineral soil at the base of crags at 800 m on Aonach Beag (NN27, v.c. 97), where it grows with both parents.

Carex viridula ssp. *brachyrrhyncha*	*Carex viridula* × *C. saxatilis*	*Carex saxatilis*
Leaves usually only 1/3 to 1/2 as long as stem, matt.	**Leaves more than half as long as stem**, shiny.	Leaves ± as long as stem, ± shiny.
Ligule 1 mm.	Ligule 1.5–2 mm.	Ligule 2–4 mm.
Lowest bracts exceeding inflorescence.	Lowest bracts equal to or exceeding inflorescence.	Lowest bracts ± equalling inflorescence.
♂ spike often on a peduncle up to 28 mm.	♂ spike ± sessile or shortly pedunculate.	♂ spike ± sessile or shortly pedunculate.
♂ glumes, orange- or red-brown; midrib green.	♂ glumes chestnut brown, darkening; midrib ± concolorous or green.	♂ glumes purple-black with paler midrib; margin hyaline.
♀ spikes 1–3(–4), 8–15 mm, orange- or red-brown, upper contiguous, or lowest distant, sessile or with short peduncle.	♀ **spikes 3** (sometimes 2), **12–17 mm, chestnut brown, ± contiguous**, lowermost shortly pedunculate.	♀ spikes 1–3, 5–20 mm, purple- to dark red-brown, ± contiguous, erect, the lowest rarely shortly pedunculate.
Utricles 3–5.5 mm, ribbed, yellow-green, patent; beak 1.5–2 mm, arcuate; stigmas 3.	Utricles 4–5 mm, **pale yellow-green, darkening above**, ribbed, **mostly empty**; beak 1–1.5 mm, arcuate; stigmas 3 (or 2).	Utricles 3–3.5 mm, ovoid, ± inflated, often dark purple-green on exposed faces; beak 0.5 mm, notched; stigmas 2.

78b × 72 *Carex* × *corstorphinei* Druce

Carex viridula subsp. *oedocarpa* × *C. binervis*   (*not mapped*)

This partially fertile hybrid has the habit of *Carex binervis* with distant female spikes, but the colour of the leaves and the inflorescence is much closer to that of *C. viridula* subsp. *oedocarpa*. It differs additionally from *C. binervis* in its lesser stature, its shorter, and thus apparently stouter, spikes and its abruptly narrowed utricles. From *C. viridula* subsp. *oedocarpa* it can be further distinguished by its shorter lower bracts, its longer male and female spikes and the slightly paler colour of its glumes and utricles.

Carex × *corstorphinei* has been collected from wet grassland in Corrie Fee (NO27, v.c. 90) in 1915 and, more recently, from tall, wet vegetation near Hinksford (SO89, v.c. 39).

Carex viridula subsp. *oedocarpa*	*Carex* × *corstorphinei*	*Carex binervis*
Stems 5–40 cm.	Stems to 40 cm.	Stems 15–150 cm.
Leaves dark yellow-green.	**Leaves yellow-green.**	Leaves dark green above, glossy light green below.
Bracts, except for lowest, exceeding inflorescence.	Bracts up to twice as long as spike.	Bracts 2–4 times as long as spike.
♂ spike 15–20 mm.	♂ spike 17–22 mm.	♂ spike 20–45 mm.
♂ glumes orange-brown to hyaline.	**♂ glumes very pale brown.**	♂ glumes purplish.
♀ spikes 2–4, 7–13 mm, ovoid, ± contiguous, but lowest usually remote.	♀ spikes 3, 17–27 mm, cylindric, distant.	♀ spikes 2–4, 15–45 mm, cylindric, distant, lowermost usually nodding.
♀ glumes brown with green midrib.	**♀ glumes pale brown with paler midrib.**	♀ glumes purple-brown; midrib green or brown.
Utricles 3–4 mm, yellow-green, abruptly narrowed to 1 mm beak.	**Utricles 4–4.5 mm, pale golden brown with darker dots, abruptly narrowed to 1 mm beak.**	Utricles 3.5–4.5 mm, purple-brown or partly green, tapering to 1.5 mm beak.

Carex viridula subsp. *brachyrrhyncha* × *C. saxatilis*
78a × 62
Carex × *corstorphinei* (*Carex viridula* subsp. *oedocarpa*
× *C. binervis*) 78b × 72

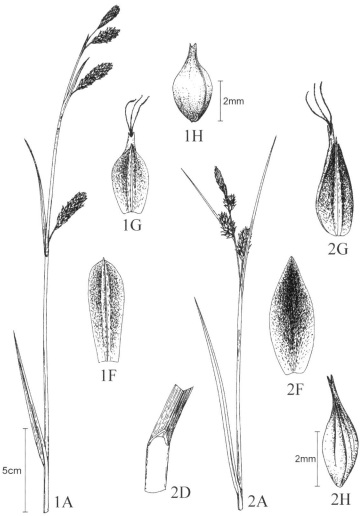

1 *Carex* × *corstorphinei* **2** *Carex viridula* subsp. *brachyrrhyncha* × *C. saxatilis*
A Fertile shoot; **D** Inner face of leaf-sheath and ligule; **F** Male glume; **G** Female
floret; **H** Utricle.

78b *Carex viridula* Michx. subsp. *oedocarpa* (Andersson) B. Schmid
Carex demissa Hornem. in previous editions

Common Yellow-sedge   *Map 78b*

Rhizome short; shoots ± densely tufted; roots pale yellow-brown; scales grey-brown, soon fibrous and decaying completely. *Stems* 5–40 cm, often shorter than leaves, subterete, solid, often slightly curved. *Leaves* 5–35 cm × 1.5–5 mm, rigid, recurved, ± flat with keeled midrib, ± abruptly tapered at apex, dark yellow-green, dying to straw colour and often overwintering; hypostomous; sheaths hyaline or white with green veins, persistent, becoming grey-brown; apex of inner face ± straight; ligule *c.* 1 mm, rounded, notched. *Inflorescence* in upper half of stem but often with solitary distant spike at base; bracts leaf-like, often reflexed, ± flaccid and, except for the lowest, well exceeding inflorescence. *Male spike* 1, 15–20 mm; *male glumes* 3–4 mm, oblong-lanceolate, orange-brown to hyaline, with paler midrib; apex obtuse. *Female spikes* 2–4, ± contiguous but usually the lowest remote, 7–13 mm, ovoid; peduncles short, the lower up to four times as long as the spike, half ensheathed; *female glumes c.* 3.5 mm, ovate, brown with green midrib; apex subacute. *Utricles* 3–4 mm, obovoid, abruptly narrowed into beak, patent, lower deflexed when ripe, yellow-green, faintly ribbed; beak *c.* 1 mm, occupying less than 1/3 of total length, bifid, not or rarely slightly deflexed (although drying may bring about an unequal collapse of the utricle apex, thus deflecting the beak); stigmas 3; nut obovoid, trigonous.   *Fr.* 7–9.

A plant of similar mire habitats to **78a** but usually found where the calcium concentration is less than 30 ppm. It can withstand a higher aluminium concentration than **78a** and is often found on inorganic soils, e.g. gravel of lake margins. It is a constant component of the following NVC communities: **M11** *C. viridula* subsp. *oedocarpa–Saxifraga aizoides* mire, **M12** *Carex saxatilis* mire, **M34** *C. viridula* subsp. *oedocarpa–Koenigia islandica* flush and **M38** *Palustriella commutata–Carex nigra* spring communities. Its ecological tolerance is shown by its occurrence in the following: **M6, M8–10, M15, M17, M23, M29, M31, M32** and **M37** mires, **SD14** dune-slacks, **MG8** mesotrophic grassland, **CG10** and **CG12** calcareous grasslands and **U5, U15** and **U17** montane communities.

Some differences between subsp. *oedocarpa* and subsp. *brachyrrhyncha* are discussed on p. 396; see also the key on p. 75. Small stunted plants can be confused with subsp. *viridula*, but the straight stems, smaller utricles and clustered spikes distinguish that subspecies.

For hybrids see p. 388.

Carex viridula subsp. *oedocarpa* 78b

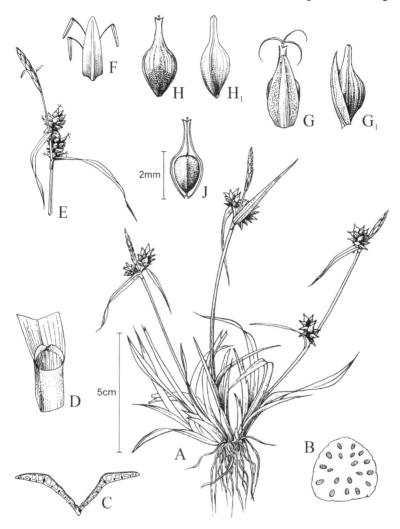

A Fertile shoot; **B** T.S. stem (culm); **C** T.S. leaf; **D** Inner face of leaf-sheath and ligule; **E** Inflorescence; **F** Male floret; **G** Female floret (abaxial view); **G₁** Female floret (side view); **H** Utricle (abaxial view); **H₁** Utricle (side view); **J** Section through utricle, showing nut.

401

M78b Carex viridula subsp. *oedocarpa*

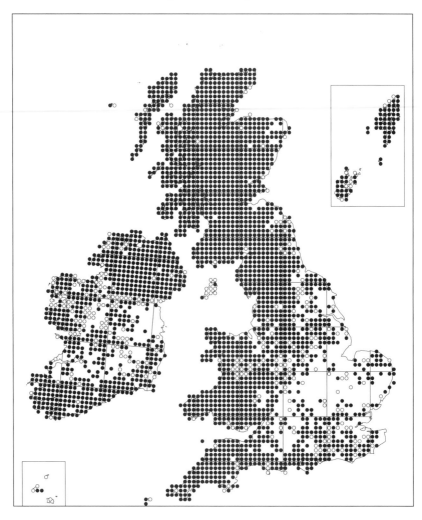

Carex viridula subsp. *oedocarpa* is widespread in Britain, especially common in the N and W (at 0–930 m: Porter & Foley 2002) but less common in the chalk and limestone areas of East Anglia, SE Midlands and S England. In Ireland it is common but scarcer in the central base-rich areas.

Carex viridula subsp. *viridula* *M78c*

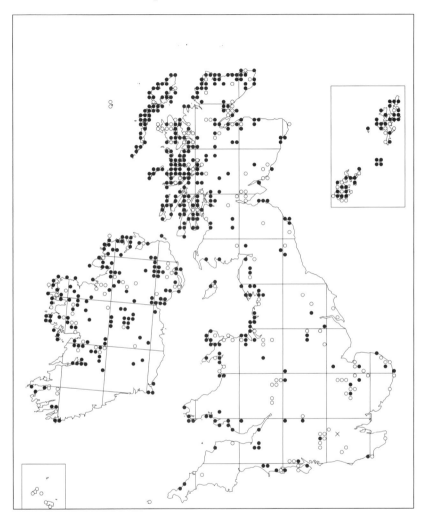

C. viridula subsp. *viridula* var. *viridula* is scattered throughout the British Isles. Var. *pulchella* is more frequent along sea-loch margins in northern Scotland and the coasts of NW Britain and has been recorded along the whole length of our Atlantic seaboard (see Perring & Sell 1968); it is occasionally found inland. Var. *bergrothii* has so far been confirmed only from Counties Clare (H9), Galway (H15/16) and Leitrim (H29) but it could occur in Britain also.

78c *Carex viridula* Michx. subsp. *viridula*

C. serotina Mérat in previous editions

Small-fruited Yellow-sedge   Map 78c

Rhizomes short; shoots 4 to many, tufted; roots pale brown; scales pink- or grey-brown, becoming fibrous. *Stems* 5–40 cm, trigonous-terete, straight. *Leaves* 15–40 cm × 0.8–3.4 mm, rigid, spreading or erect, flat or ± channelled, with midrib rounded beneath, gradually narrowed to a trigonous blunt tip, yellow- to grey-green, becoming pale grey-brown and persistent on dying, sometimes overwintering; hypostomous; sheaths white or hyaline, becoming grey-brown, persistent; apex of inner face straight; ligule *c.* 1 mm, rounded, tubular. *Inflorescence* up to 3/4 length of stem; bracts leaf-like, stiff, spreading but rarely deflexed, much exceeding inflorescence. *Male spike* 1, 5–20 mm, often pushed over by developing female spike; *male glumes c.* 4 mm, oblong-lanceolate, orange-brown with pale or green midrib; apex acute. *Female spikes* 2–5, 5–10 mm, ovoid, upper contiguous and sessile, lower occasionally remote and pedunculate; *female glumes* 1.5–3 mm, ovate, pale yellow-brown, with green midrib and subacute apex. *Utricles* 2–3 mm, obovoid to ellipsoid, abruptly or gradually contracted into beak, faintly nerved, yellow-green, slightly inflated or not; beak 0.25–1 mm, straight or only slightly deflexed, split; stigmas 3; nut obovoid, trigonous. *Fr.* 7–9.

A plant of sparsely vegetated base-rich to base-poor substrates, most commonly kept open by a fluctuating water regime, e.g. around stony lake shores in *Carex rostrata–Calliergonella cuspidata/Calliergon giganteum* mire (**M9**). In freshwater marshes, e.g. where *Juncus acutiflorus* is dominant. Most frequent in maritime situations where salt-laden winds provide calcium and magnesium: dune-slacks with *Sagina nodosa–Bryum pseudotriquetrum* (**SD13**), *Salix repens* communities with *Campylium stellatum* (**SD14**) and *Holcus lanatus* (**SD16**), *Calluna vulgaris–Scilla verna* heath (**H7**) and *Festuca rubra–Plantago* spp. maritime grassland (**MC10**). Also found in estuarine marshes and in sea-lochs, often around the high tide level.

This taxon may usually be separated from the other subspecies by the 1–8 female spikes clustered around a short, sessile to very shortly pedunculate male spike. For distinctions from **78b** subsp. *oedocarpa* see that taxon. Occasionally, especially in inland stations in southern England, the male spike is entirely absent and replaced by a terminal female spike (called *C. oederi* var. *cyperoides* Marsson in British literature but not accepted here). For hybrids see p. 388.   (*Continued on p. 406.*)

Carex viridula subsp. *viridula* 78c

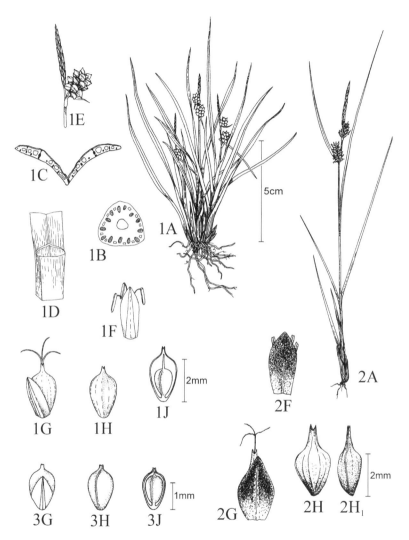

Carex viridula subsp. *viridula* **1** var. *viridula* **2** var. *bergrothii* **3** var. *pulchella*
A Fertile shoot; **B** T.S. stem (culm); **C** T.S. leaf; **D** Inner face of leaf-sheath and
ligule; **E** Upper spikes; **F** Male floret; **G** Female floret; **H** Utricle (abaxial view);
H₁ Utricle (side view); **J** Section through utricle, showing nut.

405

78c *Carex viridula* subsp. *viridula* (continued)

Besides the commonest form (var. *viridula*, described on p. 404) two other forms, which we prefer to treat as varieties, can be distinguished in this subspecies.

Carex viridula subsp. *viridula* var. *bergrothii* (Palmgr.) B. Schmid

Var. *bergrothii* is a larger form within the variation of this subspecies. It is the tallest (typically 25–30 cm) of the segregates of subsp. *viridula* and may resemble an erect form of subsp. *oedocarpa*. It may be readily distinguished from the latter taxon by its upright and straight, not curved, culm, its narrower, erect leaves and, in particular, its ecological preferences. From the other segregates within subsp. *viridula*, var. *bergrothii* may be separated by its relatively large (3.2–4 mm long), conspicuously nerved, inflated, light green utricles that become yellow at maturity; these contrast strongly with the pale reddish-brown glumes with a distinct green midrib. The beak is relatively long (0.6–1.2 mm), straight to slightly deflexed, with a minutely scabrous margin. The 2–3(–4) female spikes are contiguous to often rather distant. It has been found in wet, base-rich fens and lake-shores, usually with a fluctuating water regime (e.g. in turloughs), so far only in W Ireland.

Carex viridula subsp. *viridula* var. *pulchella* (Lönnr.) B. Schmid

Var. *pulchella* is an extreme, usually smaller, form within the range of variation seen in the subspecies; thus it is possible to find plants that are intermediate between this and var. *viridula*.

This is typically a smaller plant, 2–15(–25) cm tall, and may be distinguished from var. *viridula* by its very small, 1.5–2.5 mm long, feebly ribbed grey-green utricles with a beak 0.2–0.6 mm and completely filled by the nut. Unlike in var. *viridula*, the terminal male spike may be shortly stalked (to 10 mm) and the 2–3(–5) female spikes are often distant. The female glumes are dark brown with a pale green midrib. The dark green leaves are 0.5–2 mm wide (narrower than in var. *viridula*) and shorter than the culm. Flowering typically occurs from May to July.

Var. *pulchella* is usually found growing as small isolated tufts in areas of sparse low-growing vegetation found on the upper reaches of saltmarshes, where typical associates include *Eleocharis quinqueflora*, *Festuca rubra* and *Juncus gerardii* (*cf.* **SM19**), and especially on the vertical edges of sandy channels formed by run-off water; also inland on sandy lake-shores.

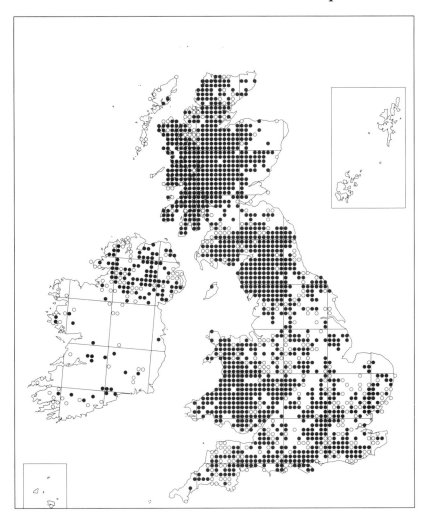

Despite a marked decline since 1950, *Carex pallescens* is still common in upland grassland in Britain, except in the east, and frequent on heavier soils further south. It is also frequent in Northern Ireland but rarely recorded in the Republic, perhaps owing to lack of suitable grasslands.

79 *Carex pallescens* L.

Pale Sedge   *Map 79*

Rhizomes very short; shoots tufted; roots usually dark red-brown; scales brown, often red-tinged. *Stems* 20–60 cm, trigonous, rough on the sharp angles. *Leaves* 15–50 cm × 2–5 mm, soft, with scattered hairs beneath, flat or often keeled, gradually tapering to a fine point, mid-green, grey-brown on dying; hypostomous; sheaths brown, hairy, persistent, with inner face hyaline, hairy; apex concave; ligule *c.* 5 mm, acute or obtuse, tubular. *Inflorescence* up to 1/4 length of stem but usually much shorter; bracts leaf-like, the lower exceeding inflorescence, usually crimped at base, uppermost setaceous. *Male spike* 1, 8–12 mm, often concealed by female spikes; *male glumes* 3–4 mm, obovate-oblong, pale brown, with midrib often darker; apex mucronate. *Female spikes* 2–3, clustered or the lower remote, 5–20 mm, subglobose to ovoid, suberect or lower nodding; peduncles smooth, the lower often longer than spike; *female glumes* 3–4 mm, ovate, pale brown or hyaline with a broad midrib; apex acuminate. *Utricles* 2.5–3.5 mm, ovoid-oblong; apex rounded, not beaked, mid-green, shiny, faintly nerved; stigmas 3; nut ellipsoid, trigonous, stalked.   *Fr.* 6–7.

Carex pallescens is particularly a plant of open *Fraxinus–Sorbus aucuparia–Mercurialis perennis* woodland (**W9**), either on heavy clays, where it may form large clumps, or on better drained soils where water is always available. Possibly a woodland relict in hilly places, where it will grow on open wet ledges and stream-banks with grasses and other sedges, although it is found in Scotland on similar wet grassy ledges at altitudes higher than the local forest limit as a component of the acid grassland vegetation of rocky hillsides (**U4, U5**), being recorded at 790 m in Atholl, E Perth (Foley & Porter 2002).

This species can be confused with little else. The utricle shape and the crimped base of the lower bracts are distinctive; when it is not fruiting, the hairs on the leaf-sheath and underside of the leaf make it easily recognisable. Occasionally subglabrous forms are found, but hairs are always present on the inner face of the leaf-sheath.

No hybrids are known. The putative one collected by John Raven in v.c. 97 and formerly thought to be a hybrid with **71** *C. laevigata* (David 1974) has now been redetermined by A.C.J. and A.O. Chater as that species. The two species are in distinctly different sections of the genus and not at all closely related.

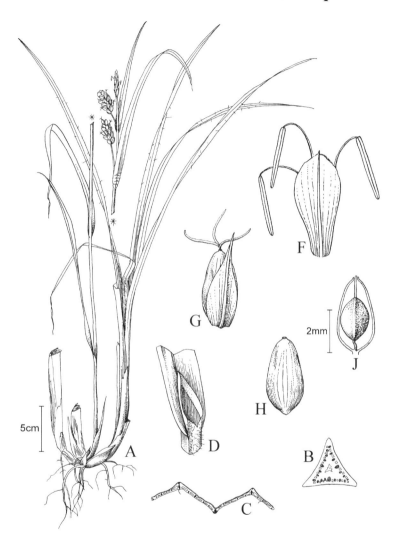

A Fertile shoot; **B** T.S. stem (culm); **C** T.S. leaf; **D** Inner face of leaf-sheath and ligule; **F** Male floret; **G** Female floret; **H** Utricle; **J** Section through utricle, showing nut.

80 *Carex digitata* L.

Fingered Sedge   *Map 80*

Rhizomes short, branched; shoots tufted, of two kinds, apical leafy shoots with overwintering terminal buds and lateral short shoots ending in a flowering stem; roots deep red-brown, wiry, fibrous; scales purplish-crimson. *Stems* 5–25 cm, slender, trigonous-subterete with 2–4 short (up to 2 cm), often setaceous leaves at base. *Leaves* 5–25 cm × 1.5–5 mm, usually sparsely hairy on upper surface, soft, ± flat or slightly keeled, tapered abruptly to a blunt point, light green to bronzy-green, often overwintering; margins rough; hypostomous; sheaths bright crimson (even in very young shoots), with the inner face herbaceous; apex concave, soon splitting; ligule 0.5–1.5 mm, rounded. *Inflorescence* 1/5 to 3/4 length of stem, the lowest branch 1 cm or more from the female spike above; bracts to 10 mm, sheathing for 3 mm. *Male spike* 1, overtopped by uppermost female spike; *male glumes* 5 mm, red-brown with a pale midrib and hyaline margin; apex rounded or even emarginate. *Female spikes* 1–2 cm, 5–10-flowered, with peduncle < 6 mm; *female glumes* 3–4.5 mm, obovate, purplish-crimson; apex obtuse or emarginate. *Utricles* 3–4.5 mm, obovoid, greenish-brown, pilose; beak almost 0, truncate; stigmas 3; nut obovoid, trigonous, stalked.   *Fr.* 4–6.

C. *digitata* is found in open woodland or scrub and amongst rocks and on stabilised screes of dry hard chalk and limestone, e.g. in the *Gymnocarpium robertianum–Arrhenatherum* association (**OV38**), in crevices in limestone pavement, and occasionally in the open shade of *Fraxinus–Acer campestre–Mercurialis perennis* woodland, *Teucrium scorodonia* sub-community (**W8g**). It seeds freely in lightly shaded habitats but dies out if the canopy becomes too dense. New plants can appear from dormant seed if the ground is disturbed (Foley & Porter 2002).

C. *digitata* flowers earlier than **81** C. *ornithopoda*, often in early April, and can withstand more shaded conditions when growing occasionally in open woodland or scrub. The purplish glumes ± equalling the utricles and the separation of the branches of the inflorescence distinguish this species from C. *ornithopoda*, in which the utricles project well beyond the straw-coloured glumes and the branches all spring from nearly the same point. C. *digitata* is usually larger in all its vegetative parts and the sheaths of even the youngest shoots are deeply tinged with crimson.

C. *digitata* hybridises with C. *ornithopoda* in mainland Europe.

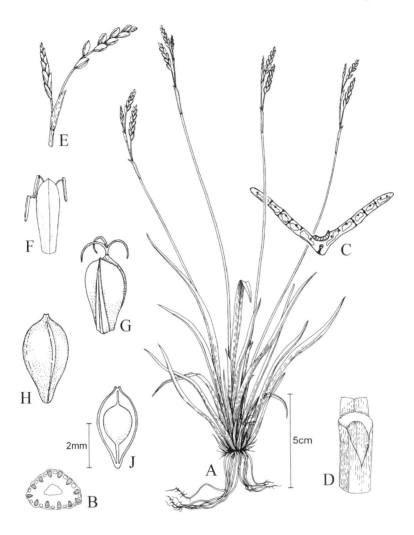

A Fertile shoot; **B** T.S. stem (culm); **C** T.S. leaf; **D** Inner face of leaf-sheath and ligule; **E** Upper spikes; **F** Male floret; **G** Female floret; **H** Utricle; **J** Section through utricle, showing nut.

M80 *Carex digitata*

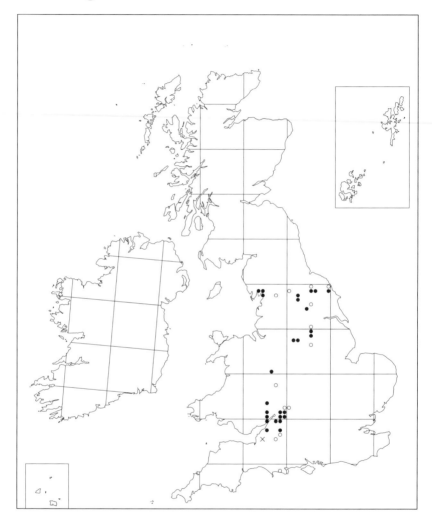

Carex digitata is very local but more widely spread than *C. ornithopoda*, extending from Somerset and Dorset to Westmorland and NE Yorks. See also David (1978a). Studies of allozyme variation (Tyler 2002, 2003) show our populations to have originated from glacial survivals found in the Caucasus and E European Russia, reaching Britain via Finland and Scandinavia.

Carex ornithopoda M81

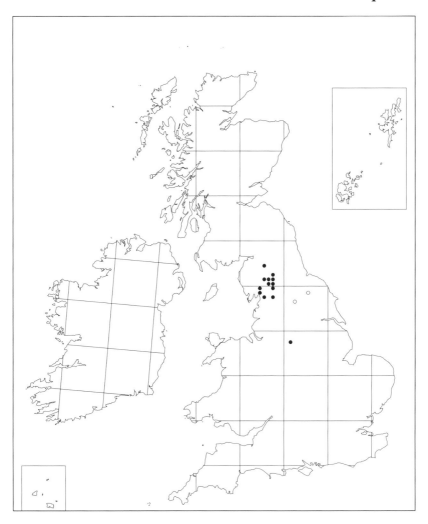

Carex ornithopoda occurs from near sea level to 600 m on Long Fell,
Westmorland (Porter & Foley 2002). Very local: in Derbyshire, Yorkshire,
Cumberland and Westmorland (Corner & Roberts 1989; David 1980a; Porter
& Roberts 1997).

81 *Carex ornithopoda* Willd.

Bird's-foot Sedge   *Map 81*

Rhizomes short, much branched; shoots tufted, of two kinds, apical leafy shoots with overwintering terminal buds and lateral short shoots ending in a flowering stem; roots wiry, fibrous, deep brown; scales deep red-brown, becoming fibrous. *Stems* 5–20 mm, slender, trigonous-subterete with 2–4, short (up to 1 cm), often setaceous leaves at the base. *Leaves* 5–20 cm × 1–3 mm, soft, ± flat or slightly keeled, tapered abruptly to a blunt point, light or mid green, often overwintering; margins rough; hypostomous; sheaths orange- to dark crimson-brown, becoming fibrous, with the inner face herbaceous; apex concave, soon splitting; ligule 0.5–1 mm, rounded. *Inflorescence* 1/8–1/10 length of stem, compact, ± digitate, with spikes arising within 5 mm; bracts glumaceous, sheathing for < 2 mm. *Male spike* 1, 5–8 mm, few-flowered, overtopped by the lower female spikes and appearing lateral; *male glumes c.* 2.5 mm, obovate, red-brown with a pale midrib and hyaline margin; apex acute or mucronate. *Female spikes* 2–3, 5–10 mm, 2–4(–5)-flowered, ± sessile or the lowest with peduncle to 3 mm; *female glumes* 2–2.5 mm, obovate, pale orange-brown with hyaline margin; apex obtuse or ± acute, often erose. *Utricles* 2–3 mm, obovoid to narrowly pyriform, yellow-green to brown, pilose, but hairs may fall as they age; beak almost 0, truncate; stigmas 3; nut obovoid, trigonous, stalked.   *Fr.* 5–6.

A plant of dry, well-drained Carboniferous limestone grasslands, particularly *Sesleria caerulea–Galium sterneri* associations (**CG9**), or in crevices in limestone pavement; occasionally in the open shade of limestone woodland, e.g. *Fraxinus–Acer campestre–Mercurialis perennis, Teucrium scorodonia* sub-community (**W8g**). In some Cumbrian sites and in Derbyshire it grows in *Festuca ovina–Agrostis capillaris–Thymus poylytrichus* grassland (**CG10**) with *Carex flacca* and *Helianthemum nummularium* (I. Taylor in Wigginton 1999). Also, in the Eden Valley (v.c. 70), it occurs on acid red Permian sandstone where it is flushed with lime-laden water (Corner & Roberts 1989).

Closely related to, and sometimes confused with, **80** *C. digitata*: for the differences see that species. It hybridises with *C. digitata* in mainland Europe but the hybrid is not recorded for Britain.

414

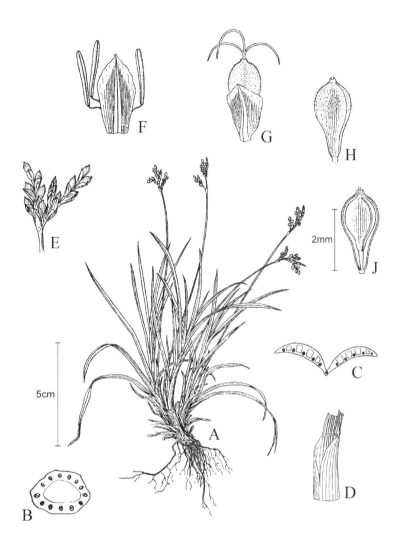

A Fertile shoot; **B** T.S. stem (culm); **C** T.S. leaf; **D** Inner face of leaf-sheath and ligule; **E** Upper spikes; **F** Male floret; **G** Female floret; **H** Utricle; **J** Section through utricle, showing nut.

82　*Carex humilis* Leyss.

Dwarf Sedge　　　　　　　　　　　　　　　　　　　*Map 82*

Rhizomes shortly creeping, becoming very tufted, often dying out in the centre; shoots densely fasciculate at branch tips; roots purple-brown; scales red-brown, persisting as fibres. **Stems** 2–10 (rarely to 15) cm, slender, often arcuate or flexuous, subterete, solid, often hidden by leaves. **Leaves** up to 20 cm × 1–1.5 mm, rough, stiff, arcuate, at first flat, later becoming channelled, tapering from base to a fine trigonous point, dark green, pale purple-brown on decay, overwintering; hypostomous; sheaths white with green veins, becoming orange- and red-brown, persistent, eventually fibrous and clothing rhizome; inner face hyaline; apex concave; ligule 0.5–1 mm, rounded. **Inflorescence** up to 3/4 length of stem; bracts with sheath 3–8 mm, glumaceous, hyaline or pale brown, almost enclosing female spike. **Male spike** 1, 10–15 mm; **male glumes** 5–7 mm, elliptic-oblanceolate, reddish- or purple-brown with very broad hyaline margin and pale midrib; apex obtuse or subacute. **Female spikes** 2–4, distant, 4–10 mm, fusiform, with 2–4 flowers only; peduncles 1–2 mm, ensheathed; whole spike ± enclosed by hyaline bracts; **female glumes** 2–3 mm, obovate to broadly elliptic, clasping utricle and appearing narrower, red-brown, hyaline at edges and base; apex obtuse, often mucronate. **Utricles** *c.* 2.5 mm, obovoid, pyriform, trigonous, hispid; beak almost 0, truncate; stigmas 3; nut ± ellipsoid, trigonous, stalked.

Fr. 4–7.

　　C. humilis is a species of short turf in species-rich limestone and chalk grasslands of *Festuca ovina–Helichtotrichon pratense* (**CG2**) and *Bromopsis erecta* associations (**CG3**), usually but not exclusively found on S-, SW- and W-facing slopes. Over limestone it can occur in grazed pastures and on field margins. It fruits freely, but regeneration from seed (distributed by ants) and colonisation of new areas have rarely been reported (Foley & Porter 2002).

　　There is no other *Carex* species that *C. humilis* could be confused with in calcareous grassland except perhaps depauperate non-fruiting **86** *C. montana*, the soft leaves of which contrast with the rigid, arcuate leaves of *C. humilis*. The latter is easily overlooked because of its narrow, *Festuca*-like leaves growing intermingled with *Festuca ovina* itself. The lemon-yellow anthers can be seen well within the tuft in early spring. Both glumes and utricles drop towards the end of the season. In winter *C. humilis* may be recognised as a characteristic red-brown turf.

　　No hybrids are known.

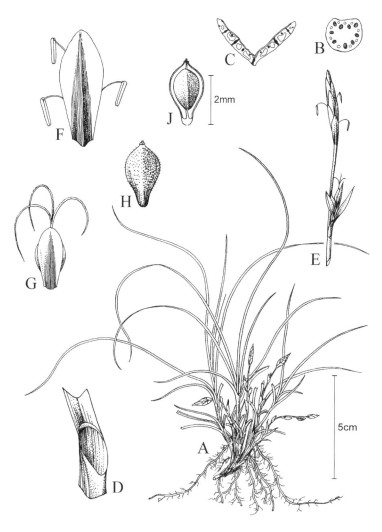

A Fertile shoot; **B** T.S. stem (culm); **C** T.S. leaf; **D** Inner face of leaf-sheath and ligule; **E** Upper spikes; **F** Male floret; **G** Female floret; **H** Utricle; **J** Section through utricle, showing nut.

M82 Carex humilis

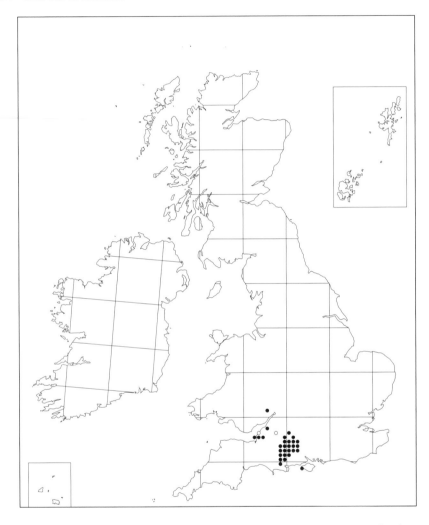

Carex humilis, although nationally scarce and possibly now confined to ancient cleared areas in only eight vice-counties, can be locally abundant, as on the Dorset and S Wiltshire downs. Rare in N Somerset, N Wiltshire, S Hampshire, W Gloucs and Herefordshire and found on the Isle of Wight in 2006. See also David (1979a, 1993).

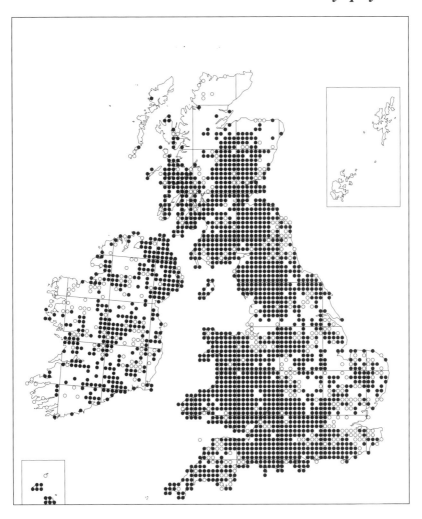

Carex caryophyllea is found throughout mainland Britain and Ireland but is local N of the Great Glen, rare in the Outer Hebrides and absent from Orkney and Shetland. It reaches 765 m on Knock Fell, Westmorland (Foley & Porter 2002).

83   *Carex caryophyllea* Latourr.

Spring-sedge   *Map 83*

Rhizomes shortly creeping; shoots loosely tufted; roots dark brown or purple-brown; scales mid brown, often shiny, soon becoming fibrous. **Stems** 2–30 cm, trigonous, leafy below. **Leaves** up to 20 cm × 1.5–3 mm, recurved, smooth on upper surface, shiny, ± flat, tapered ± abruptly to a short trigonous point, mid green, sometimes overwintering; hypostomous; sheaths herbaceous, becoming dark brown and fibrous, with inner face hyaline, soon decaying; apex straight to concave; ligule 1–2 mm, obtuse, with free margin very narrow, entire. **Inflorescence** 2–4 cm; lower bracts often leaf-like, the lowest with a sheath 3–5 mm, upper glumaceous. **Male spike** 1, 10–15 mm, clavate when in flower, oblanceoloid in fruit; **male glumes** 4–5 mm, oblanceolate-elliptic, mid brown to reddish-brown, hyaline towards base, with pale green midrib; apex ± acute or mucronate. **Female spikes** 1–3, 5–12 mm, ovoid, ± contiguous, clustered at base of male spike, sessile or with peduncles ensheathed; **female glumes** 2–2.5 mm, broadly ovate, mid brown to reddish-brown, with midrib wide at base, green, excurrent into an obtuse, mucronate or often attenuate apex. **Utricles** 2–3 mm, obovoid-ellipsoid, ± trigonous, with two prominent lateral ribs, tomentose, green; beak *c.* 0.2 mm, notched; stigmas 3; nut obovoid-ellipsoid trigonous.   **Fr.** 5–7.

 C. caryophyllea is a plant of wide ecological tolerance. It is found in most calcicolous grasslands, in particular *Festuca ovina–Carlina vulgaris* (**CG1**) and *Festuca–Helictotrichon pratense* (**CG2**) communities in S and E England, and is widespread in the western half of Britain, scattered in mesotrophic grasslands, e.g. *Anthoxanthum–Geranium sylvaticum* (**MG3**), *Cynosurus–Centaurea nigra* (**MG5**) and siliceous grassland of the *Festuca ovina–Agrostis capillaris–Galium saxatile* type (**U4**); also in maritime sites enriched with calcium and magnesium from salt-laden winds, e.g. on sea cliff-tops where *Festuca rubra* is a main component (e.g. **MC8, MC9, MC11**), and sand-dune grasslands (**SD8, SD14**).

 It can be distinguished from small **72** *C. binervis* by its blackish-brown fibrous sheaths and flatter, shiny leaves. It is similar to **85** *C. ericetorum* and, to a lesser extent, to **87** *C. pilulifera* (see those species for differences).

 Carex caryophyllea hybridises with *C. pilulifera* and *C. ericetorum*, but neither hybrid has so far been reported from the British Isles.

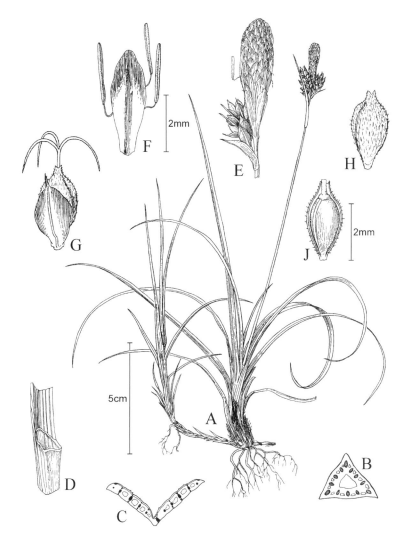

A   Fertile shoot; **B**   T.S. stem (culm); **C**   T.S. leaf; **D**   Inner face of leaf-sheath and ligule; **E**   Upper spikes; **F**   Male floret; **G**   Female floret; **H**   Utricle; **J**   Section through utricle, showing nut.

84 *Carex filiformis* L.[*]

Downy-fruited Sedge   Map 84

Rhizomes long-creeping, often very slender, sometimes forming dense patches; shoots 2–3 per tuft; roots pale; scales red-brown, shiny, with sharp points, persistent. **Stems** 20–50 cm, rough above, trigonous, slender. **Leaves** 15–40 cm × 1.5–2 mm, rough, flat, gradually tapering to a fine point, ± glaucous, grey-brown on decay, often overwintering; hypostomous; sheaths red or red-purple, becoming brown, often persistent and fibrillose on splitting, with inner face hyaline; apex concave; ligule 1–2 mm, acute to obtuse, tubular, entire. **Inflorescence** 1/6 or less of stem length; upper bracts setaceous, lower leaf-like, ± equalling inflorescence, the lowest not or shortly sheathing. **Male spikes** 1–2, 12–25 mm; **male glumes** 4–5 mm, elliptic-ovate, red-brown with paler midrib and hyaline margin; apex ± acute, often apiculate. **Female spikes** 1–2, contiguous, 5–14 mm, oblong-ovoid to subglobose; **female glumes** 2–3 mm, ovate to subrotund, purple- or red-brown with pale midrib; apex acute or lowermost in spike mucronate. **Utricles** 2–3 mm, subglobose or pyriform, trigonous, densely tomentose, green; beak 1–0.2 mm, notched; stigmas 3; nut obovoid or pyriform, trigonous. **Fr.** 6–7.

Carex filiformis is a local plant of fairly rich pastures with a substantial availability of calcium (**MG6** *Lolium* associations, though not listed by Rodwell 1992) and of damper meadows, roadsides and rough ground, especially on gravelly soils which are continuously irrigated and contain other sedges (e.g. *C. panicea*, *C. flacca* and *C. nigra*) with *Molinia caerulea*, *Filipendula ulmaria* and *Potentilla erecta* (David 1983).

The small, very hairy utricles of *C. filiformis* distinguish it from any other British sedge of comparable size; the leaf-like bracts of this species separate it from **83** *C. caryophyllea*. Vegetatively it may be similar to **67** *C. flacca* and other glaucous sedges of its habitat (e.g. **100** *C. nigra*), but the shiny, red basal leaf-sheaths and scales and the brown, persistent inner face of the leaf-sheath, usually showing some fibrillae, serve to distinguish it.

The limited distribution of this species in Britain is not easy to explain; it is possibly more widespread than recorded, as it is difficult to detect when not in flower.

A hybrid with *C. flacca* has been described from France.

---

[*]*Carex tomentosa* L. in Edition 2

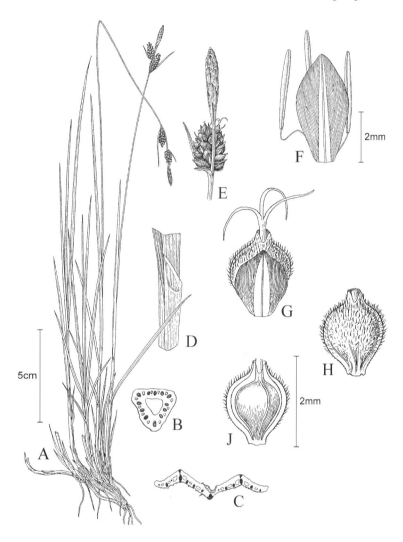

A Fertile shoot; **B** T.S. stem (culm); **C** T.S. leaf; **D** Inner face of leaf-sheath and ligule; **E** Upper spikes; **F** Male floret; **G** Female floret; **H** Utricle; **J** Section through utricle, showing nut.

M84 Carex filiformis

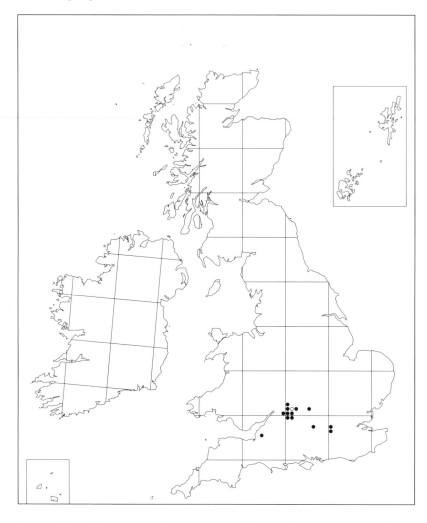

Carex filiformis is recorded for Surrey, Middlesex, where it became extinct in the 1960s (Kent 1976), Oxfordshire, E Gloucs and N Wilts; it was found in N Somerset in 2003. See also David (1983, 1993).

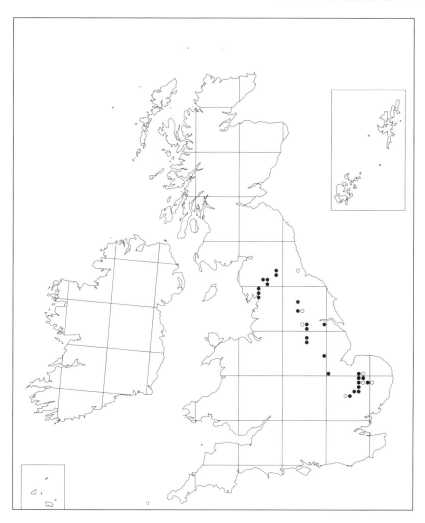

Carex ericetorum is a local species on the East Anglian chalk and on the limestones of Lincolnshire, Derbyshire, Yorks, Durham and Westmorland. Destruction of habitat and unsuitable management have led to a loss of sites since 1970 and to its inclusion in the **Red Data List** (Cheffings & Farrell 2005). See also David (1981a).

85 *Carex ericetorum* Pollich

Rare Spring-sedge   *Map 85*

Rhizomes shortly creeping; shoots tufted, often forming a close mat; roots dark brown or purple-brown; scales deep brown or blackish-brown, becoming fibrous. **Stems** 2–20 cm, bluntly trigonous, ± leafless or with 3 very short leaves at base. **Leaves** up to 15 cm × 1.5–4 mm, often recurved, papillose and feeling somewhat rough on upper surface, shiny, ± flat, tapered ± abruptly to a short trigonous point, mid green to yellow-green, serrulate with a narrow scarious margin, sometimes overwintering; hypostomous; sheaths herbaceous, becoming brown and fibrous, with inner face hyaline; apex straight; ligule less than 1 mm, rounded, with free margin minute, ± entire. **Inflorescence** (1.5–)2–3 cm; bracts glumaceous, the lowest scarcely sheathing. **Male spike** 1, 10–15 mm, narrowly cylindrical; **male glumes** 2–3 mm, oblong, deep chestnut to purple-brown, with margin scarious, fringed, and apex rounded. **Female spikes** 1–3, ± contiguous, 5–12 mm, ovoid, erect, sessile; **female glumes** 2–2.5 mm, rounded, deep chestnut, darkening through purple-brown to black, with margin scarious, fimbriate. **Utricles** 2–3 mm, subglobose-trigonous, tomentose, pale to rich green, becoming brown at apex; beak very short; stigmas 3; nut subglobose.   **Fr.** 4–6.

In dry grazed grassland on infertile calcareous soils in the following communities: *Festuca ovina–Helictotrichon pratense* grassland (**CG2**), *Festuca–Hieracium pilosella–Thymus* spp. grassland (**CG7**) and *Sesleria caerulea–Galium sterneri* grassland (**CG9**).

Often with **83** *C. caryophyllea*, from which it is not easy to separate by vegetative characters. When it is in flower or fruit the deeper, often purplish glumes, which in the female spike are obtuse with a broad scarious and usually fimbriate margin, provide an immediate identification.

Hybrids with *C. caryophyllea*, *C. pilulifera* and *C. montana* are reported, but not from Britain.

Carex ericetorum is a **Red Data List** species in Great Britain; *Status*: **Vulnerable** (Cheffings & Farrell 2005).

426

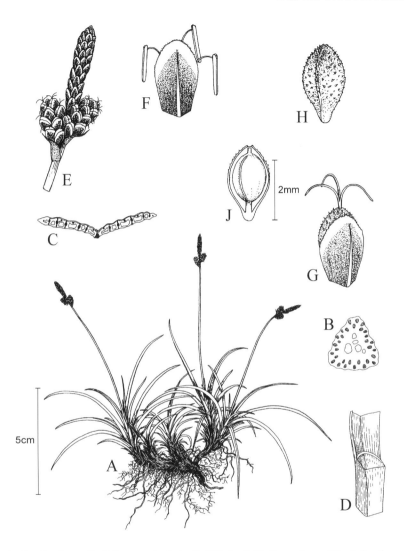

A Fertile shoot; **B** T.S. stem (culm); **C** T.S. leaf; **D** Inner face of leaf-sheath and ligule; **E** Inflorescence; **F** Male floret; **G** Female floret; **H** Utricle; **J** Section through utricle, showing nut.

86 *Carex montana* L.

Soft-leaved Sedge   *Map 86*

Rhizomes creeping, woody, much branched; clone often dying out in the centre and thus forming a ring of shoots tufted at apex; roots woody, purple-brown; scales red-brown, becoming fibrous at base. ***Stems*** 10–40 cm, slender, rough at top, flaccid, trigonous or often with 6 angles toward base, ± solid, leafless or with few short leaves at base. ***Leaves*** 10–35 cm × 1.5–2 mm, soft, flat, gradually drawn out to a slender point, sparsely hairy on upper surface near the tip and edges, becoming glabrous, light to mid green, grey-brown and persisting on dying; hypostomous; sheaths dark red-brown to almost bright red, ribbed, becoming fibrous and densely clothing rhizome, with inner face hyaline, soon decaying; apex concave; ligule *c.* 1 mm, obtuse, with free margin minutely fimbriate. ***Inflorescence*** 1–2 cm, very congested; bracts glumaceous or lowest setaceous, the lowest scarcely sheathing. ***Male spike*** 1, 10–20 mm; ***male glumes*** 4–5 mm, oblanceolate or broadly elliptic, red-brown, with pale midrib; apex acute or ± mucronate. ***Female spikes*** 1–4, 6–10 mm, ovoid, with a few lax flowers, clustered beneath male spike, erect, sessile; ***female glumes*** 3–5 mm, broadly ovate or obovate, reddish-black with pale midrib and hyaline margin; apex obtuse or even retuse, mucronate. ***Utricles*** 3.5–4 mm, obovoid-pyriform, bluntly trigonous, tapered to a stout stalk, densely hispid, lightly ribbed, brown or blackish on exposed face; beak almost 0, notched; stigmas 3; nut obovoid, trigonous, stalked.   ***Fr.*** 5–6.

C. montana is a plant of rough grassy locations, usually overlying limestone or mineral-rich igneous rocks and attributed to *Festuca ovina–Helictotrichon pratense* (**CG2**) and *Festuca–Agrostis capillaris–Thymus polytrichus* grasslands (**CG10**). This apparent association with base-rich soils may be misleading, as studies in Wales (Kay & John 1994) suggest it grows on similar sites where non-calcareous drift overlies the calcareous bedrock.

The soft, mid to pale green, sparsely hairy leaves and mat-forming rhizomes (which may die out in the middle, leaving a ring of sedge tufts) distinguish this species from the single-tufted **87** *C. pilulifera*, with stiff, papillose leaves. If the slender flowering stems lie amongst the leaves, it may resemble that species, but the mucronate female glumes and large pyriform utricles of *C. montana* are sufficient to identify it with certainty.

Carex montana is reported to hybridise with *C. ericetorum*, *C. flacca* and *C. pilulifera* but these hybrids are not recorded for Britain.

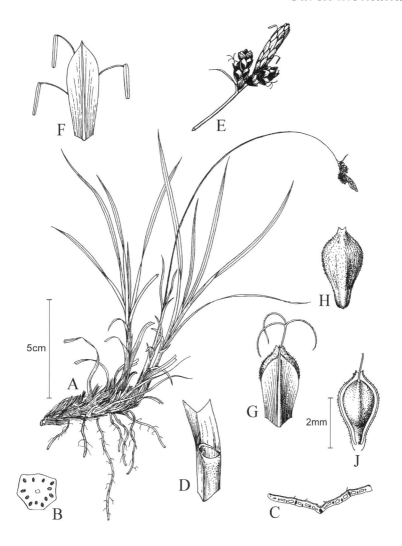

A Fertile shoot; **B** T.S. stem (culm); **C** T.S. leaf; **D** Inner face of leaf-sheath and ligule; **E** Inflorescence; **F** Male floret; **G** Female floret; **H** Utricle; **J** Section through utricle, showing nut.

M86 *Carex montana* L.

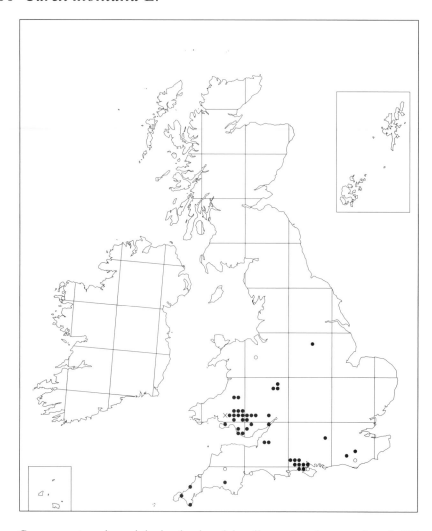

Carex montana is mainly lowland and locally scattered across S and SW England, as far north as Derbyshire, and in Wales (David 1977); it reaches an altitude of 560 m in Carmarthenshire (Foley & Porter 2002). Not recorded for Ireland.

Carex pilulifera M87

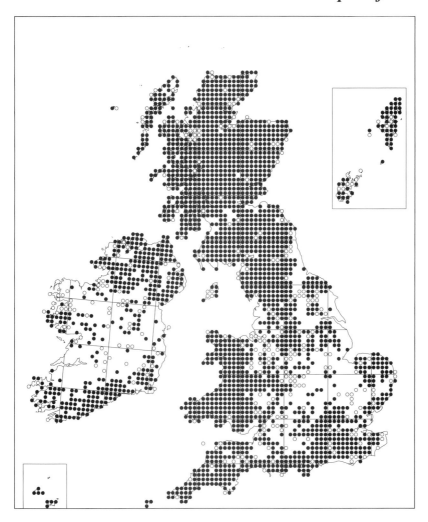

Carex pilulifera is found throughout Britain but is more frequent in acid, sandy regions in N England and common in the hill country of Wales and Scotland, where it ascends to 1140 m (Porter & Foley 2002). In Ireland it is less frequent in the centre.

87 *Carex pilulifera* L.

Pill Sedge   *Map 87*

Rhizomes short; shoots densely tufted, often decumbent; roots purple-brown; scales brown, soon becoming fibrous. *Stems* 8–30 cm, ± rough above, wiry, sharply trigonous below spike, often arcuate and elongating in fruit. *Leaves* 5–20 cm × 1.5–2 mm, rough above, ± flat, papillose on upper surface, ± abruptly tapered to a short trigonous point, dull, yellow-green or mid green, pink-brown and persistent on decay, overwintering; hypostomous; sheaths pale red-brown or wine-red, becoming fibrous, with inner face hyaline; apex straight; ligule 0.5–1 mm, rounded, with free margin minutely fimbriate. *Inflorescence* 1–4 cm; spikes clustered; bracts leaf-like or the upper setaceous, rarely exceeding inflorescence, the lowest not sheathing. *Male spike* 1, (6–)8–15 mm; *male glumes* 3.5–4 mm, oblanceolate-elliptic, brown or chestnut, hyaline towards margin; with pale midrib; apex acute to acuminate. *Female spikes* 2–4, 4–8 mm, ovoid or subglobose, erect, sessile; *female glumes* 3–3.5 mm, broadly ovate, red-brown, hyaline towards margin; midrib green, becoming yellow; apex acute. *Utricles* 2–3.5 mm, obovoid-ellipsoid, downy at least at apex, deep green; beak 0.3–0.5 mm, notched; stigmas 3; nut obovoid, trigonous.   *Fr.* 6–7.

  C. pilulifera is a plant of leached, skeletal, sandy, loamy or peaty soils with a low base content and a pH range usually between 4.5 and 6.0. It is found on various *Festuca–Agrostis* grasslands (**CG10, CG11, CG12**), in *Nardus–Galium saxatile* pasture (**U5**) and with *C. bigelowii* (**U7, U10**); also in lowland calcifugous grasslands (**U3**), open *Calluna*–moss/lichen heaths (**H12–17**) and the *Alchemilla alpina–C. pilulifera* sub-community of **H18**, often taking advantage of heath-fires to re-establish itself and spread.

  C. pilulifera varies in length of bracts and female glumes. It is distinguished from both **83** *C. caryophyllea* and **85** *C. ericetorum* by its tufted habit, reddish sheaths, dull, arcuate leaves and wiry, often incurved stems. The closely related **86** *C. montana*, also tufted and with wiry stems, differs in its more obviously creeping rhizome, softer (not rough) leaves and purple-brown glumes. Further, *C. pilulifera* is a plant of more acid soils than any of the other species.

  Carex pilulifera hybridises with *C. caryophyllea*, *C. ericetorum* and *C. montana* but these hybrids have not been recorded for Britain or Ireland.

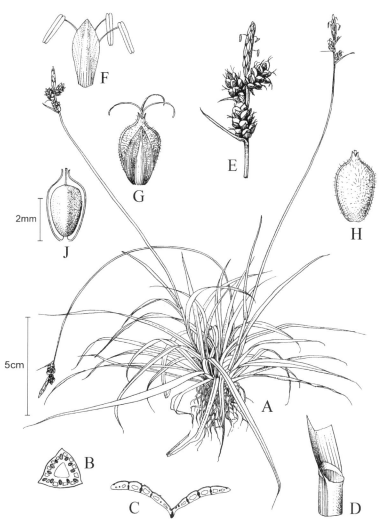

A Fertile shoot; **B** T.S. stem (culm); **C** T.S. leaf; **D** Inner face of leaf-sheath and ligule; **E** Inflorescence; **F** Male floret; **G** Female floret; **H** Utricle; **J** Section through utricle, showing nut.

88 *Carex atrofusca* Schkuhr

Scorched Alpine-sedge   *Map 88*

Rhizomes shortly creeping; shoots in loose tufts; roots yellowish; scales pale brown, soon decaying. *Stems* 5–35 cm, trigonous. *Leaves* 2–12 cm × 2–5 mm (those of sterile shoots often less than 1 mm), soft, ± flat or slightly keeled, stem-leaves abruptly tapered to a short trigonous point, those of sterile shoots more gradually tapered to a finer trigonous point 1–3 cm long, mid green, very rarely glaucous; hypostomous; sheaths pale with green veins, becoming pale yellow-brown, soon decaying, with inner face hyaline and apex concave, soon splitting; ligule 1–2.5 mm, obtuse. *Inflorescence* 1/6 to 1/4 length of stem; lower bracts narrowly leaf-like, shorter than the spike, the lowest with a sheath 5–15(–25) mm, upper glumaceous. *Male spike* 1, 5–10 mm, broadly ellipsoid; *male glumes* 3.5 mm, ovate-elliptic, dark red-brown, rarely pale, with pale or green midrib; apex acute to acuminate. *Female spikes* 2–4, 5–12 mm, clustered, lowest rarely distant, ovoid-globose, nodding; peduncles smooth, up to 3 times as long as spike, half-ensheathed; *female glumes* c. 3 mm, oblanceolate, purple- or red-black with pale, thin or often indistinct midrib; apex acuminate. *Utricles* 4–4.5 mm, narrowly obovoid or ellipsoid, purple-black; beak 0.3 mm, notched; stigmas 3; nut ± ellipsoid, trigonous, stalked.   *Fr.* 7–9.

A rare plant of micaceous stony flushes between 540 and 1000 m (on Beinn Heasgarnich, v.c. 88), although now known no lower than 680 m, on Ben Lawers, v.c. 88 (Porter & Foley 2002). In *Carex–Saxifraga* mires in which the dominant species are *C. viridula* subsp. *oedocarpa* and *S. aizoides* (**M11**) and *C. saxatilis* (**M12**) with other sedges (such as *C. dioica, C. nigra, C. panicea* and *C. pulicaris*), *Juncus alpinoarticulatus, J. biglumis, J. castaneus, Pinguicula vulgaris, Thalictrum alpinum, Blindia acuta* etc. Often in rock-flushes on steep slopes and then protected by a small rock or tuft of *Nardus stricta* or *Festuca ovina* (R.E. Thomas in Wigginton 1999).

C. atrofusca could be confused with **92** *C. atrata*, but the position of the male florets, the stiffer and distinctly glaucous leaves and the rock-ledges habitat of the latter are sufficient to distinguish them.

No hybrids of *C. atrofusca* are recorded.

Carex atrofusca is a **Red Data List** species in Great Britain; *Status*: **Vulnerable** (Cheffings & Farrell 2005).

434

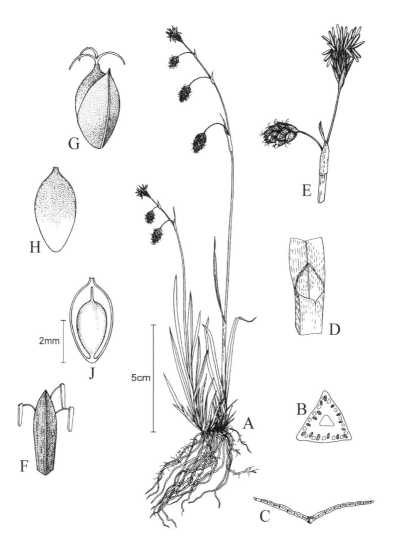

A Fertile shoot; **B** T.S. stem (culm); **C** T.S. leaf; **D** Inner face of leaf-sheath and ligule; **E** Upper spikes; **F** Male floret; **G** Female floret; **H** Utricle; **J** Section through utricle, showing nut.

M88 Carex atrofusca

Carex atrofusca has been found only on the Breadalbanes in mid Perth and in Westerness and Argyll. The record of the species on Rum (Heslop Harrison 1945) is unconfirmed and is ecologically unlikely (Pearman & Walker 2004).

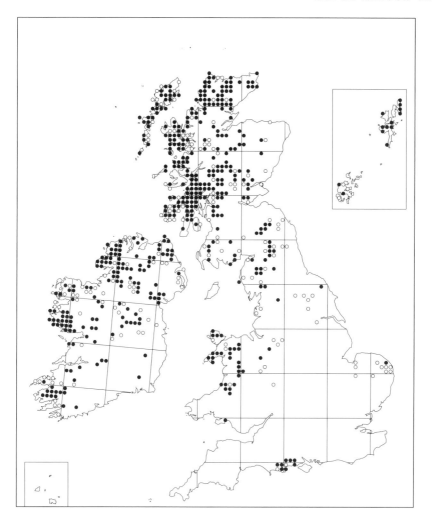

Carex limosa occurs mainly in N Wales, N England and Scotland, becoming frequent in the blanket mires of the west. Also in the S Dorset–Hampshire valley mires and formerly on the wet heaths of E Norfolk, where it was last seen in 1974 (R. Ellis pers. comm.). In Ireland it grows mainly in the north and west.

437

89 *Carex limosa* L.

Bog-sedge *Map 89*

Rhizomes often far-creeping, lying amongst mosses, partly ascending; shoots loosely tufted, initially decumbent, slender; roots yellow, felted; scales brown, persistent. In winter only wiry rhizomes with few leaves survive. **Stems** 10–40 cm, ± rough, slender, trigonous, striate, often decumbent at base. **Leaves** 15–40 cm × 1–2.5 mm, ± rough, thin, keeled, gradually tapered to a fine, rough point, pale green to bluish-grey-green, often rich brown on decay; hypostomous; sheaths red-flushed, becoming brown or red-brown, persistent, with inner face hyaline, persistent; apex concave; ligule 1–2 mm, obtuse. **Inflorescence** *c.* 1/6 length of stem; bracts leaf-like, greyish-green, lowest about as long as spike, not sheathing or with sheath less than 5 mm. **Male spike** 1, 10–25 mm; **male glumes** 3–4 mm, broadly lanceolate, red-brown, often with a green midrib; apex ± acute, apiculate. **Female spikes** 1–3, 7–20 mm, with up to 20 flowers, usually nodding; peduncles up to 40 mm, slender, smooth; **female glumes** 5–5.5 mm, slightly wider than utricle, ovate, brown or reddish-purple, with a green midrib; apex acute to aristate. **Utricles** 3–3.5 mm, obovoid to broadly ellipsoid, compressed, strongly ribbed, grey-glaucous; beak 0.5 mm, truncate; stigmas 3; nut obovoid, trigonous. **Fr.** 6–9.

Carex limosa grows in and around pools in very wet blanket and valley mires, with *Sphagnum cuspidatum, S. denticulatum, Menyanthes trifoliata, Eriophorum angustifolium* and *Utricularia* spp. (**M1**), and with *Carex rostrata, C. lasiocarpa*, other *Carex* spp., *Calliergonella cuspidata* and *Calliergon giganteum* (**M9**); also in more mesotrophic mires with *Carex rostrata, Sphagnum fallax* etc. (**M4**). Usually found below 450 m, but ascending to 830 m on Meall nan Tarmachan, v.c. 88 (Porter & Foley 2002).

Similar in appearance to **91** *C. magellanica*, but that species forms more solid clumps, with at least some of the leaves 2 mm or more wide, smooth except at the tip and of a clearer (apple) green; also, the ligule is longer, with a wider free margin than in *C. limosa*, and the lowest bract is the same colour as the leaves and usually overtops the inflorescence. In fruit the two are easy to separate, since *C. magellanica* has narrower female glumes with ± cusped apices that expose more of the pale apple green, ± beakless utricles; in *C. limosa* the silvery-glaucous utricles are ± obscured by the wider glumes.

Hybrids with *C. magellanica* and *C. rariflora* are recorded in mainland Europe but not so far in Britain or Ireland.

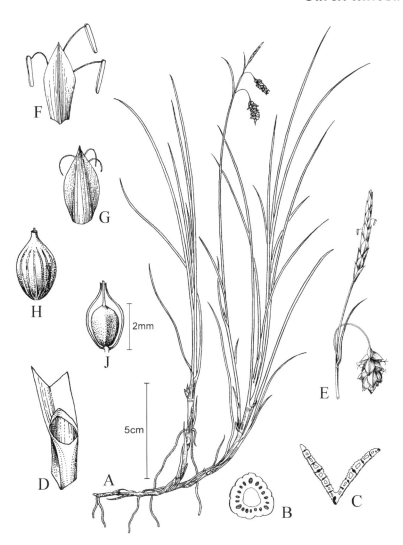

A Fertile shoot; **B** T.S. stem (culm); **C** T.S. leaf; **D** Inner face of leaf-sheath and ligule; **E** Upper spikes; **F** Male floret; **G** Female floret; **H** Utricle; **J** Section through utricle, showing nut.

90   *Carex rariflora* (Wahlenb.) Sm.

Mountain Bog-sedge   *Map 90*

Rhizomes shortly creeping, often producing a close carpet of single shoots; roots yellow, felted; scales red-brown. *Stems* up to 20 cm, mostly smooth, trigonous, ± solid. *Leaves* up to 15 cm × 1–2 mm, with *c.* 9 veins, glaucous to grey-green, deeply keeled, often strongly incurved at the tip; hypostomous; sheaths becoming fibrous, with inner face hyaline, turning brown; apex concave; ligule *c.* 2 mm, obtuse, with free margin *c.* 1 mm. *Inflorescence* 1/3–1/5(–1/9) length of stem; lower bracts narrow, 8–12 mm, shorter than inflorescence, with sheath up to 5 mm. *Male spike* 1, 8–12 mm; *male glumes* *c.* 4 mm, oblong-ovate, dark brown, with apex obtuse, mucronate. *Female spikes* usually 2, rarely 3, with up to 8 flowers; *female glumes* 3–4 mm, dark purple or chocolate-brown, oblong-ovate, with apex obtuse, mucronate. *Utricles* 3–4.5 mm, ellipsoid, narrower and shorter than female glumes, strongly ribbed, markedly tapered at either end; stigmas 3; nut ellipsoid, trigonous, stalked.   *Fr.* 7–8.

A rare and local sedge forming a characteristic association with *C. canescens*, *C. echinata*, *C. bigelowii*, *C. aquatilis*, *Sphagnum papillosum*, *S. russowii* and *Viola palustris* (**M7**) on wet slopes of oligotrophic peat, or, more often, on a fixed bank of silt in the headwaters of a mountain stream just before the gradient steepens (David 1980b). Found between 790 and 1125 m, the latter height on Ben Macdui, v.c. 94 (Porter & Foley 2002). It is very shy-flowering in some seasons, and this may have concealed its presence, and certainly its abundance, in a number of localities.

In Britain *C. rariflora* is separated from its two allies **89** *C. limosa* and **91** *C. magellanica* by the different altitudes that they normally inhabit as well as by its form (fewer flowers on the spike and much smaller size).

The species hybridises with both *C. limosa* and *C. magellanica* but neither hybrid has been recorded from Britain.

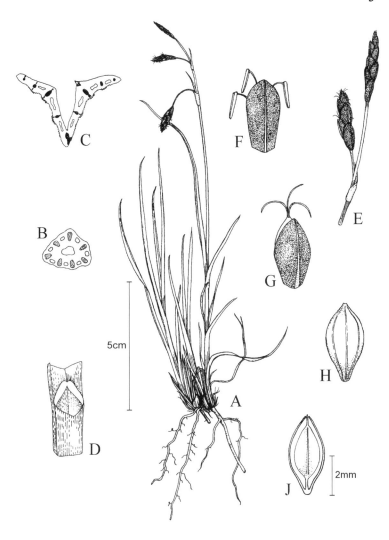

A Fertile shoot; **B** T.S. stem (culm); **C** T.S. leaf; **D** Inner face of leaf-sheath and ligule; **E** Upper spikes; **F** Male floret; **G** Female floret; **H** Utricle; **J** Section through utricle, showing nut.

441

M90 Carex rariflora

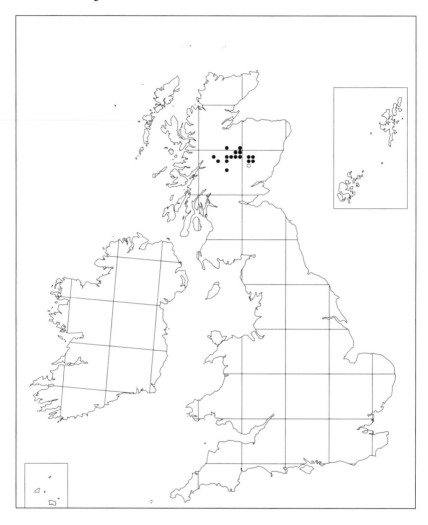

Carex rariflora, which is found in the E Central Highlands but also occurs very rarely in Breadalbane, is confined to high tablelands where snow lies late. See also David (1980b). A record from South Uist (Heslop Harrison 1945) has been shown to be unsubstantiated (J.E. Raven in Preston 2004).

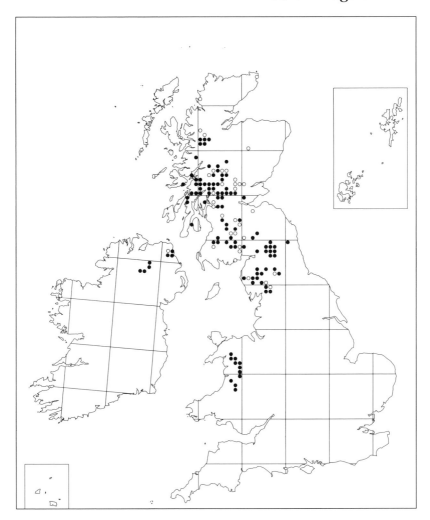

Carex magellanica is scattered from the Lake District to North Uist and West Sutherland; also in North Wales (v.cc. 46, 47, 48 and 49), but very local. In Ireland found only in Tyrone, Londonderry and Antrim.

91   *Carex magellanica* Lam.*

Tall Bog-sedge   *Map 91*

Rhizomes shortly creeping, often ascending; shoots loosely tufted; roots yellow, felted; scales shiny, red-brown, persistent. *Stems* 12–40 cm, usually smooth, trigonous, ± solid. *Leaves* up to 25 cm × 1.5–4 mm, soft, thin, with *c.* 15 veins, ± flat, rough on the margins towards the abruptly tapered tip, young ones with a waxy bloom, soon becoming mid or apple green; hypostomous; sheaths becoming red-brown, persistent, with inner face hyaline; apex concave; ligule 4–5 mm, acute, tubular. *Inflorescence c.* 1/5 length of stem; bracts leaf-like, yellow-green fading to brownish, lower usually exceeding inflorescence, the lowest sheathing to 1 mm or less. *Male spike* 1, 10–20 mm; *male glumes* 5–6 mm, lanceolate-elliptic, pale red-brown, hyaline at margins; apex acute to acuminate. *Female spikes* 2–4, 5–18 mm, ovoid, lax and up to 10(–15)-flowered, upper ± erect at first, becoming, as lower, nodding; peduncles smooth, 5–20 mm; *female glumes* 3–5(–6.5) mm long, narrower than the utricle, lanceolate, caducous, red- or purple-brown with a slightly paler midrib; apex acuminate or cusped. *Utricles* 3–3.5 mm, ovoid-globose, ± compressed, ± patent, faintly ribbed, pale apple green; beak ± absent; stigmas 3; nut ellipsoid, trigonous. *Fr.* 6–7.

    C. magellanica is a plant more of bryophyte lawns than of pools, with *Sphagnum cuspidatum* and *S. fallax* (**M1, M2**), since, unlike **89** *C. limosa*, it cannot tolerate standing water. Its favourite habitat is a level or slightly sloping ledge near the crest of a moor, wet but, being close to the watershed, neither inundated nor subject to much if any movement of the water; this is why it is frequently found on county boundaries, as these often run along a watershed. It reaches 685 m on Ben Lui, v.c. 88 (Porter & Foley 2002).

    C. magellanica is rarer than **89** *C. limosa*, but may have been overlooked or confused with that species: for differences see *C. limosa*.

    Hybrids between this species and *C. rariflora* are recorded for Sweden but not for Britain or Ireland.

    C. magellanica is protected in Northern Ireland under Schedule 8 of the Wildlife Order (Northern Ireland) 1985.

C. magellanica Lam. is bipolar in distribution and was first described from South American material. Plants in the Northern Hemisphere are often treated as subsp. *irrigua* (Wahlenb.) Hiitonen, but the differences are small.

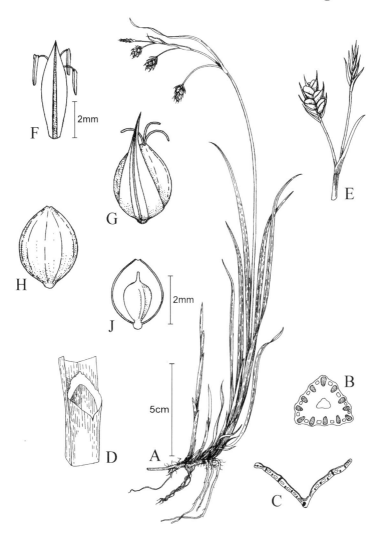

A Fertile shoot; **B** T.S. stem (culm); **C** T.S. leaf; **D** Inner face of leaf-sheath and ligule; **E** Upper spikes; **F** Male floret; **G** Female floret; **H** Utricle; **J** Section through utricle, showing nut.

92　*Carex atrata* L.

Black Alpine-sedge　　　　　　　　　　　　*Map 92*

Rhizomes short; shoots tufted; roots pale brown; scales brownish or reddish-purple, persistent. *Stems* (25–)30–55 cm, thick, rigid, trigonous, solid. *Leaves* 15–30 cm × 2–6 mm, ± flat or slightly keeled, abruptly tapered to a rough apex, mid green to deep blue-green; hypostomous; sheaths dark brown, often wine-red, persistent, with inner face hyaline (reflecting as silvery-green), persistent; apex straight; ligule 2–3 mm, obtuse to acute. *Inflorescence* 1/8 to 1/6 length of stem; bracts leaf-like, lower exceeding inflorescence, the lowest not or scarcely sheathing. *Spikes* 3–5, ovoid, 8–20 mm, clustered in an inclined head, becoming ± nodding in fruit, terminal spike female at top, male at base, lower female only; lower peduncles rough, as long as spike. *Male glumes* 4.5–6 mm, ovate-elliptic, red-black with pale midrib; apex acute or rounded. *Female glumes* 3.5–4.5 mm, ovate-elliptic, purple or reddish-black with pale midrib; apex ± acute. *Utricles* 3–4 mm, obovoid-ellipsoid, compressed at edges, green; beak 0.3–0.5 mm, slightly notched; stigmas 3; nut obovoid, trigonous.　　　　　　　　　　　　*Fr.* 7–9.

　　C. atrata is found on steep ungrazed cliff-ledges, usually where there is calcareous veining. Thus it is found on cliffs associated with the *Luzula sylvatica–Geum rivale* tall-herb community (**U17**) in Scotland, northern England and N Wales. In Scotland it also grows in *Salix lapponum–Luzula sylvatica* scrub (**W20**) and the *Dryas–Silene acaulis* ledge community (**CG14**) with *C. norvegica*, *C. vaginata* and other rare calcicolous species; usually above 700 m, reaching 1095 m on Ben Lawers, v.c. 88 (Foley & Porter 2002).

　　It occasionally grows with **88** *C. atrofusca*, with which, at first glance, it can be confused. When sterile, the creeping rhizome of *C. atrofusca* (although that may not always be obvious) is usually sufficient to separate it, as are the pale, often yellow-brown leaf-sheaths and rhizome-scales. The lack of a creeping rhizome can separate *C. atrata*. The lack of a terminal male spike and the bract exceeding the inflorescence will distinguish *C. atrata* from **102** *C. bigelowii*, with which it can also grow. Vegetatively, the lack of obvious rhizomes and the tufted shoots will distinguish *C. atrata*.

　　Hybrids between *C. atrata* and *C. norvegica* are known but are not recorded for Britain.

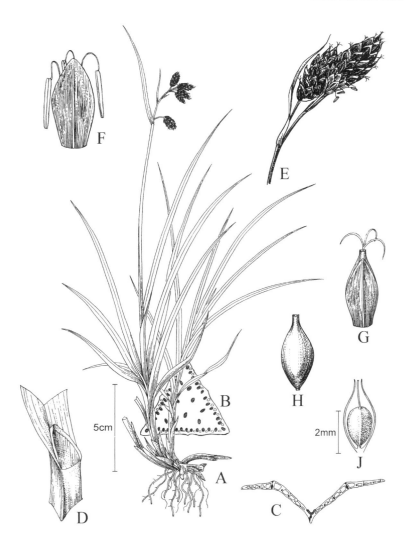

A Fertile shoot; **B** T.S. stem (culm); **C** T.S. leaf; **D** Inner face of leaf-sheath and ligule; **E** Upper spikes; **F** Male floret; **G** Female floret; **H** Utricle; **J** Section through utricle, showing nut.

447

M92 Carex atrata

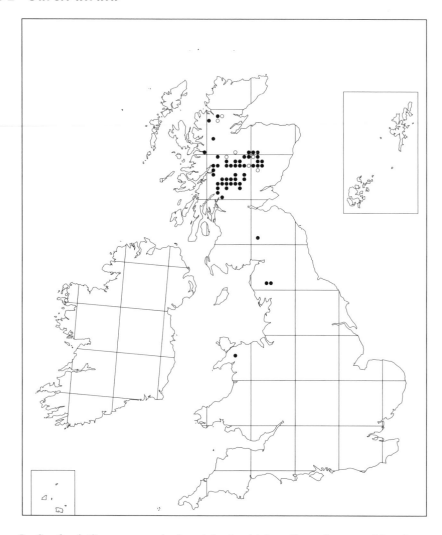

In Scotland *Carex atrata* is found in the higher Grampians, reaching just westwards into E Westerness; it also occurs at one site in Peeblesshire. In England it is found in the Lake District (v.c. 69) and in Wales in Caernarvonshire (v.c. 49). It is absent from Ireland.

Carex buxbaumii was previously known from three single localities in Scotland (in v.cc. 96, 97 and 98; mapped above). In 2006 it was recorded from Skye (v.c. 104, not included above) and it has been possibly overlooked in other sites. First discovered in our islands in Ireland in 1835 around Lough Neagh (v.c. H39), where it has long ago disappeared through drainage.

93 *Carex buxbaumii* Wahlenb.

Club Sedge   *Map 93*

Rhizomes shortly creeping; shoots single or in small tufts; roots pale yellow-brown; scales shiny, red-orange-brown, occasionally blackish, persistent. *Stems* 30–70 cm, rigid, sharply trigonous. *Leaves* 25–60 cm × 1.5–2.0 mm, ± flat or keeled, gradually tapered to a fine rough point, grey-green to glaucous, with margins ± inrolled; hypostomous; sheaths red- or orange-brown, with inner face hyaline-brown, persistent, fibrillose; ligule *c.* 3 mm, acute. *Inflorescence c.* 1/4 length of stem; upper bracts glumaceous/setaceous, lower bracts leaf-like, ranging from equalling inflorescence to slightly longer, scarcely sheathing. *Spikes* 2–5, contiguous or remote, 7–15 mm, erect, the terminal female at top, male at base, the lower spikes female; peduncles 2–12 mm, rough. *Male glumes* 4 mm, lanceolate-elliptic, reddish-black with pale midrib; apex acute. *Female glumes* 3–5 mm, ovate-triangular, asymmetrical, dark red-brown with pale midrib; apex acuminate or aristate. *Utricles* 3–4.5 mm, indistinctly ribbed, pale green, oblong-ovoid, slightly tapering with ± straight sides, ± inflated; apex obtuse; beak absent or very short, notched; stigmas 3; nut ellipsoid, trigonous.   *Fr.* 7–8.

    C. buxbaumii is a sedge of mesotrophic *C. rostrata–Calliergonella cuspidata/Calliergon giganteum* mires (**M9**), but also often associated with dwarf shrubs, *Erica tetralix* and *Myrica gale* (**M15**), although it does less well when *Myrica* invades (P. Batty in Wigginton 1999).

    Superficially like **100** *C. nigra*, but the three stigmas, shape of female glume and terminal female florets distinguish it (although very occasionally *C. nigra* has a few female flowers at the top of the male spike). Vegetatively, distinguished from **56** *C. lasiocarpa* by the acute ligule and less tapered leaf.

    Plants from Lough Neagh formerly identified as *C. hartmanii* Cajander, a plant of C Europe and Fennoscandia, are a form of *C. buxbaumii*. A northern taxon, *C. buxbaumii* subsp. *alpina* (Hartman) Liro, which has similar utricles to *C. hartmanii* but shorter, acute but not acuminate male glumes, could occur in alpine Scotland; it also has all spikes cylindrical, whilst in typical *C. buxbaumii* the terminal spike is clavate and the others ovoid or obovoid.

    No hybrids between *C. buxbaumii* and other species in this section have been recorded; the hybrids recorded with *C. acutiformis* and *C. nigra* are probably aberrant forms of those species.

    Carex buxbaumii is a **Red Data List** species in Great Britain; *Status*: **Vulnerable** (Cheffings & Farrell 2005).

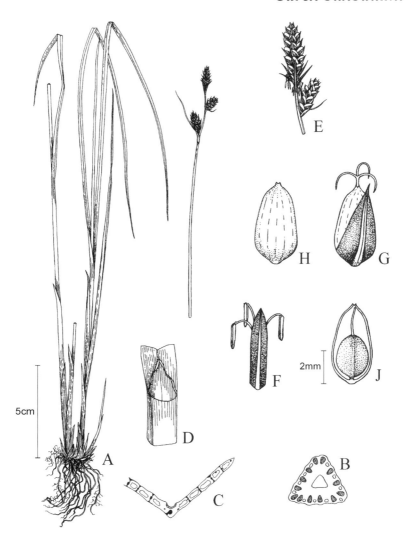

A Fertile shoot; **B** T.S. stem (culm); **C** T.S. leaf; **D** Inner face of leaf-sheath and ligule; **E** Upper spikes; **F** Male floret; **G** Female floret; **H** Utricle; **J** Section through utricle, showing nut.

94 *Carex norvegica* Retz.

Close-headed Alpine-sedge   *Map 94*

Rhizomes short; shoots tufted; roots pale yellow-brown; scales brown, red-brown or blackish, becoming fibrous in decay. *Stems* 6–30(–40) cm, trigonous. *Leaves* 5–20 cm × 1.5–3 mm, mid green, not glaucous, ± flat or keeled, gradually tapered to a short, fine trigonous point; hypostomous; sheaths white, green-veined, becoming red, red-brown or brown, persistent, with inner face hyaline; apex straight; ligule 0.5–1 mm, obtuse. *Inflorescence* a compact, terminal cluster of 1–4 subglobose, erect spikes, the terminal one of which is female at the top and male at the base (often only to be detected by the presence of white filaments), the rest being female; upper bracts glumaceous, lower bracts leaf-like, exceeding inflorescence, the lowest not or scarcely sheathing. *Male glumes* 2–2.5 mm, lanceolate-elliptic, dark red-brown with pale midrib; apex acute. *Female glumes* 1.5–2 mm, ovate, red-black with narrow, pale midrib; apex acute. *Utricles* 2–2.5 mm, obovoid-ellipsoid, minutely papillose, greenish-brown; beak 0.25 mm, slightly notched; stigmas 3; nut ellipsoid, trigonous.   *Fr.* 7–8.

A very rare plant of wet ledges and stony flushes in N-facing corries where snow lies late, on base-rich mountains, usually between 550 and 900 m but reaching 1095 m on Ben Lawers (v.c. 88) (G. Rothero, pers. comm.). It occurs with other sedges, grasses and dwarf-heath species, e.g. in the *Dryas–Silene acaulis* ledge community (**CG14**) and in *C. viridula* subsp. *oedocarpa–Saxifraga aizoides* mire (**M11**), especially where the vegetation is more open.

Sometimes confused with **100** *C. nigra* or, more likely, **101** *C. bigelowii*, but these species never form such dense tufts, have far-creeping rhizomes and two stigmas, and also have their terminal spike entirely male (although aberrant forms of these species do very rarely have female flowers at the top of the male spike).

The species hybridises in Sweden with *C. atrata*, but this hybrid has not so far been reported from Britain.

452

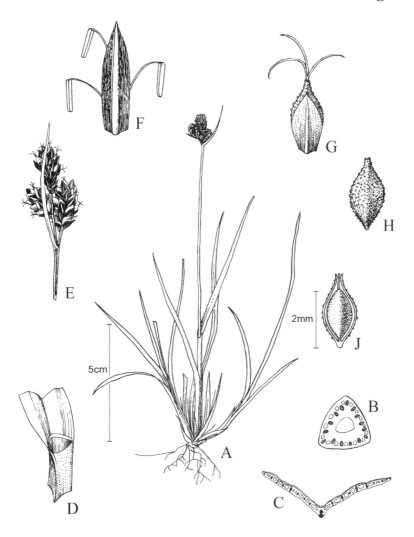

A Fertile shoot; **B** T.S. stem (culm); **C** T.S. leaf; **D** Inner face of leaf-sheath and ligule; **E** Inflorescence; **F** Male floret; **G** Female floret; **H** Utricle; **J** Section through utricle, showing nut.

M94 Carex norvegica

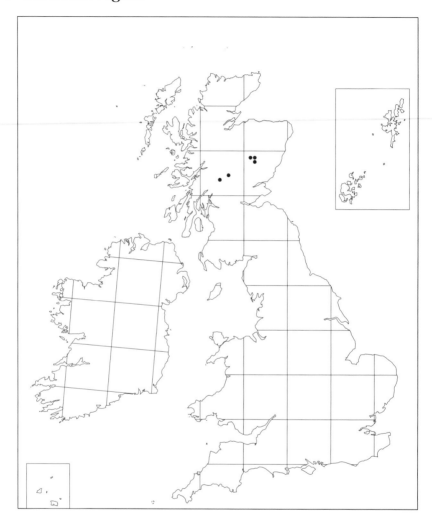

Carex norvegica is a local plant in Mid Perth, Angus and S Aberdeen. Records from Rum and unlikely sites on N and S Uist (Heslop Harrison 1945) are unsubstantiated (Pearman & Walker 2004; J.E. Raven in Preston 2004).

The following eight species (**95** *C. recta* Boott, **96** *C. salina* Wahlenb., **97** *C. aquatilis* Wahlenb., **98** *C. acuta* L., **99** *C. trinervis* Degl., **100** *C. nigra* (L.) Reichard, **101** *C. elata* All. and **102** *C. bigelowii* Torr. ex Schwein.) belong to that section of subgenus *Carex* which has two stigmas, reddish- or purplish-brown/black glumes with green or pale midribs, usually ceasing below the apex, and green, biconvex, minutely papillate utricles with a short or almost absent beak. In the main, their geographical distributions overlap and ecologically they have similar requirements. They form partially fertile hybrids that back-cross, leading commonly to introgression between the species, and in all species there are forms showing one or more characters of another close species.

In the space available here justice cannot be done to all these varieties and forms (many of which have formal Latin names) and the figures in this book illustrate the type varieties. *Carex nigra*, the most ubiquitous species of all (both geographically and ecologically), has, understandably, the greatest variation in response to habitat conditions. Kükenthal (1909) lists ten varieties (under *C. goodenowii* J. Gay) and many forms of each which are the result of habitat influence or crossing with other closely related species. Dune-slack forms (var. *stolonifera* (Hoppe) Asch.), e.g. in the *Potentilla anserina–Carex nigra* community (**SD17**) at Morfa Dyffryn (v.c. 48), have short, wide, often arcuate leaves, as do plants growing around hill sheep-shelters, perhaps reacting to higher phosphate in the soil. A spreading but tufted form (var. *tornata* (Fr.) Kük.) in calcareous mires, e.g. Tarn Moss, Malham (v.c. 64), has wide, rigid leaves and a thick dense spike. Those in mineral-poor mires have slender, channelled leaves (var. *strictiformis* (L.H. Bailey) Kük.). An ecotype in which the rhizomes grow upwards seeking aerated peat and thereby form substantial tussocks (var. *subcaespitosa* Kük.) can be found in stagnant mires, e.g. Sunbiggin Tarn (v.c. 69), where it was recorded by Holdgate (1955) erroneously as *C. juncella* (Fr.) Th. Fr., a Scandinavian species lacking creeping rhizomes.

Faulkner (1972) studied the cytology (i.e. the number and morphology of the chromosomes) of British and some European members of this group, in particular of a number of populations of '*C. recta*' from both Scotland and Scandinavia. He suggested that this taxon may best be regarded as of hybrid origin, although Scottish plants do not show the variation seen in those from Scandinavia either in morphology or chromosome number. Nevertheless, he postulated that, on the evidence of both plant and chromosome morphology,

(*Continued on p. 458.*)

Dominant parental traits within the *Carex nigra* group

Because of their tendency to vary morphologically between their two parents, all sedge hybrids can be difficult to identify and even more difficult to describe definitively. Such difficulties are exacerbated in the *Carex nigra* group, where hybrids are usually at least partially fertile and back-crossing and introgression frequently occur, thus adding to the range of forms which may be found. The following table aims to pick out the main characters by which the parent species are identified and thus to show which species may be involved in a putative hybrid.

Character	*C. acuta*	*C. aquatilis*	*C. bigelowii*	*C. elata*	*C. nigra*	*C. recta*
Habit	creeping, tufted	creeping, tufted	creeping, but shoots few	densely tussocky	creeping, tufted	creeping, tufted
Height (cm)	to 120	to 110	to 30	to 100	7–45(–70)	to 110
Angle of (trigonous) stem	acute	obtuse to subterete	acute	acute	obtuse	obtuse
Leaf width (mm)	3–10	3–5	2–7	3–6	1–3(–5)	3–7
Stomata	below	mainly above	below	below	mainly above	on both sides
Colour of upper surface of leaf	green	glaucous	glaucous	glaucous	glaucous	mid green to yellow-green
Colour of lower surface of leaf	glaucous	dark green or yellow-green	glaucous	glaucous	glaucous	mid green to yellow-green
Ligule length (mm) and shape	4–6, obtuse	4–15, obtuse/acute	1–2, acute	5–10, acute	1–3, rounded	2–4, obtuse

(*Continued on opposite page.*)

(Continued from previous page.)

Character	C. acuta	C. aquatilis	C. bigelowii	C. elata	C. nigra	C. recta
Inflorescence/stem length ratio	1/6–1/4	1/6–1/3	1/8–1/5	c. 1/7	1/6–1/4	1/6–1/3
Relationship of lower bract to inflorescence	exceeding	exceeding	shorter	much shorter	± equalling	exceeding
♂ spikes (no.)	2–4	2–4	1, rarely 2	1–3	1–2	(1–)2–5(–6)
♂ spike length (mm)	20–60	5–50	5–20	15–50	5–30	10–45
♀ spikes (no.)	2–4	2–5	2–3	2–3	1–4	2–6
♀ spike length (mm)	30–100	15–70	5–15	15–40	7–50	20–80
Utricle length (mm)	2–3.5	2–3	2.5–3	3–4	2.5–3.5	2–3.5

Characters unique to one species:

Carex nigra – male spikes dimorphic, one very much smaller than the other.

Carex acuta – female glumes often patent; inner face of leaf-sheath membranous and colourless.

Carex elata – leaf-sheaths fibrillose, yellow-brown; early fruiting (May/June).

Carex bigelowii – male spike clavate; stem very rigid, often curved.

Carex aquatilis – stem brittle; lower bract ensheathing inflorescence.

Carex recta – female glumes at bottom of spike often aristate.

Carex salina – female glumes all aristate; awn ± 1 mm long, toothed.

N.B. Carex salina is known only from a single site, with no hybrids recorded, and therefore not in the table.

457

95–102 *Carex nigra* group (*Continued from p. 455.*)

the parents of '*C. recta*' are *C. aquatilis* and *C. paleacea* Wahlenb., the latter a species of similar pan-boreal distribution but not yet found in Britain or Ireland. Because we find seed set in *C. recta*, it has been treated as a species (Jermy *et al.* 1982; Stace 1997). Hylander (1966) considered that the Scandinavian plants (as collected by Faulkner) were *C. vacillans* Drejer (a hybrid of *C. nigra* with *C. paleacea* that can similarly be fertile), different from the North American *C. recta* of Boott.

For the most recent work on this intriguing problem we must look to North America and to J. Cayouette and colleagues in Canada. In extensive cytological studies on this group they showed that hybridisation is common, the morpholgy of the offspring often being very variable, making them difficult to separate from back-crosses with one or other of their parents (Cayouette & Morisset 1985, 1986b). Complementary studies on isoenzyme analysis (Standley 1990) confirmed the *C. recta* parentage suggested above. In the same paper Standley analysed another pan-boreal maritime species, *C. salina* (found for the first time in our area in 2004: Dean *et al.* 2005), and showed it to be *C. paleacea* crossed with *C. subspathacea* Wormskjold, another pan-boreal species of hybrid origin so far not recorded for the British Isles. A detailed study of the *C. recta/paleacea* complex in Britain has been made by Dean (2006).

Though *C. recta* and *C. salina* both produce good seeds, their pollen is only partly fertile and they do have the disturbed meiosis characteristic of true hybrids (Cayouette & Morisset 1986a), a situation common to other hybrids in this section. For these reasons we see them as 'stabilised hybrids' (after Cayouette *et al.*) and treat them here as species. It has been suggested (J. Cayouette pers. comm.) that this 'stabilisation' may represent a successful means of speciation in a group of species sharing a large number of genes.

Hybrids within the section

Those below, recorded in our area, are discussed on the following pages.

C. recta × *C. aquatilis* (**95** × **97** *C.* × *grantii* A. Benn.)
C. recta × *C. nigra* (**95** × **100** *C.* × *spiculosa* Fr.)
C. aquatilis × *C. acuta* (**97** × **98**)
C. aquatilis × *C. nigra* (**97** × **100** *C.* × *hibernica* A. Benn.)
C. acuta × *C. nigra* (**98** × **100** *C.* × *elytroides* Fr.)
C. elata × *C. acuta* (**101** × **98** *C.* × *prolixa* Fr.)
C. elata × *C. nigra* (**101** × **100** *C.* × *turfosa* Fr.)
C. bigelowii × *C. aquatilis* (**102** × **97** *C.* × *limula* Fr.)
C. bigelowii × *C. nigra* (**102** × **100** *C.* × *decolorans* Wimm.)

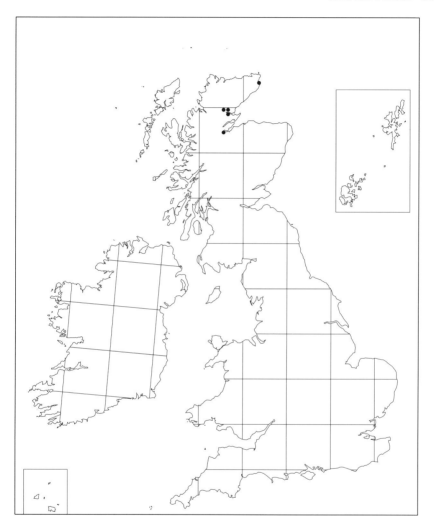

Carex recta is a very local species of estuarine or lower riverine localities in
NE Scotland (Eastererness, E Ross, E Sutherland and Caithness).

95 *Carex recta* Boott

Estuarine Sedge   *Map 95*

Rhizomes often far-creeping; shoots tufted; roots pale purple-brown; scales red-brown, often blackened, persistent. *Stems* 30–100 cm, stiff, trigonous. *Leaves* up to 130 cm × 3–7 mm, mid green to yellow-green, ± flat or weakly keeled, rough on upper surface, on margins and on keel beneath, lower culm leaves and those of sterile shoots gradually tapering to a flat, stiff point; amphistomous; sheaths herbaceous, becoming brown or tinged wine-red, persistent, with transverse septa distinct and inner face hyaline, ± persistent; ligule 2–4 mm, obtuse, tubular. *Inflorescence* 1/6 to 1/3 length of stem; bracts leaf-like with purplish auricles, at least the lower exceeding inflorescence. *Male spikes* 1–(2–5)–6, 10–45 mm, lower pedunculate; *male glumes* 4–6 mm, oblanceolate-elliptic, hyaline at margins; apex obtuse. *Female spikes* 2–6, 20–80 mm, contiguous or ± overlapping, lax-flowered at base, cylindric, upper often male at top; peduncles 0–35 mm, rough; *female glumes* 3–7 mm, ovate-lanceolate, brown to red-brown; apex acute or acuminate, usually aristate in lower florets. *Utricles* 2–3.5 mm, obovate or suborbicular, green, nerveless or faintly nerved; beak *c.* 0.2 mm, truncate; stigmas 2; nut orbicular or obovate, usually strongly indented on one face, biconvex.   *Fr.* 8–9.

C. recta often forms extensive colonies in stiff peaty alluvium or in more sandy situations, but usually where silt is periodically deposited or the water-table fluctuates seasonally. Often dominant with *Phragmites*, *Phalaris arundinacea* and other grasses in species-rich sedge communities of tall-herb fen (**S27**), with *C. rostrata*, *C. aquatilis*, *C. nigra* and *Juncus acutiflorus*.

A fertile taxon probably best thought of as a 'stabilised hybrid', showing a morphology and ecology intermediate between two closely related species, **97** *C. aquatilis* (with which it often grows and back-crosses) and *C. paleacea*, a taxon not yet found in Britain or Ireland. (see **95–102** *Carex nigra* group introduction). It is distinct in usually having aristate glumes in the lower florets of each female spike, the lower of which are distinctly pedunculate and often pendulous (both *C. paleacea* characters). *C. recta* lacks the glaucous upper surface of the leaves seen in *C. aquatilis* and its stem is not so bluntly trigonous nor is it brittle. **98** *C. acuta* is somewhat similar but has a sharper triquetrous stem and is a southern species.

For hybrids, see **95–102** *Carex nigra* group introduction.

Carex recta is a **Red Data List** species in Great Britain; *Status*: **Vulnerable** (Cheffings & Farrell 2005).

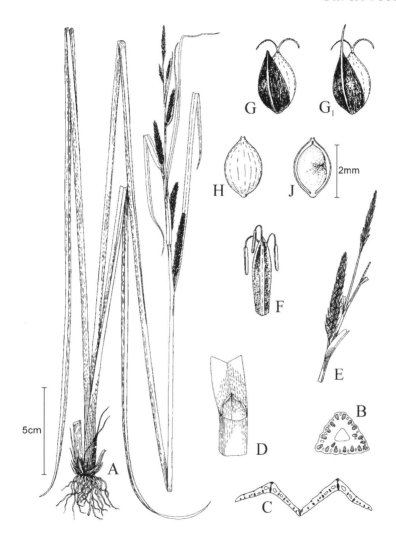

A Fertile shoot; **B** T.S. stem (culm); **C** T.S. leaf; **D** Inner face of leaf-sheath and ligule; **E** Upper spikes; **F** Male floret; **G** Female floret from mid-spike; **G₁** Female floret from near base of spike; **H** Utricle; **J** Section through utricle, showing nut.

461

95 × 97 *Carex* × *grantii* A. Benn.

Carex recta × *C. aquatilis* (*not mapped*)

In its most typical form this variable hybrid is closer to *C. aquatilis* in its brittle, bluntly trigonous stem and the glaucous upper surface of the leaves. It resembles *C. recta* in usually possessing the excurrent midrib on some of the lower glumes of the female spikes, which are longer, fatter and more clustered than those of *C. aquatilis*. *C. × grantii* usually has stomata on both surfaces of the leaf but plants have been recorded with very few or even no stomata on the upper surface.

At its only known British site, on the Wick River (ND35, v.c. 109), here tidal, various populations occur as seemingly clonal entities, since they are morphologically uniform within themselves but differ one from another. As a result of introgression, it is difficult to find the parents at this site.

Carex recta	*Carex* × *grantii*	*Carex aquatilis*
Stem 30–100 cm, trigonous, not brittle.	**Stem** to 50(–90) cm, usually **bluntly trigonous and brittle.**	Stem 20–110 cm, bluntly trigonous above, subterete at base, brittle.
Leaves mid green to yellow-green, matt.	**Leaves ± glaucous above, mid green or glaucous below, matt.**	Leaves ± glaucous above, shiny, dark green or yellow-green below.
Stomata usually present on both leaf surfaces	Stomata usually present on both leaf surfaces.	Stomata mostly confined to upper leaf surface.
♀ spikes 20–80 × 4–6 mm, contiguous or ± overlapping.	♀ **spikes** 30–80 × 4–6 mm, **overlapping or clustered.**	♀ spikes 15–70 × 4(–5) mm, upper contiguous, lowest ± distant.
♀ glumes 3–7 mm, with apex acute or acuminate, usually aristate in lower florets, exceeding utricle.	♀ **glumes** 3–5 mm, with apex acute or acuminate, **usually aristate in some lower florets**, exceeding utricle except at top of spike.	♀ glumes 2–3 mm, with apex acute to cuspidate or obtuse, usually shorter than utricle.
Utricles 2–3.5 mm, usually hard and fully formed; beak 0.2 mm.	Utricles usually 2.5–3 mm, often distorted and sterile; beak *c.* 0.2 mm.	Utricles 2–3 mm, hard and fully formed; beak almost absent.

462

Carex × *grantii* (*Carex recta* × *C. aquatilis*)   **95 × 97**
Carex × *spiculosa* (*Carex recta* × *C. nigra*)   **95 × 100**
Carex acuta × *C. aquatilis*   **97 × 98**

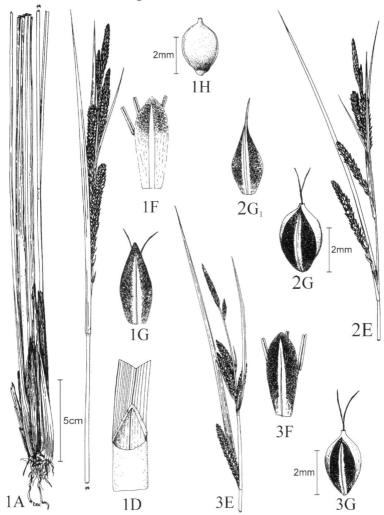

2mm

1H

1F

2G₁

2G

2mm

1G

2E

5cm

3F

1A

1D

3E

2mm

3G

1 *Carex* × *grantii* **2** *C.* × *spiculosa* **3** *C. acuta* × *C. aquatilis*
A Fertile shoot; **D** Inner face of leaf-sheath and ligule; **E** Inflorescence; **F** Male floret;
G Female floret (mid-spike); **G₁** Female glume at base of lowest spike; **H** Utricle.

95 × 100 *Carex* × *spiculosa* Fr.

Carex recta × *C. nigra*   (*not mapped*)

In its most intermediate form this hybrid resembles *C. recta* in having stomata on both leaf surfaces, although these can sometimes be very sparse below, and in possessing long female spikes, the lowest florets of which have at least some aristate glumes. It is similar to *C. nigra* in its less robust stature and in having glaucous leaves and bracts that equal or slightly exceed the inflorescence. It resembles both parents in possessing trigonous stems, pioneering rhizomes and red-brown basal sheaths.

Seen in the field with its *C. recta* parent at its only known British site in slightly shaded conditions on the upper tidal reach of the Oykell River at Invershin, East Ross (NH59, v.c. 107), it appears as a smaller, more slender plant, with narrower leaves and more pendent female spikes. In addition, it tends to grow closer to the water's edge or sometimes even slightly submerged.

Carex recta	*Carex* × *spiculosa*	*Carex nigra*
Stem height 30–100 cm.	**Stem height 45–60 cm.**	Stem height 7–45(–70) cm.
Leaves 3–7 mm wide, mid green to yellow-green; stomata usually ± equally abundant on both surfaces.	Leaves 2.5–3.5 mm wide, glaucous; **stomata occurring on both surfaces but less frequent on lower surface.**	Leaves 1–3(–5) mm wide, blue-green to glaucous; stomata mostly confined to upper surface.
Lowest bract exceeding inflorescence.	Lowest bract equalling or slightly exceeding inflorescence.	Lowest bract ± equalling inflorescence.
♀ spikes 20–80 mm, lax-flowered at base.	♀ spikes 25–70 mm, lax-flowered at base.	♀ spikes 7–50 mm.
♀ glumes 3–7 mm, ovate-lanceolate, with apex acute or acuminate, usually aristate in lower florets.	♀ **glumes 3–4.5 mm,** lanceolate, with apex acute or acuminate, **sometimes aristate in lower florets.**	♀ glumes 2–3 mm, lanceolate-oblong, with apex ± obtuse.
Beak of utricle 0.2 mm.	Beak of utricle *c.* 0.2 mm.	Beak of utricle almost nil.

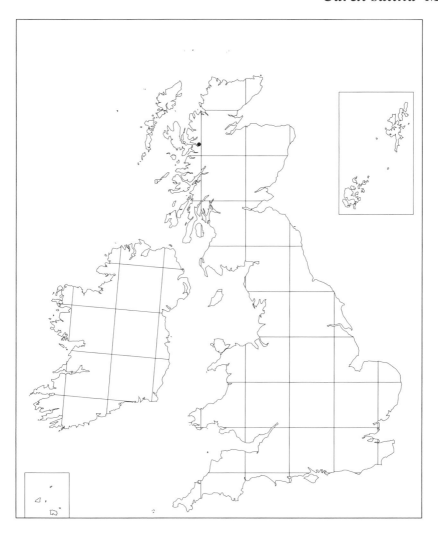

Carex salina was recorded in our area for the first time in 2004 at the head of a sheltered sea-loch at Morvich (v.c. 105). Other similar maritime areas in Scotland and possibly Ireland should be searched for this species.

96 *Carex salina* Wahlenb.

Saltmarsh Sedge Map 96

Rhizomes far-creeping; shoots tufted; roots rich brown-grey; scales red-brown, often blackened, persistent. *Stems* 10–30 cm, smooth, spongy, stiff, obtusely trigonous, soon overtopped by lower leaves and those on sterile shoots. *Leaves* up to 30 cm (or 60–70 cm where plants more sheltered) × 2–3(–4) mm, mid green, young leaves ± glaucous and matt on both surfaces, stiff, V-shaped, with upper 1/3–1/2 and tip toothed; amphistomous; not overwintering; sheaths herbaceous, pale brown, soon decaying, with inner face hyaline and transverse septa distinct; ligule acute, *c.* 5 mm; apex concave. *Inflorescence* 1/4 to almost 1/2 length of stem; lowest bract leafy, slightly shorter to slightly longer than inflorescence, often spathe-like, enclosing spike. *Male spikes* 1–2(–3), 1–2 cm; *male glumes* 4–6 mm, oblanceolate-elliptic, blackish-brown, hyaline at margins; apex obtuse. *Female spikes* 2–3, 1–3 cm, erect; lowest spike with peduncle up to 1.5 cm, sometimes lax-flowered at base; *female glumes* 4–5 mm, ovate-elliptic, mid to dark brown with broad pale centre with obvious midrib; some glumes three-veined; apex of those in upper florets apiculate; lower florets all aristate, with awn ± 1 mm long, toothed. *Utricles* 2.5–3.5 mm, ellipsoid, with 0–3 veins beneath beak; beak 0.2–0.4 mm, conic, 0.5 mm at base, obliquely truncate or not; stigmas 2; nut orbicular or obovate, biconvex, glossy, usually deeply constricted on one face. *Fr.* 6–7.

 C. salina is found in extensive clones near mean high tide level and is often inundated at high spring tides. This may explain the scarcity of fully ripe fruit through a failure in pollination. Landwards it extends into a *Puccinellia maritima* saltmarsh (**SM13**). The banks just above the sedge are *Festuca rubra–Juncus gerardii* and *Blymus rufus* saltmarsh (**SM16, SM19**).

 Like **95** *C. recta*, *C. salina* is a 'stabilised hybrid' (see **95–102** *Carex nigra* group introduction), with one parent, *C. paleacea*, in common with that taxon, the other parent being the pan-arctic coastal *C. subspathacea*, a species not (yet!) recorded for the British Isles. Compared to *C. recta*, *C. salina* flowers very early and has very short stems, overtopped by the narrower leaves that are mixed with, and could easily go undetected amongst, grass-like vegetation on saltmarshes (J. Cayouette pers. comm.). *C. recta* is usually a taller plant, has longer female spikes and longer female glumes, and usually grows in upper levels of estuaries in more silty soils.

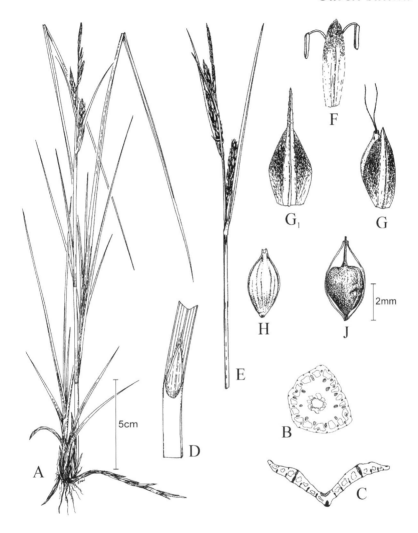

A Fertile shoot; **B** T.S. stem (culm); **C** T.S. leaf; **D** Inner face of leaf-sheath and ligule; **E** Inflorescence; **F** Male floret; **G** Female floret from mid-spike; **G₁** female glume from base of spike; **H** Utricle; **J** Section through utricle, showing nut.

467

97 *Carex aquatilis* Wahlenb.

Water Sedge   *Map 97*

Rhizomes far-creeping; shoots tufted; roots red-brown, up to 2 mm thick, much branched; scales orange- or red-brown, persistent. *Stems* 20–110 cm, smooth, bluntly trigonous above, subterete at base, brittle. *Leaves* 15–130 cm × 2.5–5(–8) mm, smooth, shiny, dark green or yellow-green beneath, rough or smooth and ± glaucous above, culm leaves flat, vegetative leaves weakly keeled, gradually tapered to a flat point, with the margins rolling inwards on drying; epistomous, with a few scattered stomata below; sheaths herbaceous, wine-red or red-brown, persistent, with inner face hyaline, soon decaying; apex straight or concave; ligule 4–15 mm, obtuse or acute, ± tubular. *Inflorescence* 1/6 to 1/3 length of the stem; bracts leaf-like, lowest conspicuously broad and ensheathing at base, exceeding inflorescence. *Male spikes* 2–4, 5–50 mm; *male glumes* 3–4 mm, obovate to oblanceolate, hyaline at margins; apex obtuse. *Female spikes* 2–5, 15–70 mm, cylindric, slender, dense-flowered, becoming lax below, upper contiguous, ± sessile, often male at top, lowest ± distant, ensheathing much of the spike; peduncles more than 20 mm, smooth; *female glumes* 2–3 mm, ovate or broadly elliptic, hyaline at margins; apex acute to cuspidate or obtuse. *Utricles* 2–3 mm, ellipsoid to obovoid, nerveless, green; beak almost absent, truncate; stigmas 2; nut ellipsoid to obovoid, biconvex, shiny.   *Fr.* 7–9.

C. *aquatilis* is predominantly a lowland swamp species. In lakes it grows with C. *vesicaria* (**S11**), C. *rostrata* (**S27**), etc. In rivers and muddy estuaries in the N it is often the only sedge in the scanty riparian flora, but further S it grows with C. *riparia* and C. *acutiformis*. In the east-central Highlands a smaller upland form (similar, except in stature, to the lowland plant and sometimes called var. *stans* (Drejer) Boott) grows with C. *canescens*, C. *rariflora*, C. *nigra* and *Sphagnum* spp. (**M7**) up to 775 m on Glas Maol (v.c. 90). This form has recently been found also at c. 800 m in the Pennines.

C. *aquatilis* is easily distinguished by the shiny bright green lower surface of the leaf, the red sheaths and the slender, more neatly packed female spikes with very long bracts and nerveless utricles. Also, the brittle, ± subterete stem (which snaps when folded) is characteristic of the species. **98** C. *acuta*, which is similar in stature, has leaves glaucous beneath, sheaths rarely red, tough, sharply angled concave-sided stems which do not snap, and robust, more open spikes with faintly ribbed utricles.

For hybrids, see **95–102** *Carex nigra* group introduction.

468

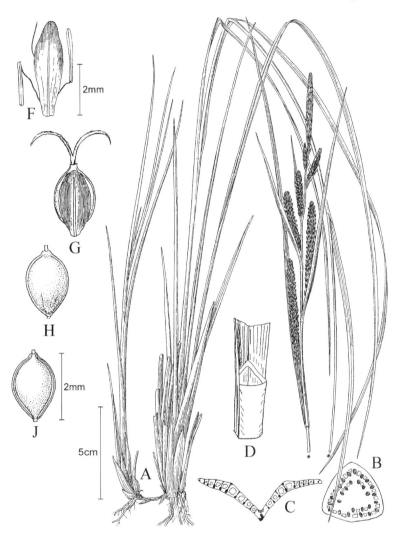

A Fertile shoot; **B** T.S. stem (culm); **C** T.S. leaf; **D** Inner face of leaf-sheath and ligule; **F** Male floret; **G** Female floret; **H** Utricle; **J** Section through utricle, showing nut.

M97 *Carex aquatilis*

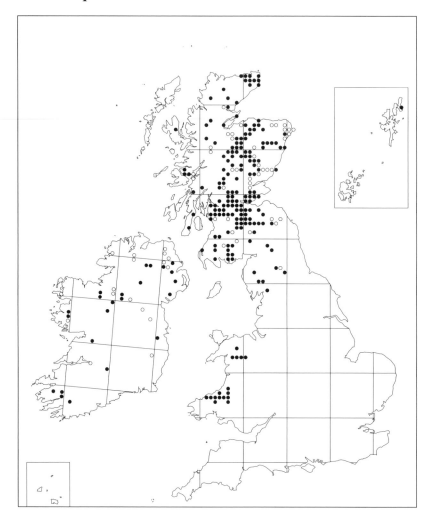

Carex *aquatilis* is basically a northern species from Shetland to the Scottish border, although extinct in many former localities; local in the English Lakes, rare in Teesdale and in the northern Pennines and in N and W Wales, where it is considered a glacial relict. In Ireland, uncommon and scattered.

Carex aquatilis × C. acuta

Map 97 × 98

This hybrid differs from both parents in possessing dense stomata on both surfaces of the leaves. In general appearance it is similar to *C. acuta*, especially in its extremely long leaves which ± conceal the inflorescences, but differs from this parent in its less trigonous stem, its shorter female spikes and its channelled rather than plicate leaves. Compared to *C. aquatilis* its leaves are glaucous rather than dark or yellow-green on the underside and the female spikes are less smooth and generally broader than in this parent.

Carex aquatilis	*Carex aquatilis* × *C. acuta*	*Carex acuta*
Upper half of stem bluntly trigonous, snapping on bending.	Upper half of stem trigonous, partially snapping on bending.	Upper half of stem sharply trigonous, not snapping on bending.
Leaves 2.5–5(–8) mm wide, dark or yellow-green below, ± glaucous above, channelled.	Leaves to 6 mm wide, ± glaucous on both sides, channelled.	Leaves 3–10 mm wide, deep green above, glaucous below, plicate.
Stomata mostly on upper leaf surface.	**Stomata abundant on both leaf surfaces.**	Stomata confined to lower leaf surface.
Lowest bract exceeding and ensheathing inflorescence.	Lowest bract exceeding but not ensheathing inflorescence.	Lowest bract exceeding but not ensheathing inflorescence.
♀ spike cylindric, 15–70 mm long, 4 (< 5) mm broad, feeling smooth; glumes and utricles appressed.	♀ spike cylindric or fusiform, 30–50 mm long, 5–6 mm broad; glumes and utricles somewhat patent.	♀ spike cylindric, 30–100 mm long, up to 6 mm broad, feeling rough; glumes and utricles patent.
♀ glumes 2–3 mm, ovate or broadly elliptic, usually shorter than utricle.	♀ glumes 3–4 mm, oblong-obovate, ± equalling or slightly exceeding utricle.	♀ glumes 2.5–4 mm, oblong-obovate, longer or sometimes shorter than utricle.
Utricles 2–3 mm, ellipsoid to obovoid, not ribbed.	**Utricles *c.* 3 mm, often strongly obovoid and irregularly wrinkled and shrunken.**	Utricles 2–3.5 mm, ellipsoid-obovoid to subglobose, faintly ribbed.

M97 × 98 *Carex aquatilis* × *C. acuta*

Carex aquatilis × *C. acuta* is known only from Wales, at Cors Caron NNR
(v.c. 46) and at four sites at Lake Bala and one at Llandderfel (all v.c. 48).
It grows with both parents in ditches, on lakesides and on river-margins.

Carex × *hibernica* (*Carex aquatilis* × *C. nigra*)   *M97 × 100*

Carex × *hibernica* is found in scattered localities in Scotland and western Ireland.

97 × 100 *Carex* × *hibernica* A. Benn.

Carex aquatilis × *C. nigra*   *Map 97 × 100*

Carex nigra hybridises with both the normal form of *C. aquatilis* and also the much shorter upland form which occurs at altitudes above 700 m in the Grampians. The resultant hybrid, *Carex* × *hibernica*, thus varies greatly in height but is generally of considerably lesser stature than its *C. aquatilis* parent. It differs additionally from *C. aquatilis* in its more trigonous stem, narrower leaves and shorter lowest bract and female spikes. It is taller than *C. nigra*, with slightly broader leaves, an often broader lowest bract and often longer female spikes. The often deformed and empty utricles are closer in size to those of *C. aquatilis*.

Carex × *hibernica* is found from near sea level to at least 950 m, usually in the presence of both parents and most commonly where *C. aquatilis* is a component of upland flushes and saddle mires with *Sphagnum papillosum* (**M7**) and in lowland situations on river banks and the margins of lochs (**S11**).

Carex aquatilis	*Carex* × *hibernica*	*Carex nigra*
Stem height to 110 cm (to 50 cm in upland form), bluntly trigonous to subterete, brittle.	**Stem height to 70 cm (to 30 cm when a hybrid of upland *C. aquatilis*), trigonous.**	Stem height 7–45(–70) cm, usually shorter at high altitudes, trigonous.
Leaves 2.5–5(–8) mm broad, smooth, shiny, dark green or yellow-green below, glaucous above.	**Leaves to 3.5 mm broad,** glaucous, varying between those of parents in colour, often yellow-green in mountain mires.	Leaves 1–3(–5) mm broad, glaucous on both sides.
Lowest bract exceeding inflorescence and usually wider than 2 mm.	**Lowest bract usually ± equalling or shortly exceeding inflorescence, wider than 2 mm.**	Lowest bract ± equalling inflorescence, usually up to 2 mm wide.
♀ spikes 15–70 mm.	♀ spikes (10–)20–40 mm.	♀ spikes 7–50 mm.
Utricles 2–3 mm.	**Utricles 2–2.8 mm, often empty and deformed.**	Utricles 2.5–3.5 mm.

Carex × hibernica (*Carex aquatilis* × *C. nigra*) 97 × 100
Carex × elytroides (*Carex acuta* × *C. nigra*) 98 × 100

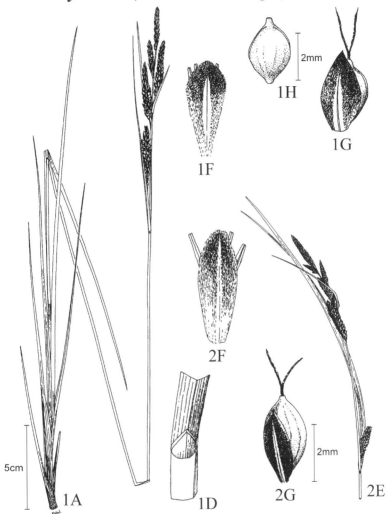

1 *Carex × hibernica* **2** *C. × elytroides*
A Fertile shoot; **D** Inner face of leaf-sheath and ligule; **E** Inflorescence; **F** Male floret; **G** Female floret; **H** Utricle.

M98 × 100 **Carex × elytroides** (*Carex acuta × C. nigra*)

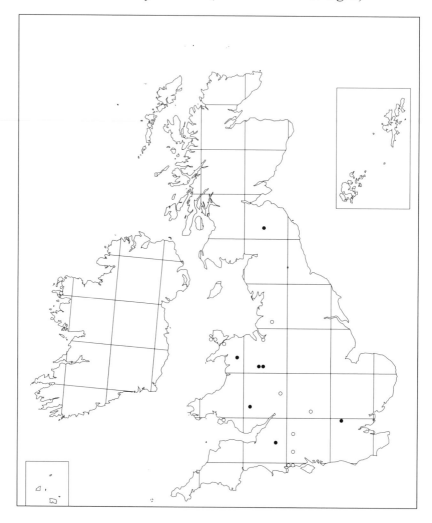

Carex × elytroides has been recorded from more than ten vice-counties northwards to the central belt of Scotland, sometimes in the absence of *C. acuta* in the more northerly sites. There is also a recent record from Westmorland (v.c. 69) which is not mapped.

Carex × *elytroides* Fr.

98 × 100

Carex acuta × *C. nigra*

Map 98 × 100

Carex × *elytroides* is distinguished from its parents by the presence of abundant stomata on both surfaces of the leaves. It differs additionally from *C. acuta* in usually having a shorter lowest bract which more or less equals or slightly exceeds the inflorescence, a less sharply trigonous stem and a lesser stature. From *C. nigra* it is distinguished by its greater height, somewhat broader leaves and its generally longer male and female spikes. As in *C. acuta*, the female glumes are usually markedly narrower than their utricles; however, particularly near the tip, they often also exhibit the hyaline margin of *C. nigra*.

C. × *elytroides* occurs on pond margins and riversides and in dykes and wet fields.

Carex acuta	*Carex* × *elytroides*	*Carex nigra*
Stems 30–120 cm high, sharply trigonous above, subterete at base.	Stems to 85 cm high, trigonous throughout.	Stems 7–45(–70) cm high, trigonous throughout.
Leaves 3–10 mm broad; stomata confined to lower surface.	Leaves 2–5.2 mm broad; **stomata ± abundant on both surfaces.**	Leaves 1–3(–5) mm broad; stomata mostly confined to upper surface.
Lowest bract exceeding inflorescence.	Lowest bract usually ± equalling inflorescence, but occasionally much exceeding it.	Lowest bract ± equalling inflorescence.
♂ spikes 2–4, 20–60 mm.	♂ **spikes 1–3, 15–40 mm.**	♂ spikes 1–2, 5–30 mm.
♀ spikes 2–4, 30–100 mm.	♀ **spikes 2–4, 20–55 mm.**	♀ spikes 1–4, 7–50 mm.
♀ glumes usually markedly narrower than utricle and with inrolled margins often forming a cusp, often ± patent.	♀ **glumes usually markedly narrower than utricle**; margins sometimes hyaline near the tip, often ± patent.	♀ glumes usually slightly narrower than utricle and often with hyaline margins, closely appressed to utricle.

98 *Carex acuta* L.

Slender Tufted-sedge   *Map 98*

Rhizomes far-creeping; shoots tufted (occasionally tussocky); roots red to brown; scales red-brown, often soon decaying. **Stems** 30–120 cm, rough, sharply trigonous with concave faces distally, subterete at base. **Leaves** 30–140 cm × 3–10 mm, rough on edges, thin, distinctly plicate, gradually narrowed to a pendulous tip, deep green and glossy above, glaucous below, with margins rolling outwards on drying; hypostomous; sheaths brown or red-brown, persistent, with transverse septa prominent; inner face hyaline, persisting as a brown membranous strip; apex straight or concave; ligule 4–6 mm, obtuse, truncate with a free margin. **Inflorescence** 1/6 to 1/4 length of stem; bracts leaf-like, lowest exceeding inflorescence. **Male spikes** usually 2–4, 20–60 mm; **male glumes** 4.5–5.5 mm, elliptic- to obovate-oblong; apex obtuse or subacute. **Female spikes** 2–4, 30–100 mm, cylindric, usually contiguous, often lax-flowered at base, erect, upper sessile, often 3 at top, lower shortly pedunculate; **female glumes** 2.5–4 mm, oblong-obovate; apex obtuse or margin inrolled forming a cusp. **Utricles** 2–3.5 mm, ellipsoid-obovoid to subglobose, either longer or shorter than glume, faintly nerved, green; beak almost absent, truncate; stigmas 2; nut obovoid, biconvex, shortly stalked.   ***Fr.*** 6–7.

C. acuta is a species of ponds, dykes and riversides in the following swamp communities where there is a more or less constantly high water level: *Phragmites* (**S4**), *Glyceria maxima* (**S5**), *C. riparia* (**S6**). Also in tall-herb fens with other sedges where *Phragmites* is dominant (**S25** and **S26**).

Similar to **57** *C. acutiformis* in leaf-texture and inflorescence, but the serrulate acumen of the female glume and particularly the three stigmas of that species separate them. When not flowering, the fibrillose leaf-sheaths with distinct aerenchyma blocks and dark, more yellow-green upper leaf surface distinguish *C. acutiformis*. *C. acuta* can also be confused with **97** *C. aquatilis* where their distributions overlap: for differences see that species. A robust form of open water habitats has, at the base of the lowermost female spike, glumes with an elongated apex; this should not be confused with **95** *C. recta*, which has a blunter angled stem and leaves not glaucous beneath.

C. acuta hybridises with *C. acutiformis* (**57** × **98** *C.* × *subgracilis* Druce), producing a hybrid not easy to identify. For other hybrids, see **95–102** *Carex nigra* group introduction.

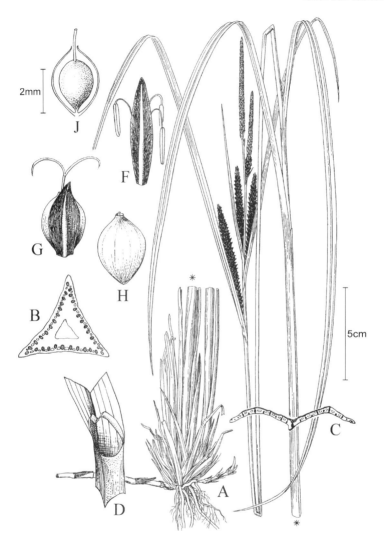

2mm

5cm

A Fertile shoot; **B** T.S. stem (culm); **C** T.S. leaf; **D** Inner face of leaf-sheath and ligule; **F** Male floret; **G** Female floret; **H** Utricle; **J** Section through utricle, showing nut.

M98 *Carex acuta*

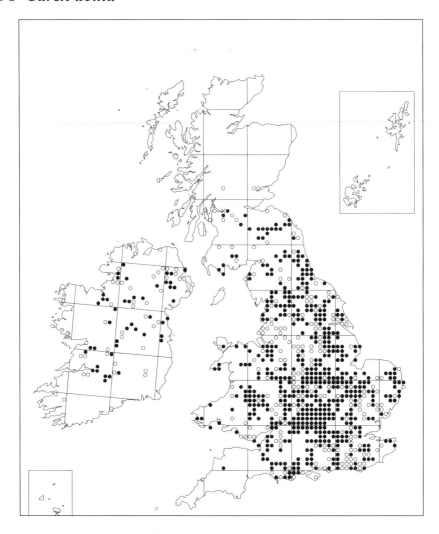

In Britain *Carex acuta* is found mainly in major river valleys of the Midlands
up to the Tees, then becomes scarcer further north to the Clyde–Forth basin.
Records further north usually show introgression with *C. aquatilis*. In Ireland
an uncommon plant (T. O'Mahony pers. comm.), scattered in the C and N.

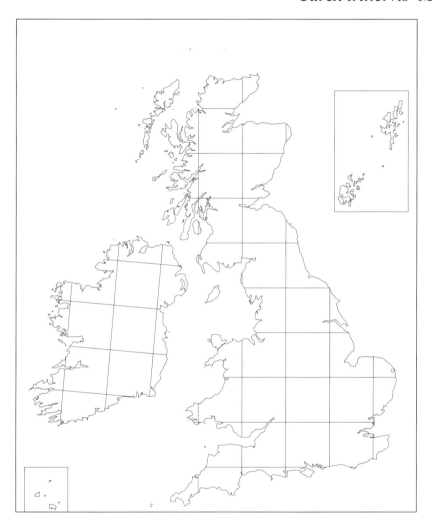

Carex trinervis was found at Ormesby Common, E Norfolk (v.c. 27), in 1869 and not collected there after 1890. The area is now built over and the species is accepted as extinct in Britain, but there could be suitable coastal habitats further south on the E coast. It is not recorded for Ireland.

99 *Carex trinervis* Degl.

Rhizomes far-creeping, often thick (< 4 mm); shoots clustered; roots pale brown or red-brown; scales brown, dull, becoming fibrous or persistent and blackish when in anaerobic soils. **Stems** 10–40(–60) cm, slender, trigonous, smooth below, rough on angles above. **Leaves** up to 60 cm × 1–2(–3) mm, stiffly erect, usually inrolled, gradually tapering to a fine trigonous point, pale green to glaucous; amphistomous; sheaths pale biscuit-brown, with inner face hyaline, thin and persistent; apex straight; ligule 1–3 mm, rounded. **Inflorescence** 1/6 to 1/3 length of stem; bracts leaf-like, canaliculate, often stiff and patent, the lowest overtopping the inflorescence. **Male spikes** (1–)2–3(–4), linear, (5–)20–50 mm; **male glumes** 3–5 mm, obovate-oblong, purple-brown with wide, pale midrib; apex obtuse or subacute with narrow hyaline margin. **Female spikes** (1–)2–4, (7–)20–50 mm, oblong-cylindric, clustered, subsessile, erect, ± contiguous or lowest sometimes distant with short peduncle; **female glumes** 1.5–3 mm, elliptic to oblong-ovate, red-brown to black with wide green midrib and hyaline margin; apex obtuse and acuminate, becoming shortly aristate in lower florets of lowest spike. **Utricles** 3.5–5 mm, broader and longer than glumes, ovoid-ellipsoid, grey-green, often with fine purple-brown spots and 3 or more distinct nerves on adaxial face; beak almost absent, truncate; stigmas 2; nut ellipsoid, biconvex.   **Fr.** 6–9.

Closest to **100** *C. nigra*, but the female glumes on the lower florets of the clustered spikes of *C. trinervis* often have excurrent midribs. Vegetatively this species has distinctive inrolled leaves (*cf.* those of *Ammophila arenaria*) and thicker rhizomes (> 2.5 mm). It is a species of dune-slacks and upper saltmarsh communities on the coasts of W Europe, occasionally growing 50–100 km from the coast, e.g. in the Netherlands. The only British population was found in E Norfolk (v.c. 27) between 1869 and 1890 *c.* 8 km from the sea, but the area was coastal in the Romano-British period and sandy hollows may have existed in the glacial till.

Material from this site was grown and distributed by several botanists and still grew in A.W. Stelfox's garden in Co. Down, Northern Ireland, in 1962 (*fide* A.C.J.). Some of it appears to have been only partly fertile, with smaller and rarely cuspidate female glumes, perhaps as a result of hybridisation with **100** *C. nigra* (*C.* × *timmiana* Junge). *C. trinervis* hybridises with that species and *C. flacca* in mainland Europe: see Foley (2005).

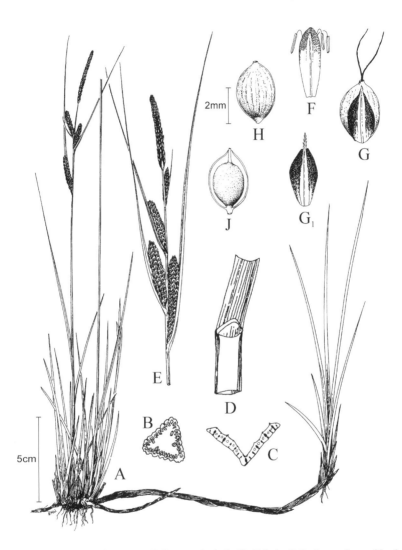

A Fertile and sterile shoots; **B** T.S. stem (culm); **C** T.S. leaf; **D** Inner face of leaf-sheath and ligule; **E** Inflorescence; **F** Male floret; **G** Female floret; **G₁** Female glume from base of lower spike; **H** Utricle; **J** Section through utricle, showing nut.

100 *Carex nigra* (L.) Reichard

Common Sedge   *Map 100*

Rhizomes predominantly far-creeping but tussocky in stagnant mires; shoots tufted; roots pale brown or red-brown; scales brown or red-brown, ± shiny, persistent or becoming fibrous. *Stems* 7–45(–70) cm, rough above, < 2 mm wide, trigonous, solid. *Leaves* up to 90 cm × 1–3(–5) mm, thin, ± flat, gradually tapering to a fine point, blue-green to glaucous on both sides, with upper surface becoming olivaceous, tinged purple-brown in autumn; margins rolling inwards on drying; epistomous but sometimes with a few stomata on lower surface also; sheaths brown, black or rarely red, ± fibrous, with inner face hyaline; apex straight; ligule 1–3 mm, rounded, shortly tubular, with free tissue *c.* 0.5–0.6 mm wide, variably papillate at its margin. *Inflorescence* 1/6–1/4 length of stem; bracts leaf-like, lowest ± equalling inflorescence. *Male spikes* 1–2, 5–30 mm; *male glumes* 3–5 mm, obovate-oblong, black with green midrib; apex obtuse or subacute. *Female spikes* 1–4, 7–50 mm, ± contiguous, cylindric, erect, upper often male at top, lower sometimes distant, with short peduncle; *female glumes* 2–3 mm, lanceolate-oblong, black with green midrib; margins narrow, hyaline-papillate; apex ± obtuse. *Utricles* 2.5–3.5 mm, ovoid-ellipsoid, faintly nerved, minutely papillate, green, often tinged dark purple; beak almost nil, truncate; nut ellipsoid, biconvex.   *Fr.* 6–8.

C. nigra shows a wide habitat tolerance and is found in 26 of the 38 mire types described by Rodwell (1991b). Common in those with some degree of water movement or mineral (? calcium and magnesium) enrichment, e.g. *Palustriella commutata–C. nigra* limestone springs (**M38**), and constant in *Molinia–Crepis paludosa* mire (**M26**); also found in *Sphagnum*-dominated mires, e.g. *S. squarrosum* (**M5**) and *S. warnstorfii* (**M8**) with *C. rostrata*, *C. echinata–S. fallax/denticulatum* (**M6**) and *C. canescens–S. russowii* (**M7**). It grows with *Littorella* (**A22**) and *Eleocharis palustris* (**S19**) around lakes and with other sedges bordering ponds, e.g. *C. elata* (**S1**), *C. rostrata* (**S9**) and *C. vesicaria* (**S11**). It also occurs in coastal communities: *Calluna–Scilla verna* heath (**H7**); saltmarshes with *Blysmus rufus* and *Eleocharis uniglumis* (**SM19, SM20**); dune-slack communities with *Salix repens*, *Hydrocotyle* and *C. flacca* (**SD14, SD15**); with *Potentilla anserina* (**SD17**), where it resembles **102** *C. bigelowii*; and in *Festuca rubra* maritime grasslands (**MC9, MC10**).

For further discussion and for hybrids, see **95–102** *Carex nigra* group introduction.

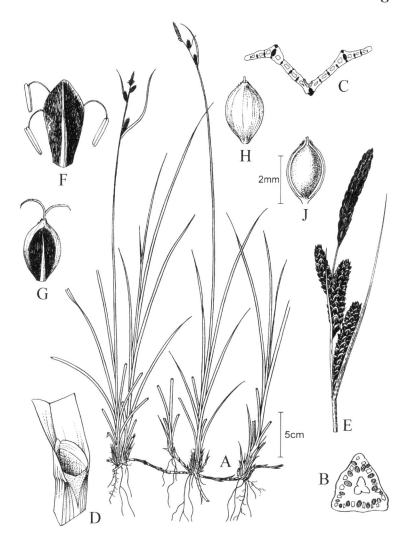

A Fertile and sterile shoots; **B** T.S. stem (culm); **C** T.S. leaf; **D** Inner face of leaf-sheath and ligule; **E** Upper spikes; **F** Male floret; **G** Female floret; **H** Utricle; **J** Section through utricle, showing nut.

M100 Carex nigra

Carex nigra is widespread and common throughout most of the British Isles with some gaps in the highly arable Oxford clay–Fenland basin (v.cc. 29 and 30).

486

Carex elata M101

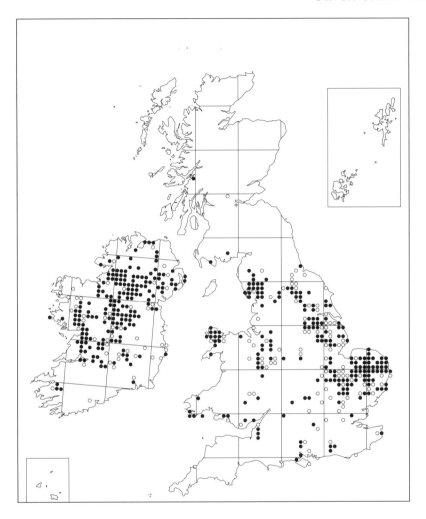

Carex elata is most frequent in the east of England, reaching as far north as the River Tees. It also occurs commonly in the Cheshire/Shropshire basin, Anglesey and Cumbria (reaching an altitude of 260 m at Sunbiggin Tarn), but is otherwise scarce in England and Wales. Very rare in Scotland, with a northerly outlier in W Argyll (v.c. 98) and an old record for Tiree (v.c. 103). In Ireland mainly in the centre and rare in the south.

487

101 *Carex elata* All.

Tufted-sedge   *Map 101*

Rhizomes very short, erect, forming dense tussocks up to 40 cm high; roots < 2 mm thick, purple-brown; scales light brown, shiny, persistent. **Stems** 25–100 cm, rough, sharply trigonous. **Leaves** 40–100 cm × 3–8 mm, rough, thin, plicate, gradually tapering, blue-green to glaucous on both sides, with margins rolling outwards on drying; hypostomous; sheaths becoming yellow-brown, persistent, with inner face hyaline, fibrillose, and minutely red-flecked concave apex; ligule 5–13 mm, acute, with free tissue < 1 mm, ± tubular. **Inflorescence** 1/7 length of stem; bracts leaf-like to setaceous, lowest less than half length of inflorescence. **Male spikes** 1–3, 15–50 mm, lowermost occasionally female at base; **male glumes** *c.* 5 mm, oblanceolate, hyaline at margins; apex obtuse. **Female spikes** 2–3, 15–40 mm, usually contiguous, cylindric, erect, ± sessile, often male at top; **female glumes** 3–4 mm, ovate-elliptic, hyaline at margins; apex obtuse or subacute. **Utricles** 3–4 mm, broadly ovoid-ellipsoid, ribbed, green; beak 0.2 mm, truncate; nut obovoid, biconvex, stalked.   *Fr.* 4–6.

C. elata is found in eutrophic mires where there is at least seasonal flooding and is common by ditches, rivers and lakes. A characteristic component of East Anglian sedge-swamp (**S1**); also with *C. riparia* (**S6**), *Cladium mariscus* (**S2**) and sub-communities of *Phragmites*–tall herb fens (**S24, S25**), in places preceding bush colonisation. In mesotrophic mires with *C. rostrata, Menyanthes trifoliata* and *Potentilla palustris* (**S27**).

A variable species but distinct amongst those in this group found in our area in completely lacking leading rhizomes and in having fibrillose sheaths. Depauperate specimens, e.g. in drained ponds and mown fen-meadow (with *Juncus subnodulosus* in **M22**) forming tufts rather than tussocks, are difficult to separate from non-fruiting *C. acutiformis*, but this has red-tinged sheaths and long rhizomes and a more yellow-green upper leaf-surface. A very similar species, *C. cespitosa* L. of N and C Europe (which has been confused with *C. caespitosa* auct., a synonym of *C. elata*, and thereby erroneously recorded for Britain) has red-brown scales.

C. elata hybridises with *C. acuta* (**101** × **98** *C.* × *prolixa* Fr.) and *C. nigra* (**101** × **100** *C.* × *turfosa* Fr.). Arthur Bennett (1897) wrongly assumed that *C. elata* was one parent of his *C.* × *hibernica* (see hybrid text **97** × **100**). Hybrids with *C. acutiformis* and *C. riparia* have been found in Europe.

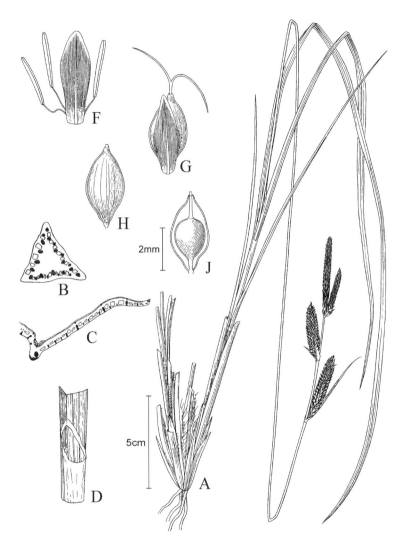

A Fertile shoot; **B** T.S. stem (culm); **C** T.S. leaf; **D** Inner face of leaf-sheath and ligule; **F** Male floret; **G** Female floret; **H** Utricle; **J** Section through utricle, showing nut.

101 × 98 *Carex × prolixa* Fr.

Carex elata × *C. acuta*   *Map 101 × 98*

Carex × prolixa combines the long thin male and female spikes of *C. acuta* with the short lowest bract of *C. elata*. Additionally, it resembles *C. elata* in its pale-coloured somewhat fibrillose basal sheaths, in the hyaline tips of the male glumes, in its longer, slightly beaked and ribbed utricles and in its early flowering time (May–June). It is closer to *C. acuta* in its spreading, non-tussock-forming habit. The utricles of specimens examined were flat and empty.

Carex × prolixa is found in wet, sometimes shaded, sites such as by ponds and waterways, in the presence of both parents.

Carex elata	*Carex × prolixa*	*Carex acuta*
Sheaths becoming yellow-brown; inner face fibrillose on splitting.	**Sheaths pale brown, somewhat fibrillose on splitting.**	Sheaths brown or red-brown, not fibrillose on splitting.
Lowest bract less than half the length of the inflorescence.	Lowest bract usually more than half the length of the inflorescence but not exceeding it.	Lowest bract exceeding the inflorescence.
♂ spikes 15–50 mm.	♂ spikes 30–65 mm.	♂ spikes 20–60 mm.
♂ glumes with hyaline margin.	**♂ glumes in upper part of spike sometimes with hyaline tip.**	♂ glumes with no hyaline margin.
♀ spikes 15–40 mm in length, 5–7 mm wide.	♀ spikes to 60 mm in length, 5–5.5 mm wide.	♀ spikes 30–100 mm in length, 4–6 mm wide.
Utricles 3–4 mm, broadly ovoid-ellipsoid, ribbed; beak 0.2 mm.	**Utricles** 3.2–4 mm, (narrowly) ovoid-ellipsoid, **ribbed**, flat; beak to 0.2 mm.	Utricles 2–3.5 mm, ellipsoid-ovoid to subglobose, faintly ribbed; beak almost absent.

Carex × *prolixa* (*Carex elata* × *C. acuta*)   **101 × 98**
Carex × *turfosa* (*Carex elata* × *C. nigra*)   **101 × 100**

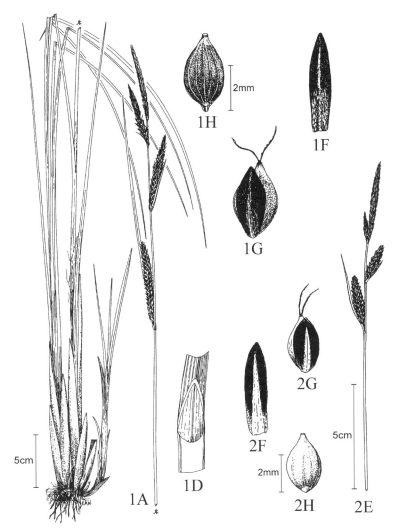

1 *Carex* × *prolixa* **2** *C.* × *turfosa*
A Fertile shoot; **D** Inner face of leaf-sheath and ligule; **E** Inflorescence; **F** Male glume; **G** Female floret; **H** Utricle.

M101 × 98 Carex × prolixa (*Carex elata × C. acuta*)

Carex × prolixa has been recorded from scattered localities in southern England and Wales, with confirmed records from Axbridge (v.c. 6), E and W Norfolk (v.cc. 27 and 28), Upware and Reach (v.c. 29), Langorse (v.c. 42) and Cors Costell (v.c. 52).

Carex × *turfosa* Fr. 101 × 100

Carex elata × *C. nigra* *Map 101 × 100*

This hybrid is variably intermediate between the parents in leaf width, bract length and ligule length and shape and in having abundant stomata on both leaf surfaces. It differs additionally from *C. elata* in its generally non-tussock-forming habit and longer lowest bract, but resembles it in its early flowering time. From *C. nigra* it differs in its broader leaves, generally taller stems, fibrillose basal sheaths, less slender spikes and shortly beaked utricles.

Seen in the field it appears closer to *C. nigra*, often existing as a complex of forms approaching that parent in habit and morphology. As a result, this hybrid is likely to be under-recorded and may well be frequent where the parents occur together, i.e. in mires and fen-carr, by slow-moving rivers and around pool margins.

Carex elata	*Carex* × *turfosa*	*Carex nigra*
Shoots densely tufted, forming tussocks.	Shoots variably tufted, rarely tussock-forming.	Shoots variably tufted, occasionally forming tussocks.
Basal sheaths fibrillose.	**Basal sheaths fibrillose.**	Basal sheaths not fibrillose.
Stems 25–100 cm.	Stems generally *c.* 50 cm.	Stems 7–45(–70) cm.
Leaves 3–8 mm broad.	Leaves (2–)4.5–6 mm broad.	Leaves 1–3(–5) mm broad.
Stomata confined to lower surface of leaf.	**Stomata occurring ± abundantly on both leaf surfaces.**	Stomata mostly confined to upper surface of leaf.
Ligule 5–13 mm, acute.	**Ligule** 3–5 mm, **obtuse to subacute.**	Ligule 1–3 mm, rounded.
Lowest bract up to half length of inflorescence.	**Lowest bract longer than in *C. elata* but usually shorter than inflorescence.**	Lowest bract ± equalling inflorescence.
♀ spikes 5–7 mm wide.	**♀ spikes 4.5–5.5 mm wide.**	♀ spikes 4–5 mm wide.
Utricles ribbed, with short beak to 0.2 mm.	Utricles faintly ribbed, with short beak to 0.2 mm.	Utricles faintly ribbed, almost without beak.

M101 × *100* **Carex** × ***turfosa*** (*Carex elata* × *C. nigra*)

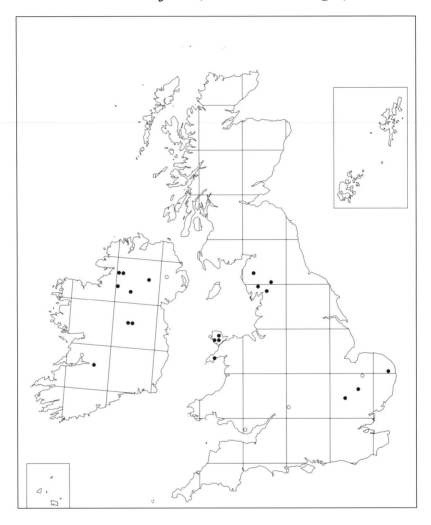

Carex × *turfosa* is scattered in the British Isles, reflecting the distribution of of its less common parent species, *C. elata*.

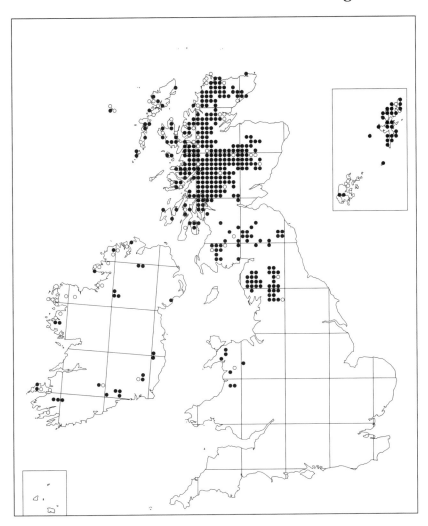

C. bigelowii is a mountain plant, occurring above 600 m for most of its range and reaching 1305 m on Ben Macdui, although in Shetland growing at 15 m (Foley & Porter 2002). Through Scotland to the High Pennines and Lake District, south to North Wales. In Ireland a local plant of mountain summits and ridges and, as in Scotland, at a lower altitude on west coast headlands.

102 *Carex bigelowii* Torr. ex Schwein.

Stiff Sedge   *Map 102*

Rhizomes short- or long-creeping; shoots solitary or in pairs, ± close together; roots often as thick as rhizomes, grey-brown; scales red- or purple-brown, shiny, persistent. **Stems** 4–30 cm, usually rough, rigid, usually >2 mm wide near base, sharply trigonous. **Leaves** up to 25 cm × 2–7 mm, stiff or arcuate, ± rough, keeled, ± abruptly tapered to a flat apex, with margins often revolute and rolling outwards on drying, glaucous and papillous below, less glaucous, ± glossy and devoid of papillae above, dying to a red-brown; hypostomous; sheaths brown or red-brown and shiny, persistent, with inner face hyaline, soon decaying, and apex ± straight; ligule 1–2 mm, acute, shortly tubular. **Inflorescence** 1/8 to 1/5 (up to 1/2) length of stem; bracts leaf-like, with blackish auricles, lowest shorter than inflorescence. **Male spike** 1, rarely 2, 5–20 mm; **male glumes** 3–4 mm, obovate-elliptic, black with green midrib; apex acute or rounded. **Female spikes** 2–3, contiguous or lower ± distant, 5–15 mm, cylindric-ovoid, erect, sessile, lowest only sometimes shortly pedunculate; **female glumes** 2.5–3.5 mm, ovate-elliptic, black with green midrib; apex obtuse. **Utricles** 2.5–3 mm, broader than glumes, suborbicular-ellipsoid, nerveless, green; beak *c.* 0.2 mm, truncate or slightly notched; nut ovoid-ellipsoid, biconvex. ***Fr.* 7–8.**

   C. bigelowii can be a dominant sedge on exposed humic, base-poor soils in the *Rhacomitrium lanuginosum–Vaccinium myrtillus–Cladonia* lichen-rich heaths (**H19, H20**) and prominent with *C. canescens, C. echinata* and *Sphagnum lindbergii* (**M7a**) and on edges of *Calluna–Eriophorum* blanket mire (**M19**). A component of 13 windswept montane communities (**U5–14, U16–18**), e.g. constant with *Nardus stricta* and *Galium saxatile* (**U7**), *Dicranum fuscescens* and *Polytrichastrum alpinum* (**U8**), *Juncus trifidus* (**U9**) or *Rhacomitrium lanuginosum* (**U10**). On ledges of flushed gullies it can be a robust plant.

   The purplish, not orange-brown, scales and glaucous, not dark green, leaves (often showing a thin band of red on decaying) distinguish this species from **72** *C. binervis*, which can grow at the lower ranges of *C. bigelowii*, while the shiny red- or purple-brown rhizome scales help to distinguish it from **100** *C. nigra*, with which it commonly hybridises (**102** × **100** *C.* × *decolorans* Wimm.). It also hybridises with **97** *C. aquatilis* (**102** × **97** *C.* × *limula* Fr.). With both of these hybrids there is the possibility of back-crossing, so identification can be difficult (see, e.g., Corner 2002).

496

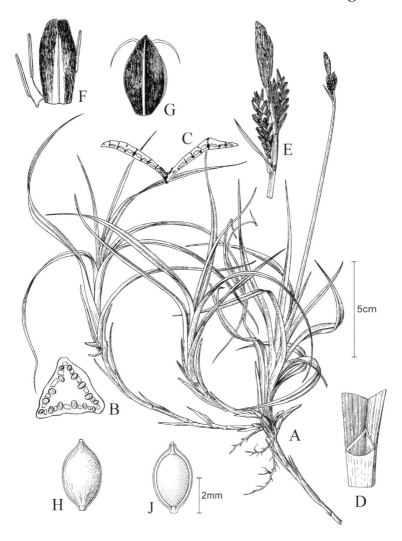

A Fertile shoot; **B** T.S. stem (culm); **C** T.S. leaf; **D** Inner face of leaf-sheath and ligule; **E** Inflorescence; **F** Male floret; **G** Female floret; **H** Utricle; **J** Section through utricle, showing nut.

102 × 97 *Carex × limula* Fr.

Carex bigelowii × *C. aquatilis* (upland form)   *Map 102 × 97*

This hybrid is intermediate between its parents in leaf width, in having stomata on both surfaces of the leaves, in its stem section and in having a lowest bract which more or less equals the inflorescence. From *C. aquatilis* it is distinguished by its smaller stature, its more sharply trigonous stem, its sometimes broader leaves, its shorter lowest bract and shorter female spikes and its usually single male spike. It differs from *C. bigelowii* in the more yellow-green underside to the leaf, its longer, less clustered male and female spikes and its longer, broader lowest bract, but it retains the rigid trigonous stem and short acute ligule of that species.

C. × limula occurs with both parents in boggy situations or on drier, acidic grassland adjacent to wet areas at altitudes usually above 700 metres.

Carex bigelowii	*Carex × limula*	*Carex aquatilis*
Stems 4–30 cm, sharply trigonous, rigid.	Stems generally intermediate in height, often 30–35 cm, trigonous, rigid.	Stems (of upland form) up to 50 cm, bluntly trigonous to subterete, brittle.
Stomata confined to lower leaf surface.	**Stomata ± abundant on both leaf surfaces.**	Stomata mainly confined to upper surface of leaf.
Leaves 2–7 mm wide, glaucous.	Leaves up to 5.5 mm wide, glaucous above, yellow-green beneath.	Leaves 2.5–5(–8) mm wide, glaucous above, dark green or yellow-green beneath.
Ligule 1–2 mm.	Ligule 2–3 mm.	Ligule 4–15 mm.
Lowest bract shorter than inflorescence, up to 2 mm broad.	**Lowest bract ± equalling inflorescence**, up to 4 mm broad.	Lowest bract exceeding inflorescence, up to 4 mm broad.
♂ spike 1, rarely 2, 5–20 mm in length.	**♂ spike 1, rarely 2, *c*. 30 mm in length.**	♂ spikes 2–4, 5–50 mm in length.
♀ spikes 5–15 mm in length; ± patent glumes giving uneven appearance.	**♀ spikes 15–30 mm in length**; appressed glumes and utricles giving smooth appearance.	♀ spikes 15–70 mm in length; appressed glumes and utricles giving smooth appearance.

Carex × limula (*Carex bigelowii* × *C. aquatilis*)   **102 × 97**
Carex × decolorans (*Carex bigelowii* × *C. nigra*)   **102 × 100**

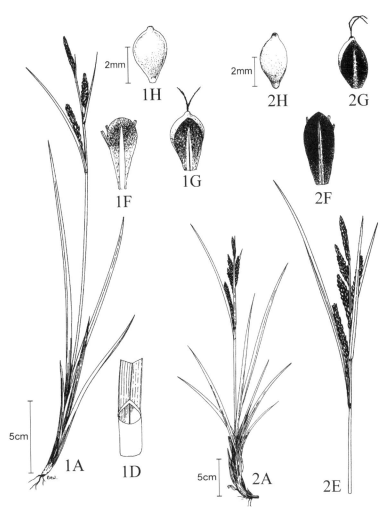

1 *Carex* × *decolorans* 2 *C.* × *limula*
A Fertile shoot; **D** Inner face of leaf-sheath and ligule; **E** Inflorescence; **F** Male floret; **G** Female floret; **H** Utricle.

M102 × 97 Carex × limula (*Carex bigelowii × C. aquatilis*)

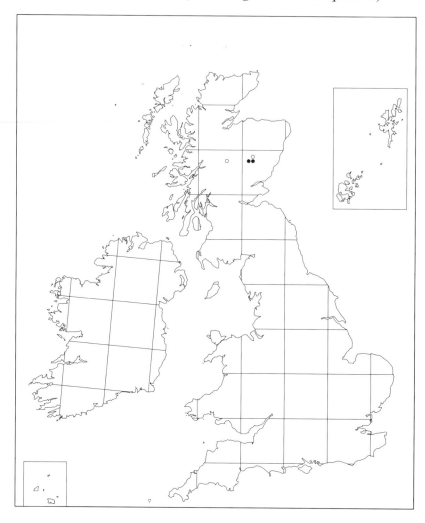

Carex × limula is recorded close to high-level associations of the upland form of *C. aquatilis* with *C. nigra* and *Sphagnum papillosum* (**M7b**) in the Grampian mountains, e.g. at 750 m on Glas Maol (v.c. 90).

Carex × *decolorans* (*Carex bigelowii* × *C. nigra*) **M102 × 100**

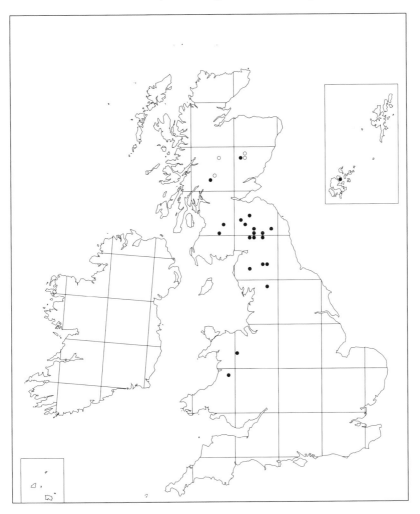

Carex × *decolorans* is found in Orkney, the Scottish Highlands, the Southern Uplands, the northern Pennines, the Lake District and north and mid Wales.

102 × 100 *Carex × decolorans* Wimm.

Carex bigelowii × C. nigra　　　　　　　*Map 102 × 100*

This hybrid can exist in a wide range of forms varying between the two parents. In its most intermediate form it possesses abundant stomata on both surfaces of the leaves, rigid stems and bracts that scarcely exceed the inflorescence. From *C. nigra* it differs in its more rigid stems, in its red-purple stem-bases and in having stomata on the under surface of its rather broader leaves. From *C. bigelowii* it differs in its longer lowest bracts, its greater stature and the presence of stomata on the upper surface of the leaves.

Carex × decolorans occurs in damp, acidic upland habitats, especially mires, above 500 m, usually in the presence of both parents. For observations on introgression between *C. bigelowii* and *C. nigra* see Corner (2002).

Carex bigelowii	*Carex × decolorans*	*Carex nigra*
Rhizome scales red- or purple-brown.	Rhizome scales red- or purple-brown.	Rhizome scales brown or red-brown.
Stems 4–30 cm high, rigid, usually more than 2 mm wide near base.	**Stems** often *c.* 35 cm high **(usually taller than in** *C. bigelowii*), rigid, *c.* 1.5 mm wide.	Stems 7–45(–70) cm high, slender, not rigid, up to 2 mm wide.
Leaves 2–7 mm broad, stiff or arcuate; stomata confined to lower surface.	Leaves often more than 3 mm broad, somewhat stiff; **stomata ± abundant on both surfaces.**	Leaves 1–3(–5) mm broad, not stiff; stomata ± confined to upper surface.
Lowest bract much shorter than inflorescence.	**Lowest bract ± equalling inflorescence.**	Lowest bract ± equalling inflorescence.
Inflorescence short; spikes often clustered together.	Inflorescence usually longer and spikes less clustered than in *C. bigelowii* but less spaced than in *C. nigra*.	Inflorescence spikes spaced out and usually occupying a greater proportion of stem than in *C. × decolorans*.
♂ spike 1, rarely 2, broadly ellipsoid.	♂ spike(s) 1 or 2, ellipsoid.	♂ spike(s) 1 or 2, narrowly ellipsoid.

Carex microglochin M103

Carex microglochin was first found in 1923 on the Ben Lawers massif in v.c.
88, its only British station. The record for Harris (v.c. 110), based on living
material sent to Kew (Clark 1941), has never been confirmed for the island, a
most unlikely site (J.E. Raven in Preston 2004).

103 *Carex microglochin* Wahlenb.

Bristle Sedge   *Map 103*

Rhizomes slender, shortly creeping; shoots often single; roots pale yellow-brown; scales pale brown, persistent. *Stems* 5–12 cm, stiff, erect, subterete, striate, solid. *Leaves* 1–5 cm × 0.5–1 mm, thick, stiff, erect, channelled, ± truncate and rounded at apex, mid green; hypostomous; sheaths soon becoming brown and decaying, rarely fibrous, with inner face hyaline, becoming brown; apex straight, serrate; ligule *c*. 0.5 mm, rounded, tubular. *Inflorescence* a single, few-flowered, terminal spike 3–5 mm, male above, female below; bracts absent. *Male glumes* 2.5–3 mm, ovate-lanceolate, red-brown, with pale midrib; apex ± acute. *Female glumes* *c*. 2 mm, ovate-lanceolate, red-brown, with pale margins, caducous, with hyaline, acute apex. *Utricles* 3.5–4.5(–5) mm, narrowly conical, rounded at base, faintly ribbed, pale yellow-green, becoming straw-coloured; apex tapered into conical beak *c*. 1 mm long, deflexed at maturity; a stiff bristle (rachilla), arising within the utricle from the base of the nut, protrudes from the top of the beak; stigmas 3; nut cylindric-trigonous.   *Fr.* 7–9.

C. microglochin is a member of a distinctive high-level facies (**aii**), of *Carex viridula* subsp. *oedocarpa–Saxifraga aizoides* mire (**M11**) in which other alpine rarities occur (*C. atrofusca, Juncus biglumis, J. castaneus* etc.), together with *C. dioica, Thalictrum alpinum* and the bryophytes *Aneura pinguis, Blindia acuta, Campylium stellatum* and *Scorpidium revolvens*, in gently sloping, stony, micaceous flushes between 600 and 900 m where the total plant cover is usually less than 50 per cent.

This species could be confused with **104** *C. pauciflora*, which has been found in the proximity of *C. microglochin*. The latter is distinctive in having an exserted bristle arising from well below the nut but within the utricle wall; its outward appearance is very similar to but should not be mistaken for the persistent style of *C. pauciflora*. Also the utricles of *C. microglochin* are fewer on each inflorescence and, on average, smaller than in *C. pauciflora*. The shoots of the latter species are loosely clustered, not solitary or 2 or 3 together, and the lower leaf-sheaths have a short subulate lamina 1–2 mm long, a feature not seen in *C. microglochin*.

No hybrids of this species are known.

Carex microglochin is a **Red Data List** species in Britain; *Status*: **Vulnerable** (Cheffings & Farrell 2005).

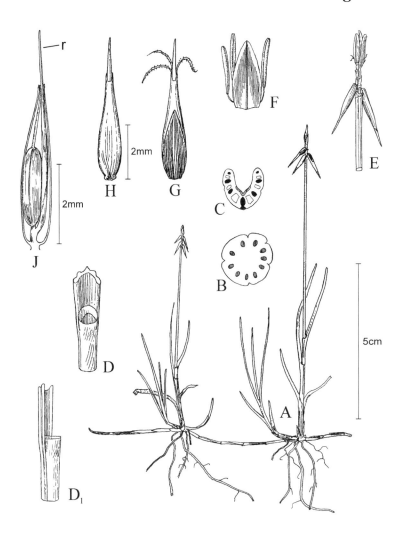

A Fertile shoots; **B** T.S. stem (culm); **C** T.S. leaf; **D** Inner face of leaf-sheath and ligule; **D₁** Side view of ligule; **E** Inflorescence; **F** Male floret; **G** Female floret; **H** Utricle; **J** Section through utricle, showing nut and whole length of rachilla (**r**).

104 *Carex pauciflora* Lightf.

Few-flowered Sedge   *Map 104*

Rhizomes slender, shortly creeping, often much branched, forming an open mat; shoots loosely tufted; roots cream or pale yellow-brown; scales pale (rarely dark) brown, striate, persistent. ***Stems*** 7–27 cm, stiff, trigonous, often curved, solid. ***Leaves*** up to 20 cm × 1–2 mm, with *c.* 9 veins, stiff, thick, ± channelled, mid green, gradually narrowed to a wide, rounded apex, those of sterile shoots often narrower and setaceous; hypostomous; sheaths pink- (rarely red-) brown, persistent, the lower ones with very short subulate green tips, with inner face hyaline; apex straight; ligule *c.* 0.5 mm, rounded, tubular. ***Inflorescence*** a single, few-flowered, terminal spike 3–8 mm, male above, female below; bracts absent. ***Male glumes*** 3.5–5 mm, lanceolate, pale red-brown, with hyaline margins; apex ± acute. ***Female glumes*** 3.5–4.5 mm, broadly lanceolate, clasping the utricle, caducous, pale red-brown, with margins hyaline towards the ± acute apex. ***Utricles*** 5–7 mm, subfusiform, tapered more abruptly below, faintly nerved, pale yellow- or rarely red-brown, tapered above to a beak-like apex; stigmas 3; style persistent in fruit, protruding from apex of utricle; nut oblong-cylindric, trigonous. ***Fr.*** 6–7.

C. pauciflora is a species of oligotrophic bogs characterised by *Sphagnum cuspidatum/fallax* bog-pool communities (**M2**), growing in the *Sphagnum* with *Andromeda polifolia*, *Drosera* spp., *Eriophorum angustifolium*, *Narthecium ossifragum*, *Rhynchospora alba* and the dwarf shrubs *Calluna vulgaris*, *Erica tetralix*, *Vaccinium oxycoccus* etc. Lowland to 820 m (Foley & Porter 2002).

C. pauciflora, because of its persistent style, may be confused with **103** *C. microglochin* with its bristle or rachilla; for differences see that species. It may initially also appear similar to **106** *C. pulicaris*, although in the field their ecological preferences are distinctive. *C. pulicaris* is always easily distinguished by the fine red-brown roots (only a rooting shoot needs to be lifted to see this) and the darker brown ellipsoid utricles which lack the persistent style of *C. pauciflora*. **51** *C. dioica* is vegetatively similar but has a narrower, channelled and inrolled leaf with only three veins.

No hybrids of *C. pauciflora* are known.

C. pauciflora is protected in Northern Ireland under Schedule 8 of the Wildlife Order (Northern Ireland) 1985.

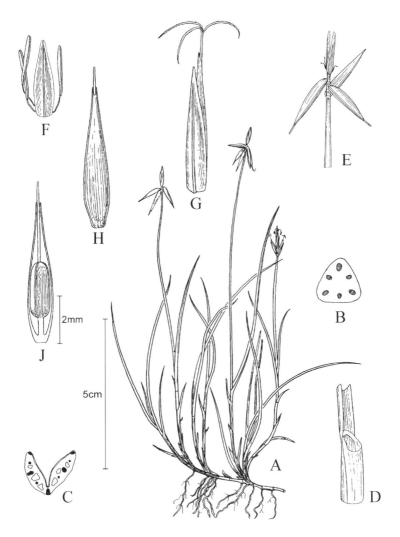

A Fertile shoots; **B** T.S. stem (culm); **C** T.S. leaf; **D** Inner face of leaf-sheath and ligule; **E** Inflorescence; **F** Male floret; **G** Female floret; **H** Utricle; **J** Section through utricle, showing nut.

M104 Carex pauciflora

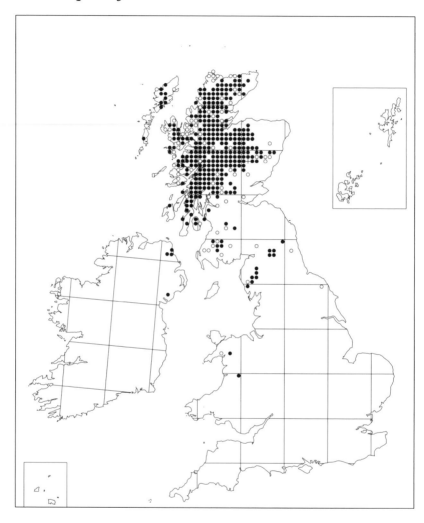

Carex pauciflora is found throughout the Highlands and N Scotland and is scattered in the Outer Isles; in England, in the Lake District and N Pennines, with one isolated locality in v.c. 62; in Wales, only in v.cc. 47 and 49. In Ireland, only in Antrim and Co. Down.

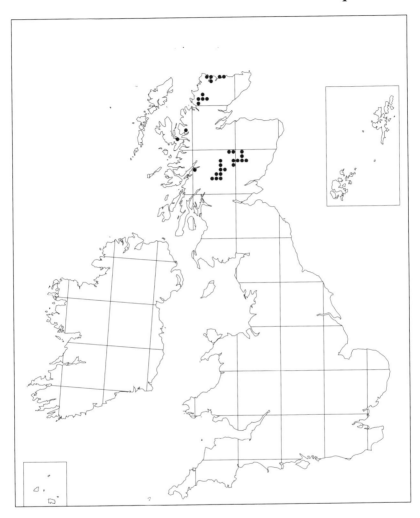

Carex rupestris is a local plant found in Scotland in the Grampians and Breadalbanes, W Ross, W Sutherland and E Skye. See also David (1979c). The record from a hill in South Uist (Heslop Harrison 1945), where no base-rich rock exists, is considered an error (J.E. Raven in Preston 2004).

105 *Carex rupestris* All.

Rock Sedge   *Map 105*

Rhizomes shortly creeping, often much branched; shoots ± tufted; roots purple-brown, slender; scales shiny, red-brown, persistent. ***Stems*** 7–20 cm, stiff, trigonous, solid. ***Leaves*** 5–20 cm × 1–1.5 mm, often curled or twisted, flat below, becoming keeled towards the gradually attenuated, trigonous apex, dull dark green, persistent on dying; hypostomous; sheaths red- or orange-brown, ribbed, persistent; inner face hyaline, becoming brown and persisting, with a straight, brown apex; ligule 0.5–2 mm, rounded, ± tubular. ***Inflorescence*** a single, terminal spike 7–15 mm, male above, female below, with a single bract at base of spike, glumaceous with a setaceous point, caducous. ***Male glumes*** 2.5–3 mm, ovate, red- or purple-brown, with obscure midrib; apex acute. ***Female glumes*** 2.5–3.5 mm, elliptic to broadly ovate, dark red- or purple-brown, with obscure midrib and narrowly hyaline margins, persistent; apex obtuse, sometimes mucronate. ***Utricles*** *c.* 3 mm, obovoid, trigonous, faintly ribbed below, grey-green to brown, erecto-patent to erect at maturity; beak *c.* 0.3 mm, slightly notched; stigmas 3; nut broadly ellipsoid, trigonous.   ***Fr.*** 7–8.

   C. rupestris is found on shallow skeletal soils on limestone cliff-ledges or on siliceous rock-ledges influenced by calcareous flushing, often on unstable slopes. Associated with general dry flush sedges, e.g. *C. flacca* and *C. pulicaris*, in the *Dryas–Silene acaulis* ledge community (**CG14**), often in association with other high-altitude sedge rarities such as *C. atrata*, *C. norvegica* and *C. vaginata*, usually above 600 m (to 935 m on Ben Lawers, v.c. 88: Foley & Porter 2002). In NW Scotland found in shallow calcareous rendzinas and other skeletal soils over Durness, Dalradian and Jurassic limestones in *Dryas octopetala–Carex flacca* dwarf shrub heath (**CG13**), where the pH can be as high as 7.5 (Averis *et al.* 2004) and where, with *C. capillaris*, it descends to sea level.

   C. rupestris can be confused with **106** *C. pulicaris*, with which it often grows. The latter species has narrow, straighter (not curled or twisted) leaves, V-shaped (keeled) in transverse section, and the leaf-sheaths are fibrous and brown, not red-brown as in *C. rupestris*. The young inflorescence looks similar, but *C. pulicaris* has only two stigmas and the female glume has a broader hyaline margin.

   No hybrids of *C. rupestris* are known.

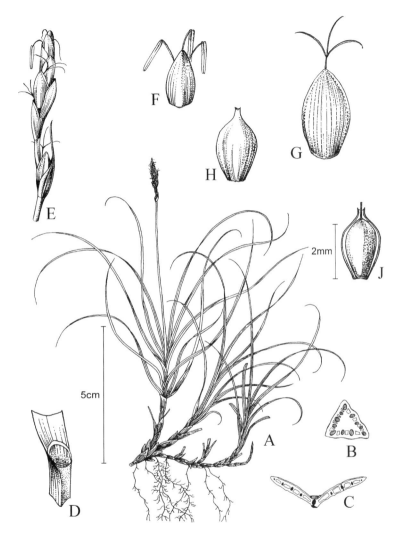

A Fertile shoot; **B** T.S. stem (culm); **C** T.S. leaf; **D** Inner face of leaf-sheath and ligule; **E** Inflorescence; **F** Male floret; **G** Female floret; **H** Utricle; **J** Section through utricle, showing nut.

106 *Carex pulicaris* L.

Flea Sedge   *Map 106*

Rhizomes shortly creeping; shoots often densely tufted; roots red-brown, very fine; scales pale brown or purplish-brown, becoming fibrous. *Stems* 10–30 cm, slender, stiff, terete. *Leaves* 5–25 cm × 0.5–1 mm, with *c.* 9 veins, ± stiff, keeled below, blunt at apex, dark green; hypostomous; sheaths becoming deep brown, ribbed, lower fibrous or soon decaying, with inner face hyaline and apex ± straight; ligule *c.* 0.5 mm, rounded. *Inflorescence* a single, few-flowered, terminal spike 10–25 mm, male above, female below; bracts absent. *Male glumes* 4.5–5 mm, oblong-elliptic, purple- or red-brown, with paler margins; apex obtuse or ± acute. *Female glumes* ± 3 mm, caducous, broadly lanceolate, red- or purple-brown, with midrib keeled and margins sometimes narrowly hyaline; apex acute or obtuse. *Utricles* 4–6 mm, ellipsoid or oblanceoloid, dark brown, shiny, usually deflexed at maturity on a short, stout pedicel and sensitive to touch (e.g. from a raindrop or insect), abscissing and 'jumping' away from the parent spike – hence the English name; beak 0.2 mm, slightly notched; stigmas 2; nut narrowly obovoid, biconvex, tapered to thick stalk.   *Fr.* 6–7.

C. pulicaris is found in a range of habitats, e.g. in mesotrophic mires of *C. rostrata–Sphagnum* (**M4, M8**) and *Molinia–Crepis paludosa* (**M26**), on stony flushes with *C. viridula* subsp. *oedocarpa* and *C. panicea* (**M11**), in *Calluna–Erica* heath with *Thymus polytrichus* (**H10d**) and in grass-heaths with *Alchemilla alpina* (**CG11**); also on limestone, in open vegetation within the *Sesleria–Galium sterneri* community (**CG9c**), in damper areas with *C. panicea* within the *Festuca–Agrostis* community (**CG10b**), in *Dryas–C. flacca* heath with *Pilosella–Ctenidium molluscum* (**CG13a**) and on ledges and in tall-herb communities at higher altitudes (in **CG14, U15** and **U17**).

C. pulicaris, before the utricles are deflexed, may be mistaken for **105** *C. rupestris*, with which it often grows (see that species). When not in flower it may be confused with **51** *C. dioica*, which has three-veined, inrolled leaves, and **104** *C. pauciflora*, which grows mainly in oligotrophic mires and has seven-veined leaves (like *C. pulicaris*), *c.* 2 mm wide and ± channelled. The leaf-sheaths of *C. pulicaris* are deep brown and ribbed; those of *C. dioica* and *C. pauciflora* are pale and barely striate. The mature utricles of *C. pulicaris* sometimes do not reflex and then simulate a female *C. dioica*, but the utricle shape and lack of ribs still distinguish it. No hybrids of *C. pulicaris* are known.

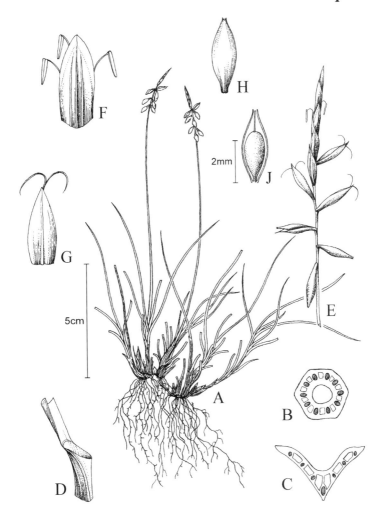

A Fertile shoot; **B** T.S. stem (culm); **C** T.S. leaf; **D** Inner face of leaf-sheath and ligule; **E** Inflorescence; **F** Male floret; **G** Female floret; **H** Utricle; **J** Section through utricle, showing nut.

M106 *Carex pulicaris*

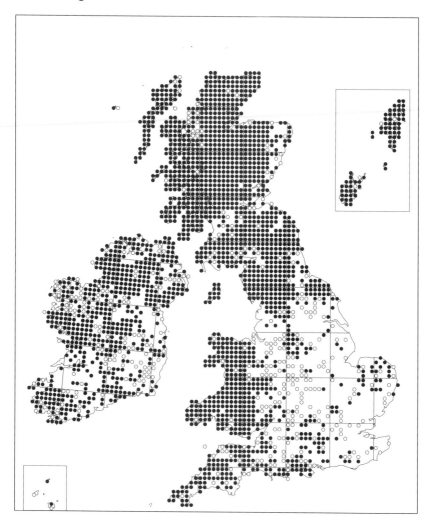

Carex pulicaris is a frequent plant of Scotland, N England and Wales; in E and S England most often found associated with valley mires but increasingly lost through drainage. In Ireland, frequent in a variety of habitats throughout.

8 DUBIOUS RECORDS, EXTINCT SPECIES AND ALIENS

Dubious records

Dandy (1958) listed three species of *Carex* that had been recorded dubiously in the British Isles, namely *C. bicolor* All., *C. glacialis* Mackenzie and *C. capitata* L. The first two were recorded for Rum, v.c. 104 (Heslop Harrison 1941, 1945), and the last for South Uist in the Outer Hebrides, v.c. 110 (Heslop Harrison 1945), all as single tufts. All three species have since disappeared from these localities and are believed to have been planted (Raven 1949; Jermy *et al.* 1982; Sabbagh 1999; Pearman & Walker 2004; Preston 2004). *C. bicolor*, a northern European species, is unlikely to occur in Britain, but the occurrence of *C. capitata* and *C. glacialis*, both present in montane areas of southern Norway, is feasible.

Smith (1830) mentioned that he had been sent a specimen by Drummond "from near Panmure, Forfar", which he identified as *C. secalina* sensu Schkuhr and which was later recorded by Babington (1843) and others as *C. hordeiformis* Wahlenb. (= *C. hordeistichos* Vill.). This is a species of southern and western Europe likely to have been introduced by G. Don, to whose garden Drummond eventually succeeded. Another western European species, *C. brizoides* L., recorded in a later edition of Babington's *Manual of British Botany* (1851) from Studley Wood, Yorkshire, and not found since, must also remain dubious, although it has been recorded from just across the English Channel in northern France; it was probably brought in on the roots of trees when the estate was being planted in the 19th century. We have seen a specimen in Keighley Museum.

Extinct species

Two species that we have included in the descriptions earlier in this book are considered extinct, **6a** *Trichophorum alpinum* (L.) Pers. and **99** *Carex trinervis* Degl. They have been included on the grounds that the habitats which each occupied may still be found in the areas where they were originally recorded. *Trichophorum alpinum*, which has not been seen in the wild since 1813, was found in a saddle mire in Angus and such remnant habitats in Scotland might still harbour the species, although when in fruit it is very distinctive and unlikely to have been missed if still extant. It was indeed recorded from near Kinlochleven in the 1930s by a visiting American botanist, Professor Fernald, but, although searched for subsequently, was not refound (see Forty & Rich 2005). The other species, *Carex trinervis*, has not been found since 1890 in East Norfolk and is characteristic of the mature brackish dune-slacks found on the nearby Dutch coast as well as on the coast of other western European countries. The coast of East Suffolk might still contain the species, easily mistaken for a form of *C. nigra*.

A third species, *Carex davalliana* Sm., which grew in a calcareous mire at Lansdown, near Bath, until the 1830s but has been lost through drainage, is not described since its habitat has completely disappeared. It is a densely tufted plant similar to **51** *C. dioica*, some 15–25 cm high, usually with a single, terminal unisexual spike and rough setaceous channelled leaves. The female spikes have 15–20 flowers, the female glumes are dark brown with hyaline margins and the utricles are 4–5 mm long, dark brown and faintly ribbed with a long beak (see Plate **51**, *C. dioica*, Figure H_2). Other records of this species in Britain have proved to be forms of *C. dioica*.

Aliens

The recording of aliens (neophytes) in the flora of the British Isles has been an activity taken seriously by members of the B.S.B.I. for many decades and, since its inception, by the Biological Records Centre. There has been a steady increase in the number of neophytes generally, especially of those recorded after 1850 (Preston *et al.* 2002), but these include rather few members of Cyperaceae. In the 19th century botanists travelling in Europe occasionally brought home live rootstocks that were cultivated in botanic gardens or their own gardens and may have escaped (see example above). From time to time the ornamental horticultural trade introduces a vigorous species for ground cover in urban landscaping which may have potential for spreading into natural habitats.

Clement & Foster (1994) list the following members of Cyperaceae that have been recorded rarely or occasionally in the British Isles. The more frequent of these species are printed in bold type and described more fully below (in alphabetical order).

From Australia or New Zealand (mostly as wool aliens)
Carex appressa R. Br., *C. brunnea* Thunb., *C. buchananii* Berggr., *C. devia* Cheeseman, *C. flagellifera* Colenso, *C. hubbardii* Nelmes, *C. inversa* R. Br., *C. longebrachiata* Boeck., *C. secta* Boott, *C. solanderi* Boott, *C. tereticaulis* F. Muell., *C. virgata* Sol. ex Boott

From North America
C. crawfordii Fernald, *C. deweyana* Schwein., *C. vulpinoidea* Michx.

From South Africa
Bulbostylis humilis (Kunth) C.B. Clarke, *B. striatella* C.B. Clarke

From South America
Scleria bracteata Cav.

Carex buchananii Berggr. (Silver-spiked Sedge)

An upright tufted sedge reaching a height of 75 cm. *Leaves* arching, narrow sharp-edged, of a distinctive reddish or coppery colour, with curled tips. *Stems* very slender, reddish. *Male spike* c. 2 cm long, cylindric. *Female spikes* up to 3, 1.5–2 cm long, cylindric; lowest bract much longer than inflorescence, reddish; *female glumes* silvery, pale and ± translucent, contrasting with utricle, with long excurrent midrib. *Utricles* reddish-brown, with prominent bifid beak.

Frequently cultivated in gardens and sometimes escaping. Recorded from Cessnock, v.c. 77, in 1990 and from Orchardstown, v.c. H6, in 2004.

Carex crawfordii Fernald

A tufted species resembling **49** *C. leporina* but differing as follows: *Leaves* usually about equalling stems. *Spikes* 7–15; *female glumes* 2.5–3 mm. somewhat darker, brown-hyaline. *Utricles* 4–5 mm, lanceoloid-ellipsoid.

Possibly introduced with fodder or other seed. Recorded from W Kent and Surrey (v.cc. 16 and 17) but not seen recently.

Carex longebrachiata Boeck.

A tufted plant with *stems* often up to 75 cm. *Leaves* 40 cm × 2–5 mm; sheaths brown, shiny, fibrous. *Inflorescence* of 4–7 distant or remote spikes (often 2 per node) on long (10–15cm) peduncles; *spikes* 15–25 mm, slender; *female glumes* 4 mm, brown-hyaline, aristate or mucronate. *Utricles* 6 mm, obovoid-ellipsoid, ribbed, rough, tapered to a fine beak 1.5 mm long.

It has been found with wool shoddy in Hampshire.

Carex inversa R. Br.

A shortly creeping plant with *stems* 30–40 cm, slender, acutely trigonous. *Leaves* 20–35 cm × 0.75–1.5 mm. *Inflorescence* a terminal cluster of 2–3 short spikes, male at base, female above, with long overtopping bracts; *female glumes* 2 mm, hyaline or pale brown with green midrib, attenuate. *Utricles* 3 mm, ovoid, green, ribbed, with rough beak 1 mm long.

Found with wool shoddy in Yorkshire and the Home Counties but not recorded for many years.

Carex secta Boott

A very large, tussock-forming sedge up to 1.5 m. *Leaves* up to 7 mm wide, light green to yellow-green. *Inflorescence* branched, slender, up to 1 m long, with pale brown spikes. *Utricles* chestnut-brown, weakly winged; stigmas 2.

Best distinguished from its close relative **35** *C. paniculata* by its extremely long, branched inflorescence and its paler, yellowish leaves.

Carex vulpinoidea Michx. (American Fox-sedge)

A tufted plant with *stems* 30–90 cm. *Leaves* often longer than stem (up to 180 cm), 2–4 mm wide. *Inflorescence* spike-like, narrow, with many short branches; *glumes* pale reddish-brown, aristate, giving 'bristly' appearance to inflorescence. *Utricles* 2–2.5 mm, ovoid to ovoid-orbicular, plano-convex; beak short, up to 1.2 mm; stigmas 2.

Possibly introduced with fodder or other seed and recorded from 10 vice-counties in England and Scotland, although only four of these records have occurred since 1970.

GLOSSARY

Abaxial: facing outwards, away from the axis of the stem (*cf.* **adaxial**).

Acicular: stiff and pointed, like a needle.

Acuminate: tapering to a long fine point (*cf.* **acute**).

Acute: narrowed into a short point (see Figure 2.11; *cf.* **acuminate**).

Adaxial: facing inwards, towards the axis of the stem (*cf.* **abaxial**).

Aerenchyma: tissue containing large, regular air-spaces.

Aerenchymatous: (of a root or stem) possessing large, regular air-spaces in the tissue.

Allozyme: see **isoenzymes**.

Amphistomous: having stomata on both leaf surfaces (*cf.* **epistomous**, **hypostomous**).

Anaerobic: without air/oxygen.

Anther: the terminal pollen-bearing portion of a stamen.

Antrorse: (of hairs or teeth) forward-pointing (*cf.* **retrorse**).

Apiculate: rounded but with a short point.

Apomixis (adjective **apomictic**): production of a fertile seed without the fusion of male and female nuclei (*cf.* **vivipary**).

Appressed: (of a utricle or a glume) inserted at an acute angle and lying close to the axis.

Arcuate: curved like a bow.

Arista: a bristle, usually the excurrent midrib of a glume (*cf.* **awn**, **rachilla**).

Aristate: possessing an arista (*cf.* **setaceous**).

Auriculate: furnished with ear-like appendages.

Awn: (on a glume) a bristle formed by the excurrent midrib (*cf.* **arista**).

Basal: (of a leaf) growing from the base of the plant (*cf.* **cauline**).

Basifixed: (of an anther) having the filament attached at or near the base.

Biconvex: convex on two sides (*cf.* **plano-convex**).

Bifid: (of a utricle beak) deeply forked at the apex (see Figure 2.44).

Bract: a modified, sometimes glume-like leaf subtending (having in its axil) a flower or branch of the inflorescence (see Figures 2.15–21, 31 and 33).

Bullate: with a surface raised into blister-like swellings.

Caducous: dropping off early.

Caespitose: tufted.

Canaliculate: (of a leaf-section) U-shaped, channelled (see Figure 2.4).

Capitate: (of an inflorescence) with flowers clustered and arising more or less from the stem apex.

Carr: wet woodland (usually of alder or sallow), a climax of lowland mires.

Cauline: (of a leaf) attached to the stem (*cf.* **basal**).

Ciliate: with an edge fringed with hairs.

Ciliolate: as above where the hairs are very small.

Cladoprophyll: a sterile utricle found at the base of a *Carex* spike.

Clavate: club-shaped.

Confluent: (of a style-base, e.g. in *Eleocharis*) not or hardly constricted at the junction with the nut.

Connate: joined so as not to be separable without tearing.

Connective: sterile apical portion of an anther.

Contiguous: (of spikes) touching each other end to end or overlapping.

Corymb (adjective **corymbose**): an inflorescence in which the pedicels become shorter upwards so that all the flowers are at approximately the same level.

Culm: the flowering or fruiting stem of a sedge or grass.

Decumbent: procumbent but with the apex turning up to become ascending or erect.

Dehisce (noun **dehiscence**): to burst or split open, releasing pollen.

Dentate: toothed.

Denticulate: with very small teeth.

Dichotomous: forked into two equal branches.

Dioecious: having the two sexes on different plants (*cf.* **monoecious**).

Distal(ly): at the end further from the point of attachment (*cf.* **proximal(ly)**).

Distant: (of spikes) with the distance between spikes about twice the length of those spikes (*cf.* **remote**).

Distichous: (of flowers or spikelets) arranged in two opposite rows down the stem.

Divaricate: diverging at a wide angle.

Dorsifixed: (of an anther) having the filament attached at or near the middle of the back.

Dystrophic: containing soil water which has very low concentrations of dissolved nutrients of any kind (*cf.* **oligotrophic**).

Ecotype: a form of a plant that is influenced by characteristics of the habitat in which it grows.

Edaphic: relating to the soil.

Elaiosome: tissue containing oil-bodies attractive to ants formed at the base of a utricle in some species (*e.g.* *Carex caryophyllea*) and disappearing as the seed matures.

Ellipsoid: (of a solid body) with an elliptic silhouette.

Elliptic: broadest in the middle and with the length up to about three times the breadth (*cf.* **oblong, ovate**).

Emarginate: (e.g. of a glume) with a pronounced angled notch at the apex.

Epistomous: having stomata on the upper (adaxial) surface of the leaf only (*cf.* **hypostomous, amphistomous**).

Eutrophic: nutrient-rich (usually either from a fertile soil or from being fed by a mineral-rich flow of water, with pH generally above 6: *cf.* **oligotrophic, mesotrophic**).

Excurrent: (of a vein, usually the midrib) running out beyond the margin of a leaf, bract or glume.

Exserted: protruding.

Falcate: curved like the blade of a reaper's sickle.

Fascicle: a bundle or bunch.

Felty: (of a root) having a thick covering of root-hairs.

Fibrillae (singular **fibrilla**, adjective **fibrillose**): thin strands of leaf-sheath tissue usually forming a ladder-like network (see p. 11).

Fibrous: (of a scale or sheath) with only the vascular bundles (veins) remaining as a result of decay of the tissue.

Filament: the stalk of a stamen, bearing the anther.

Filiform: thread-like.

Fimbriate: fringed.

Flaccid: not able to hold up its own weight.

Flexuous: wavy, twisted or bent alternately in opposite directions.

Fusiform: swollen in the middle and tapering to each end like a spindle or cigar.

Glaucous: bluish-green or bluish-grey.

Globose: (of a solid body) round, like a ball.

Glumaceous: glume-like.

Glume: a scale at the base of a male, female or hermaphrodite flower (see Figures 2.22–23).

Hispid: with short, stiff hairs.

Hyaline: colourless and transparent.

Hypostomous: having stomata on the lower (abaxial) surface of the leaf only (*cf.* **epistomous, amphistomous**).

Imbricate: regularly arranged in an overlapping pattern like roof-tiles.

Inflated: (of a utricle) swollen more than is necessary to contain the nut.

Inflorescence: a group of flowers with any branching system and associated bracts (see pp. 13 and 19–21 and Figures 2.15–21 and 31–37).

Inrolled: having the margins rolled upwards towards the midrib (see Figure 2.5).

Introgression: the transfer of genes (gene flow) from one taxon to another after hybridisation between them and subsequent back-crossing with one of them.

Involucral: (of bracts) forming an **involucre**, a structure round or just below an inflorescence (see p. 13 and Figures 2.15–21).

Involute: (of a leaf-edge) rolled inwards on the upper surface.

Isodiametric: (of a shape or organ) measuring more or less the same across in any direction.

Isoenzymes: complex chemical substances possessing different amino-acid sequences that can be extracted from plants of one taxon and compared with those of similar taxa, thereby indicating the degree of relationship between them in evolutionary terms. (The words **isoenzyme, isozyme** and **allozyme** are all used in this context.)

Keeled: (of a leaf) with a prominent midrib (like a keel) on the underside (see Figure 2.6).

Lanceolate: shaped like a lance, i.e. broadest below the middle with the length three or more times the breadth (*cf.* **ovate**).

Lanceoloid: (of a solid body) with a lanceolate silhouette.

Ligule: a membranous flap at the base of a leaf-blade.

Linear: long and narrow with more or less parallel margins (*cf.* **oblong**).

Lingulate: (e.g. of the apex of the inner face of a leaf-sheath) tongue-shaped (see Figure 2.10).

Mamillate: teat-like (*cf.* **papillate**).

Membranous: (of tissue) thin and often translucent (*cf.* **scarious**).

Mesotrophic: neither nutrient-rich (**eutrophic**) nor excessively nutrient-poor (**oligotrophic**); only occasionally flushed with nutrient-rich water.

Midrib: the median vein including, in the case of a glume, the nearby tissue.

Mitriform: shaped like a bishop's mitre.

Monoecious: having separate male and female flowers on the same plant (*cf.* **dioecious**).

Monopodial: (of a rhizome) developing so that the apical bud continues to grow horizontally while the upright shoots are produced from lateral buds (see Figure 2.2; *cf.* **sympodial**).

Morphometric: relating to the measurement of readily visible characteristics (as opposed to genetic or molecular features).

Mucro: a short, stiff point (e.g. at the apex of the midrib of a glume).

Mucronate: abruptly terminating in a short, stiff point.

Mucronulate: as above but with the mucro extremely small.

Nerved: (of a utricle) having conspicuous non-projecting veins (*cf.* **ribbed**).

Node: a more or less swollen point on a stem where leaves, flowers or lateral stems arise.

Nodose: (of a stem) bearing nodes.

Nothosubspecies: a hybrid subspecies.

Ob-: prefix signifying an inversion of a shape (e.g. **obovate**: egg-shaped with the broader end at the top).

Oblong: with the middle part more or less parallel-sided and the length up to about three times the breadth (*cf.* **elliptic, linear, ovate**).

Obtuse: blunt (see Figure 2.12).

Oceanic: (of distribution) confined to areas affected by the Atlantic Ocean.

Oligotrophic: nutrient-poor (usually from an infertile peaty soil with a low pH, generally below 5.5: *cf.* **dystrophic, eutrophic, mesotrophic**).

Orbicular: circular.

Ovate: shaped like an egg, i.e. broadest below the middle and with the length up to about three times the breadth (*cf.* **elliptic, lanceolate, oblong**).

Overwintering: (of leaves) remaining green throughout the winter season.

Ovoid: (of a solid body) with an ovate silhouette.

Panicle: a compound or much branched inflorescence.

Paniculate: (of an inflorescence) dichotomously branched as in a panicle.

Papilla: a small protuberance.

Papillate/papillose: with small protuberances (*cf.* **mamillate**).

Patent: diverging from the axis almost at a right-angle.

Peduncle: the stalk of a group of flowers (e.g. the spike in *Carex*).

Perigynium: the structure surrounding an ovary (in *Carex* a utricle).

Persistent: (of scales or sheaths) not quickly decaying, remaining intact on dying.

Phenotype (adjective **phenotypic**): the outward, physical manifestation of an organism, especially as influenced by its environment; a form of a taxon displaying particular physical characters.

Pilose: bearing long hairs.

Plano-convex: (of a utricle) more or less flat on the inner (adaxial) side and rounded on the opposite (abaxial) side (*cf.* **biconvex**).

Plicate: folded longitudinally (see Figure 2.7).

Procumbent: trailing along the ground.

Prophyll: a two-keeled structure at the base of a branch within an inflorescence, which may be glume-like, tubular or, in *Kobresia* and *Carex*, developed into a utricle.

Protandrous (noun **protandry**): having pollen maturing before the stigmas are receptive.

Protogynous (noun **protogyny**): having the stigmas receptive before the pollen is ripe.

Proximal(ly): at the end nearer the point of attachment (*cf.* **distal(ly)**).

Pruinose: having a waxy, whitish, powdery 'bloom' on the surface.

Pseudolateral: (of a main stem) appearing to branch from the side; (of a flower or inflorescence) appearing as if attached to the side.

Pseudostem: (in a sterile shoot) leaf-bases that remain folded around each other and upright, giving the impression of a false stem.

Pubescent: shortly and softly hairy.

Pyriform: shaped like a pear.

Rachilla: a bristle-like secondary axis of a spikelet (see Figure 2.42 and p. 505; *cf.* **arista**).

Rachis: (of a spikelet or inflorescence) the axis.

Remote: (of spikes) with the distance between spikes at least three times the length of those spikes (*cf.* **distant**).

Rendzina: a shallow structureless soil that forms on calcareous rocks usually having a neutral to high pH but being low in nutrients.

Reticulate: covered with a network, usually of veins.

Retrorse: (of hairs or teeth) backward-pointing (*cf.* **antrorse**).

Retuse: with a rounded, shallowly notched end.

Rhizome (adjective **rhizomatous**): a perennial underground stem (*cf.* **stolon**).

Ribbed: (of a utricle) having pronounced veins near the surface (*cf.* **nerved**).

Scaberulous: rough, with minute teeth.

Scabrid: rough to the touch.

Scarious: of a thin, dry, membranous texture and usually colourless (*cf.* **membranous**).

Sclerenchyma: supportive tissue of thickened cells.

Septa (singular **septum**): cellular cross-walls dividing longitudinal air-tubes of leaf-sheaths into a brickwork-like arrangement.

Serrate: with upward-pointing teeth.

Serrulate: finely serrate.

Sessile: without a stalk.

Setaceous: bristle-like (*cf.* **aristate**).

Soligenous: (of a mire) irrigated by ground-water moving down a slope.

Spike: a branch axis bearing flowers; a floral unit representing a spikelet that has been reduced to a single flower subtended by a prophyll (the utricle) and a glume-like bract.

Spikelet: the ultimate unit of a branched inflorescence bearing flowers (see Figures 2.22–23).

Stamen: the male organ, consisting of a filament bearing an anther (in Cyperaceae usually three per flower but in some species two: see Figures 2.24–27).

Stele: a central core of tissue (in a stem or root).

Stigma: the tip of the style, receptive to pollen (in Cyperaceae divided into two or three lobes: see Figures 2.24–27).

Stolon (adjective **stoloniferous**): a usually slender stem, on the surface or just below it, joining two plantlets or a plant and a storage organ (e.g. a tuber) (*cf.* **rhizome**).

Stoma (plural **stomata**): one of many tiny pores on the leaves and stems of vascular plants; stomata appear as lines of tiny white dots on the surface of the leaf.

Striate: marked with fine lines or grooves.

Style: the part of the female organ connecting the stigma to the ovary (in *Carex* largely contained within the utricle).

Style-base: a conical or pyramid-shaped structure remaining attached to the nut (see Figures 2.28–29).

Sub-: prefix meaning almost, not completely (e.g. **subfusiform**: more or less cigar-shaped).

Subtend: to have in its axil (see **bract**).

Subulate: awl-shaped (usually with a fine, sharp point).

Sympodial: (of a rhizome) developing so that the apical bud has finite growth in the form of an aerial shoot and lateral buds from its base produce further creeping stems (see Figure 2.1; *cf.* **monopodial**).

Terete: circular in transverse section.

Tomentose: covered with short, stiff, dense hairs.

Trabeculate: with longitudinal ridges and vertical lines of horizontally oblong epidermal cells.

Trigonous: having three angles and three faces between them in transverse section.

Triquetrous: sharply trigonous.

Truncate: (of a utricle beak) ending abruptly as if cut straight across (see Figures 2.46–47).

Tuberculate: with a surface covered in small swellings.

Unemergent (of an anther): never protruding from a male floret (and thus suggesting hybridity).

Utricle: a prophyll which has developed into a characteristic bottle-like structure and partially (in *Kobresia*) or completely (in *Carex*) surrounds the nut (see Figures 2.39–42).

Vivipary (adjective **viviparous**): production within the ovary of a seedling without prior fertilisation (*cf.* **apomixis**); used also of 'bulbils' (buds in leaf or pedicel axes which can produce young independent plantlets).

REFERENCES AND SELECTED BIBLIOGRAPHY

AVERIS, A.M., AVERIS, A.B.G., BIRKS, H.J.B., HORSFIELD, D., THOMPSON, D.B.A. & YEO, M.J.M. 2004. *An illustrated guide to British upland vegetation.* Joint Nature Conservation Committee, Peterborough.

BABINGTON, C.C. 1843, 1851. *Manual of British Botany.* London.

BECKETT, G. & BULL, A. 1999. *A Flora of Norfolk.* Gillian Beckett, Stanhoe, Norfolk.

BENNETT, A. 1886. *Carex trinervis* Degland from the coast of Norfolk. *Proceedings of the Linnean Society of London* **1886**: 84.

BENNETT, A. 1895. *Carex salina* Wahl., var. *Journal of Botany* **33**: 315.

BENNETT, A. 1897. Notes on British plants. II. – *Carex. Journal of Botany* **35**: 244–252, 259–264.

BENNETT, A. 1925. Notes on British Carices. *Transactions of the Botanical Society of Edinburgh* **29**: 127–129.

BENOIT, P.M. 1958. A new hybrid sedge. [*Carex binervis* × *C. punctata.*] *Watsonia* **4**: 122–124.

BERGGREN, G. 1969. *Atlas of seeds and small fruits of N.W. European plant species with morphological descriptions. Part. 2. Cyperaceae.* Swedish Natural Sciences Council, Stockholm.

BERNARD, J. M. 1976. The life history and population dynamics of shoots of *Carex rostrata. Journal of Ecology* **64**: 1045–1048.

BERTON, A. 1977. Sur l' anatomie des *Scirpus. Monde des Plantes* **72**: 1–5.

BIRKINSHAW, C.R. 1990. The ecology of *Carex depauperata* and its reinforcement at Cheddar Wood, Somerset. *Nature Conservancy Council, CSD Report* No. 1: 152.

BIRKINSHAW, C.R. 1991. The habitat preferences of *Carex depauperata* Curtis ex With. *Bulletin of the British Ecological Society* **22**: 26–31.

BIRSE, E.L. & ROBERTSON, J.S. 1967. The vegetation in the soils around Haddington and Eyemouth, in Ragg, J.M. & Futty, D.W. eds, *Memoirs of the Soil Survey of Scotland*, Sheets 33, 34 and 41 (part). Aberdeen.

BIRSE, E.L. & ROBERTSON, J.S. 1973. The vegetation in the soils around Carrick and the country around Girvan, in Brown, C.J. ed., *Memoirs of the Soil Survey of Scotland*, Sheets 7 and 8. Aberdeen.

BIRSE, E.L. & ROBERTSON, J.S. 1976. *Plant communities and soils of the lowland and southern upland regions of Scotland.* Macaulay Institute for Soil Research, Aberdeen.

BLACKSTOCK, N. 2007. A reassessment of the yellow sedges – *Carex flava* L. agg. (Cyperaceae) in the British Isles. Unpublished Ph.D. thesis, University of Lancaster.

BLACKSTOCK, N. & ASHTON, P.A. 2001. A re-assessment of the putative *Carex flava* agg. (Cyperaceae) hybrids at Malham Tarn (v.c. 64): A morphometric analysis. *Watsonia* **23**: 505–516.

BLACKSTOCK, N. & JERMY, [A.]C. 2001. Identification – Yellow-sedges *Carex flava* aggregate. *British Wildlife* **12**: 345–351.

BREWIS, A., BOWMAN, P. & ROSE, F. 1996. *The Flora of Hampshire*. Harley Books, Colchester.

BROWNING, J. & GORDON GRAY, K.D. 2000. Patterns of fruit morphology in *Bolboschoenus* (Cyperaceae) and their global distribution. *South African Journal of Botany* **66**: 63–71.

BROWNING, J., GORDON GRAY, K.D., SMITH, S.G. & VAN STADEN, J. 1997. *Bolboschoenus maritimus* s.l. in the Netherlands: a study of pericarp anatomy based on the work of Irene Robertus-Koster. *Annales Botanici Fennici* **34**: 115–126.

BRUHL, J.J. 1995. Sedge genera of the world: Relationships and a new classification of the Cyperaceae. *Australian Systematic Botany* **8**: 125–305.

BURES, P. 1998. A high polyploid *Eleocharis uniglumis* s.l. (Cyperaceae) from central and southeastern Europe. *Folia Geobotanica* **33**: 429–439.

BURNETT, J.H. ed. 1964. *The Vegetation of Scotland*. Oliver & Boyd. Edinburgh and London.

CALLAGHAN, T.V. 1976. Growth and population dynamics of *Carex bigelowii* in an alpine environment. Strategies of growth and population dynamics of Tundra plants 3. *Oikos* **27**: 402–413.

CAMPBELL, M.S. 1937. Three weeks botanising in the Outer Hebrides. *Report of the Botanical Society and Exchange Club of the British Isles* **11**: 304–318.

CAMPBELL, M.S. 1938. Further botanising in the Outer Hebrides. *Report of the Botanical Society and Exchange Club of the British Isles* **11**: 534–560.

CAYOUETTE, J. & CATLING, P.M. 1991. Notulae cyperologicae. 4. Naming, filing and conservation of sedge hybrids. *Cyperaceae Newsletter* No. 9: 6–7.

CAYOUETTE, J. & CATLING, P.M. 1992. Hybridization in the genus *Carex* with special reference to North America. *The Botanical Review* **58**: 351–438.

CAYOUETTE, J. & MORISSET, P. 1985. Chromosome studies on natural hybrids between maritime species of *Carex* (sections *Phacocystis* and *Cryptocarpae*) in northeastern North America, and their taxonomic implications. *Canadian Journal of Botany* **63**: 1957–1982.

CAYOUETTE, J. & MORISSET, P. 1986a. Chromosome studies on the *Carex salina* complex (Cyperaceae, Section *Cryptocarpae*) in northeastern North America. *Cytologia* **51**: 817–856.

CAYOUETTE, J. & MORISSET, P. 1986b. Chromosome studies on *Carex paleacea* Wahl., *C. nigra* (L.) Reichard and *C. aquatilis* Wahl. in northeastern North America. *Cytologia* **51**: 857–883.

CHATER, A.O. 1980. *Carex* L., in Tutin, T.G. *et al.* eds, *Flora Europaea* **5**: 290–323. Cambridge University Press, Cambridge.

CHATER, A.O. 1998. *Carex*, in Rich, T.C.G. & Jermy, A.C. eds, *Plant Crib 1998*. Botanical Society of the British Isles, London.

CHATTERS, C. 1988. Sand sedge in the Hampshire Avon Valley. *Proceedings of the Hampshire Field Club Archaeological Society* **44**: 119–126.

CLAPHAM, A.R., TUTIN, T.G. & WARBURG, E.F. (3rd ed. MOORE, D.M.) 1952, 1962, 1987. *Flora of the British Isles*. Cambridge University Press, Cambridge.

CHEFFINS, C.M. & FARRELL, L. eds. 2005. *Species Status No. 7: The Vascular Plant Red Data List for Great Britain.* Joint Nature Conservation Committee, Peterborough (ISSN 1473-0154, available on line at www.jncc.gov.uk/page-3354 or printed to order by Natural History Book Service).

CLEMENT, E.J. & FOSTER, M.C. 1994. *Alien Plants of the British Isles.* Botanical Society of the British Isles, London.

CLEVERING, O.A. & GULICK, W.M.G. van 1997. Restoration of *Scirpus lacustris* and *Scirpus maritimus* stands in a former tidal area. *Aquatic Botany* **55**: 229–246.

Climatological Atlas. 1952. Meteorological Office, London.

CLYMO, R.S. 1962. An experimental approach to part of the calcicole problem. *Journal of Ecology* **50**: 707–731.

COLLINS, R.P., McNALLY, S.F., SIMPSON, D.A. & JONES, M.B. 1988. Infraspecific variation of *Cyperus longus* L. in Europe. *New Phytologist* **10**: 279–289.

CONWAY, V.M. 1942. Biological Flora of the British Isles. *Cladium Mariscus* (L.) R. Br. *Journal of Ecology* **30**: 211–216.

COOMBE, D.E. 1954. *Carex humilis* Leyss, in Pigott, C.D. & Walters, S.M., On the interpretation of the discontinuous distributions shown by certain British species of open habitats, 111–113. *Journal of Ecology* **42**: 95–116.

CORNER, R.W.M. 1975. *Eleocharis austriaca* Hayek new to Scotland. *Watsonia* **10**: 411–412.

CORNER, R.W.M. 1981. *Carex vaginata* Tausch in southern Scotland. *Watsonia* **13**: 317–318.

CORNER, R.W.M. 2002. Observations on introgression between *Carex nigra* and *C. bigelowii* (Cyperaceae). *Watsonia* **24**: 217–220.

CORNER, R.W.M. 2004. *Carex vaginata* Tausch (Cyperaceae): a sedge new to England. *Watsonia* **25**: 127–130.

CORNER, R.W.M. & ROBERTS, F.J. 1989. *Carex ornithopoda* Willd. in Cumberland. *Watsonia* **17**: 437–438.

CORNER R., ROBERTS J., & ROBINSON, L. 2006. Sheathed Sedge (*Carex vaginata*): an update on its status in the Northern Pennines. *BSBI News* No. 101: 6–8.

COWIE, N.R. & SYDES, C. 1995. Status, distribution, ecology and management of String Sedge *Carex chordorrhiza. Scottish Natural Heritage Review* No. 41.

CRAWFORD, F.C. 1910. *Anatomy of the British Carices.* Edinburgh.

CRINS, W.J. & BALL, P.W. 1989. Taxonomy of the *Carex flava* complex (Cyperaceae) in North America and northern Eurasia II. Taxonomic treatment. *Canadian Journal of Botany* **67**: 1048–1065.

CURTIS, T.G.F. & FITZGERALD, R.A. 1994. The re-discovery of *Carex divisa*, the Divided Sedge, in Ireland. *Irish Naturalists' Journal* **24**: 496–498.

DAHLGREN, R.M.T., CLIFFORD, H.T. & YEO, P.F. 1985. *The families of the monocotyledons: structure, evolution, and taxonomy.* Springer-Verlag, Berlin.

DALBY, D.H. & DALBY, C. 1989. An overlooked taxonomic character in *Eleocharis multicaulis. Transactions of the Botanical Society of Edinburgh* **45**: 319–322.

DAMMAN, A.W.H. 1963. *Key to the* Carex *species of Newfoundland by vegetative characteristics.* Department of Forestry Publication No. 1017, Ottawa.

DANDY, J. E. 1958. *List of British Vascular Plants.* British Museum (Natural History) and Botanical Society of the British Isles, London.

DAVID, R.W. 1974. A *Carex* hybrid previously unknown. [supposedly *C. pallescens* × *C. laevigata.*] *Watsonia* 10: 165–166.

DAVID, R.W. 1976. Nomenclature of the British taxa of the *Carex muricata* L. aggregate. *Watsonia* 11: 59–65.

DAVID, R.W. 1977. The distribution of *Carex montana* L. in Britain. *Watsonia* 11: 377–378.

DAVID, R.W. 1978a. The distribution of *Carex digitata* L. in Britain. *Watsonia* 12: 47–49.

DAVID, R.W. 1978b. The distribution of *Carex elongata* L. in the British Isles. *Watsonia* 12: 158–160.

DAVID, R.W. 1979a. The distribution of *Carex humilis* Leyss. in Britain. *Watsonia* 12: 257–258.

DAVID, R.W. 1979b. Another British locality for *Carex muricata* L. *sensu stricto.* *Watsonia* 12: 335.

DAVID, R.W. 1979c. The distribution of *Carex rupestris* All. in Britain. *Watsonia* 12: 335–337.

DAVID, R.W. 1980a. The distribution of *Carex ornithopoda* Willd. in Britain. *Watsonia* 13: 53–54.

DAVID, R.W. 1980b. The distribution of *Carex rariflora* (Wahlenb.) Sm. in Britain. *Watsonia* 13: 124–125.

DAVID, R.W. 1981a. The distribution of *Carex ericetorum* Poll. in Britain. *Watsonia* 13: 225–226.

DAVID. R.W. 1981b. The distribution of *Carex punctata* Gaud. in Britain, Ireland and the Isle of Man. *Watsonia* 13: 318–321.

DAVID, R.W. 1982. The distribution of *Carex maritima* Gunn. in Britain. *Watsonia* 14: 178–180.

DAVID, R.W. 1983. The distribution of *Carex tomentosa* (*C. filiformis* auct.) in Britain. *Watsonia* 14: 412–414.

DAVID, R.W. 1990. The distribution of *Carex appropinquata* Schumacher (*C. paradoxa* Willd.) in Great Britain and Ireland. *Watsonia* 18: 201–204.

DAVID, R.W. 1993. *Carex filiformis* L. Downy-fruited sedge and *Carex humilis* Leyss., Dwarf Sedge, in Gillam, B. ed., *The Wiltshire Flora.* Pisces Publications, Newbury.

DAVID, R.W. & KELCEY, J.G. 1985. Biological Flora of the British Isles. *Carex muricata* L. aggregate. *Carex spicata* Huds. *Carex muricata* L. *Carex divulsa* Stokes. *Journal of Ecology* 73: 1021–1039.

DAVIES, E.W. 1953a. Notes on *Carex flava* and its allies. I – A sedge new to the British Isles. *Watsonia* 3: 66–69 and Plate 5.

DAVIES, E.W. 1953b. Notes on *Carex flava* and its allies. II – *Carex lepidocarpa* in the British Isles. *Watsonia* 3: 70–73 and Plate 6.

529

DAVIES, E.W. 1953c. Notes on *Carex flava* and its allies. III – The taxonomy and morphology of the British representatives. *Watsonia* **3**: 74–79 and Plates 7–9.

DAVIES, E.W. 1953d. Notes on *Carex flava* and its allies. IV – Geographic distribution. *Watsonia* **3**: 80–84.

DAVIES, E.W. 1956. Cytology, evolution and origin of the aneuploid series in the genus *Carex*. *Hereditas* **42**: 349–365.

DEAN, M. 2006. Morphological studies in genus *Carex* section *Phacocystis* (Cyperaceae) in the British Isles. Unpublished Ph.D. thesis, University of Lancaster.

DEAN, M. & ASHTON, P.A. 2006. A reassessment of the distribution of *Carex recta* Boott (Cyperaceae) in the British Isles. *Watsonia* **26**: 31–39.

DEAN, M., HUTCHEON, K., JERMY, A.C., CAYOUETTE, J. & ASHTON, P.A. 2005. *Carex salina* – a new species of sedge for Britain. *BSBI News* No. 99: 17–19.

DINES, T.D. & PRESTON, C.D. 2000. *Eleocharis parvula* discovered in Scotland. *Watsonia* **23**: 341–342.

DONOVAN, J.W. 1976. Common spike-rush (*Eleocharis palustris*) – a peculiar growth-form. *Nature in Wales* **15**: 25–26.

DRUCE, G.C. 1926. *Carex flava* × *saxatilis* = *C. Marshalli* Arth. Bennett, in Plant notes, etc., for 1925. *Report of the Botanical Society and Exchange Club of the British Isles* **7**: 789.

DUMONT, J.-M. 1976. Les deux sous-espèces de *Scirpus cespitosus* L. en Haute Ardenne, particulièrement au Plateau des Tailles. *Bulletin de la Société Royale de Botanique de Belgique* **109**: 307–318.

DUNBAR, A. 1973. Pollen development in the *Eleocharis palustris* group (Cyperaceae). I. Ultrastructure and ontogeny. *Botaniska Notiser* **126**: 197–254.

EASY, G. (1990). A note on Cambridgeshire bulrushes. *Nature in Cambridgeshire* No. 32: 58.

EDDY, A. & WELCH, D. 1969. The vegetation of Moor House National Nature Reserve. *Vegetatio* **16**: 239–284.

EGOROVA, T.V. 1999. *The sedges* (*Carex* L.) *of Russia and adjacent states* (*within the limits of the former USSR*). St Petersburg State Chemical-Pharmaceutical Academy, St Petersburg, and Missouri Botanical Garden Press, St Louis.

ELLENBERG, H. 1988. *Vegetation Ecology of Central Europe*. 4th ed., English translation. Cambridge University Press, Cambridge.

ERNST, W.H.O., VIS, R.D. & PICCOLI, F. 1995. Silicon in developing nuts of the Sedge *Schoenus nigricans*. *Journal of Plant Physiology* **146**: 481–488.

ERSKINE, S.E. & LAMBRICK, C.L. 2000. *True Fox Sedge,* Carex vulpina, *in Oxfordshire in 2000*. Ashmolean Natural History Society of Oxfordshire, Rare Plants Group, Oxford.

EWING, P. 1910. On some Scottish alpine forms of *Carex*. *Annals of Scottish Natural History* **75**: 174–181.

FAULKNER, J.S. 1970. Experimental studies on *Carex* section Acutae. Unpublished D.Phil. thesis, University of Oxford.

FAULKNER, J.S. 1972. Chromosome studies on *Carex* section Acutae in N.W. Europe. *Botanical Journal of the Linnean Society* **65**: 272–301.

FAULKNER, J.S. 1973. Experimental hybridisation of north-west European species in *Carex* section Acutae (Cyperaceae). *Botanical Journal of the Linnean Society* **67**: 233–253.

FAY, M.F., COWAN, R.S. & SIMPSON, D.A. 2003. Hybridisation between *Schoenoplectus tabernaemontani* and *S. triqueter* (Cyperaceae) in the British Isles. *Watsonia* **24**: 433–442.

FAY, M.F., O'ROURKE, A. & RICH, T.C.G. 2003. A preliminary investigation of genetic variation in Western European *Carex depauperata* Curtis ex With. (Cyperaceae), Starved Wood-sedge. *Watsonia* **24**: 507–511.

FITTER, A. & SMITH, C. 1979. *A Wood in Ascam: a Study in Wetland Conservation – Askham Bog 1879–1979.* York.

FITTER, R. & FITTER, A. 1984. *Collins Guide to the Grasses, Sedges, Rushes and Ferns of Britain and Northern Europe.* Collins, London.

FLORA OF NORTH AMERICA EDITORIAL COMMITTEE. 2002. *Flora of North America* **23**: *Cyperaceae.* Oxford University Press, New York and Oxford.

FOLEY, M.J.Y. 2005. *Carex trinervis* Degl. (Cyperaceae) – a western European coastal endemic. *Candollea* **60**: 87–95.

FOLEY, M.J.Y. 2006. Epitypification of *Carex vulpina* L. (Cyperaceae). *Watsonia* **26**: 27–30.

FOLEY, M.J.Y. & PORTER, M.S. 2000. *Carex muricata* L. subsp. *muricata* (Cyperaceae) – a review of its present status in Britain. *Watsonia* **23**: 279–286.

FOLEY, M.J.Y. & PORTER, M.S. 2002. Cyperaceae [some taxa], in Preston, C.D., Pearman, D.A. & Dines, T.D. eds, *New Atlas of the British and Irish Flora.* Oxford University Press, Oxford.

FORTY, M. & RICH, T. eds. 2005. *The Botanist. The botanical diary of Eleanor Vachell (1879–1948).* National Museum of Wales, Cardiff.

FREMSTAD, E. & SKOGEN, A. 1978. *Trichophorum caespitosum* ssp. *germanicum* i Norge. (*Trichophorum caespitosum* ssp. *germanicum* in Norway.) *Blyttia* **36**: 135–144.

FRENCH, G.C., HOLLINGSWORTH, P.M., CORNER, R.W.M., ROBERTS, F.J. & TAYLOR, I. 2005. Clonal diversity in two recently discovered English populations of *Carex vaginata* Tausch (Cyperaceae). *Watsonia* **25**: 389–395.

GEORGE, M. 1992. *The Land Use, Ecology and Conservation of Broadland.* Packard Publishing, Chichester.

GOETGHEBEUR, P. 1998. Cyperaceae, in Kubitzki, K. ed., *The families and genera of vascular plants.* **4**: *Flowering plants, monocotyledons:* Alismatanae *and* Commelinanae (*except* Gramineae), 141–190. Springer-Verlag, Berlin.

GRIME, J.P., HODGSON, J.G. & HUNT, R. 1988. *Comparative Plant Ecology.* Unwin Hyman, London.

HALLKA, L., TOIVONEN, H., SAARIO, S. & PYKÄLÄ, J. 1992. Chromosome counts in the *Carex flava* complex (Cyperaceae) in Finland. *Nordic Journal of Botany* **12**: 651–655.

HARBORNE, J.B. 1971. Distribution and taxonomic significance of flavonoids in the leaves of the Cyperaceae. *Phytochemistry* **10**: 1569–1594.

HARRAP, S. 2006. *Isolepis cernua*: do different? *BSBI News* No. 103: 13.

HEDRÉN, M. 1997. Genetic variation and hybridization in Swedish *Schoenus* (Cyperaceae). *Plant Systematics and Evolution* **204**: 21–37.

HEDRÉN, M. 2003. Patterns of allozyme and morphological differentiation in the *Carex flava* complex (Cyperaceae) in Fennoscandia. *Nordic Journal of Botany* **22**: 257–301.

HESLOP HARRISON, J.W. 1941. *Carex bicolor* All., a sedge new to the British Isles, in the Isle of Rhum. *Journal of Botany* **79**: 111–113.

HESLOP HARRISON, J.W. 1945. Noteworthy sedges from the Inner and Outer Hebrides, with an account of two species new to the British Isles. *Transactions and Proceedings of the Botanical Society of Edinburgh* **34**: 270–277.

HILBIG, W. 1994. Das segetale Auftreten von *Bolboschoenus maritimus* (L.) Palla. *Berichte der Bayerischen Botanischen Gesellschaft* **64**: 81–85.

HILL, M.O., MOUNTFORD, J.O., ROY, D.B. & BUNCE, R.G.H. 1999. *Ellenberg indicator values for British plants.* Department of the Environment, Transport and Rural Affairs, London.

HILL, M.O., PRESTON, C.D. & SMITH, A.J.E. eds. 1991. *Atlas of bryophytes of Britain and Ireland 1. Liverworts.* Harley Books, Colchester.

HJELMQVIST, H. & NYHOLM, E. 1947. Some anatomical species-characteristics in the Scandinavian Carices Distigmaticae (in Swedish, with English summary at end). *Botaniska Notiser* **1947**: 1–31.

HOLDEN, A.V. 1961. Concentration of chloride in fresh waters and rainwater. *Nature* **192**: 961.

HOLDGATE, M.W. 1955. The vegetation of some British upland fens. *Journal of Ecology* **43**: 389–403.

HOLLINGSWORTH, P.M. & SWAN, G.A. 1999. Genetic differentiation and hybridisation among subspecies of Deergrass (*Trichophorum cespitosum* (L.) Hartman) in Northumberland. *Watsonia* **22**: 235–242.

HORSFIELD, D., HOBBS, A.M., AVERIS, A.B.G. & KINNES, L.H. 1991. *The vegetation of Connemara in relation to plant communities of Great Britain.* Nature Conservancy Council, Edinburgh.

HYLANDER, N. 1966. *Carex*, in *Nordisk Kärlväxtfloro* **2**: 42–188. Stockholm.

JALAS, J. & HIRVELÄ, U. 1964. Notes on the taxonomy and leaf anatomy of *Carex elata* All., *C. omskiana* Meinsh. and *C.* × *turfosa* Fr. *Annales Botanici Fennici* **1**: 47–54.

JARDINE, E. 1994. An analysis of the genetic and phenotypic variation within and between two populations of the rare sedge, *Carex chordorrhiza* L. fil. Unpublished B.Sc. thesis, University of Edinburgh.

JARVIS, C. 2007. *Order out of Chaos: Linnaean Plant Names and their Types.* Linnean Society of London in association with the Natural History Museum, London.

JERMY, A.C. 1967. *Carex* Section *Carex* (= *Acutae* Fr.). *Proceedings of the Botanical Society of the British Isles* **6**: 375–379.

JERMY, A.C., CHATER, A.O. & DAVID, R.W. 1982. *Sedges of the British Isles.* B.S.B.I. Handbook No. 1, Edition 2. Botanical Society of the British Isles, London.

JERMY, A.C., HIBBERD, D.J. & SIMS, P.A. 1978. Brackish and freshwater ecosystems. Chapter 9 in Jermy, A.C. & Crabbe, J.A. eds, *The Island of Mull: a Survey of its Flora and Environment*. British Museum (Natural History), London.

JERMY, A.C., JAMES, P.W. & EDDY, A. 1978. Terrestrial ecosystems. Chapter 10 in Jermy, A.C. & Crabbe, J.A. eds, *The Island of Mull: a Survey of its Flora and Environment*. British Museum (Natural History), London.

JERMY, A.C. & TUTIN, T.G. 1968. *British Sedges*. Botanical Society of the British Isles, London.

KAY, Q. & JOHN, R. 1994. *Population genetics and demographic ecology of some scarce and declining vascular plants of Welsh lowland grassland and related habitats*. Science Report No. 93. Countryside Council for Wales, Bangor.

KENT, D.H. 1976. *Historical Flora of Middlesex*. Ray Society, London.

KENT, D.H. 1992. *List of Vascular Plants of the British Isles*. Botanical Society of the British Isles, London.

KENT, D.H. 1996 [correctly 1997]. *List of Vascular Plants of the British Isles. Supplement 1*. Botanical Society of the British Isles, Leicester.

KENT, D.H. & STACE, C.A. 2000. *List of Vascular Plants of the British Isles. Supplement 2*. Botanical Society of the British Isles, Leicester.

KERN, J.H. & REICHGELT, T.J. 1954. *Carex*, in *Flora Neerlandica*, 1 (3). Amsterdam.

KERSHAW, K.A. 1962. Quantitative ecological studies from Landmannahellir, Iceland. II. The rhizome behaviour of *Carex bigelowii* and *Calamagrostis neglecta*. *Journal of Ecology* 50: 171–179.

KERTLAND, M.P.H. 1971. *Eriophorum gracile* Roth in Ireland. *Irish Naturalists' Journal* 17: 62.

KJELLSSON, G. 1985. Seed fate in a population of *Carex pilulifera* L. *Oecologia (Berlin)* 67: 416-429

KLIMKO, M. & KREFT, A. 1999. Interpopulational variation of nutlets and glumes of *Bolboschoenus maritimus* (L.) Palla in Poland. *Biological Bulletin of Poznan* 36: 57–69.

KOYAMA, T. 1962. Classification of the family Cyperaceae (2). *Journal of the Faculty of Science, University of Tokyo, Sect. 3, Bot.* 8: 149–278.

KRAHULEC, F., FRANTÍK, T. & HROUDOVÁ, Z. 1996. Morphological variation of *Bolboschoenus maritimus* population over a ten year period. *Preslia, Praha* 68: 13–22.

KRECZETOWICZ, V.I. 1936. Are the sedges of subgenus *Primocarex* Kük. primitive? [in Russian]. *Botanicheskij Zhurnal SSSR (Journal Botanique de l' URSS)* 21: 295–424.

KÜKENTHAL, G. 1909. *Cyperaceae–Caricoideae*, in Engler, A., *Das Pflanzenreich* 4 (20), Heft 38. Leipzig.

KÜKENTHAL, G. 1935–1936. *Cyperaceae–Scirpoideae–Cypereae*, in Engler, A., *Das Pflanzenreich* 4 (20), Heft 101. Leipzig.

KUKKONEN, I. 1984. On the inflorescence structure in the family Cyperaceae. *Annales Botanici Fennici* 21: 257–264.

KUKKONEN, I. 1986. Special features of the inflorescence structure in the family Cyperaceae. *Annales Botanici Fennici* **23**: 107–120.

LAMBERT, J. M. 1951. Alluvial stratigraphy and vegetational succession in the region of the Bure Valley Broads. III. Classification, status and distribution of communities. *Journal of Ecology* **39**: 149–170 and Plates 11–13.

LEACH, S.J. 1986. Botanical Notes: *Eleocharis uniglumis* L. in Co. Down. *Irish Naturalists' Journal* **22**: 121.

LEACH, S.J., McMULLEN, A.S. & NORTHRIDGE, R.H. 1987. Botanical notes. *Rhynchospora fusca* (L.) Alt. f. in Co. Fermanagh. *Irish Naturalists' Journal* **22**: 262.

LECK, M.A. & SCHUTZ, W. 2005. Regeneration of Cyperaceae, with particular reference to seed ecology and seed banks. *Perspectives in Plant Ecology, Evolution and Systematics* **7**: 95–133.

LEEREVELD, H., MEEUSE, A.D.J. & STELLEMAN, P. 1981. Anthecological relations between reputedly anemophilous flowers and syrphid flies: 4. A note on the anthecology of *Scirpus maritimus* L. *Acta Botanica Neerlandica* **30**: 465–473.

LEGG, C., COWIE, N. & HAMILTON, A. 1995. *Experimental investigation of the response of the String Sedge* Carex chordorrhiza *to changes in water depth in summer.* Research, Survey and Monitoring Report No. 41. Scottish Natural Heritage, Edinburgh.

LEWIS, K.R. & JOHN, B. 1961. Hybridisation in a wild population of *Eleocharis palustris*. *Chromosoma* **12**: 433–468.

LOUSLEY, J.E. 1975. *Scirpus* L., in Stace, C.A. ed., *Hybridization and the Flora of the British Isles*, 510–512. Academic Press, London.

LOUSLEY, J.E. 1976. *Flora of Surrey*. David & Charles, Newton Abbot and London.

LOWE, C.J. 2004. *Carex divulsa* in North Yorkshire. *BSBI News* No. 96: 29–30.

MARSHALL, E.S. 1911. Dalmally plants, 1910. *Journal of Botany* **49**: 191–198.

McKENNA, P.H. 2000. The comparison of National Vegetation Classifications for two sites in Britain where *Carex flava* L. is extant. Unpublished B.Sc. dissertation, Department of Natural and Applied Sciences, Edge Hill College of Higher Education, Ormskirk.

McVEAN, D.N. & RATCLIFFE, D.A. 1962. *Plant Communities of the Scottish Highlands*. Her Majesty's Stationery Office, London.

METCALFE, C.R. 1971. *Anatomy of the Monocotyledons. V. Cyperaceae.* Oxford.

MITCHELL, J. & STIRLING, A. McG. 1980. *Carex elongata* in Scotland. *Glasgow Naturalist* **20**: 65–70.

MUASYA, A.[M.], BRUHL, J.J., SIMPSON, D.A., CULHAM, A. & CHASE, M.W. 2000. Suprageneric phylogeny of Cyperaceae, in Wilson, K.L. & Morrison, D. eds, *Monocots: Systematics and Evolution*, 593–601. CSIRO Publishing, Melbourne.

MUASYA, A.M. & SIMPSON, D.A. 2002. A monograph of the genus *Isolepis*. *Kew Bulletin* **57**: 257–362.

MUASYA, A.[M.], SIMPSON, D.A., CHASE, M.W. & CULHAM, A. 2000. Phylogenetic relationships within the heterogeneous *Scirpus* s.lat. (Cyperaceae) inferred from *rbcL* and *trnL-F* sequence data, in Wilson, K.L. & Morrison, D. eds, *Monocots: Systematics and Evolution* 610–614. CSIRO Publishing, Melbourne.

MUASYA, A.[M.], SIMPSON, D.A., CHASE, M.W. & CULHAM, A. 2001. A phylogeny of *Isolepis* (Cyperaceae) inferred using plastid *rbcL* and *trnL-F* sequence data. *Systematic Botany* **26**: 342–353.

MUASYA, A.M., SIMPSON, D.A., CULHAM, A. & CHASE, M.W. 1998. An assessment of suprageneric phylogeny in Cyperaceae using *rbcL* sequence data. *Plant Systematics and Evolution* **211**: 257–271.

MUASYA, A.M., SIMPSON, D.A., VERBOOM, G.A., GOETGHEBEUR, P., NACZI, R.F.C., CHASE, M.W. & SMETS, E. In press. Phylogeny of Cyperaceae based on DNA sequence data: current progress and future prospects. *The Botanical Review*.

MUNDELL, T. 2002. *Scirpus* or *Carex*? BSBI News No. 90: 18–19.

NELMES, E. 1939. Notes on British Carices. – IV. *Carex* vulpina L. *Journal of Botany* **77**: 259–266.

NELMES, E. 1947. A hybrid sedge new to the British Isles. [*Carex hirta* × *C. vesicaria*.] *Report of the Botanical Society and Exchange Club of the British Isles* **13**: 93–94.

NEUMANN, A. 1952. Vorläufiger Bestimmungsschlüssel für *Carex*-Arten Nordwestdeutschlands in blütenlosen Zustande. *Mitteilungen der Floristisch-Soziologischen Arbeitsgemeinschaft* NF **3**: 44–77.

NILSSON, Ö. & HJELMQVIST, H. 1967. Studies on the nutlet structure of the south Scandinavian species of *Carex*. *Botaniska Notiser* **120**: 460–485.

NOBLE, J.C. 1982. Biological Flora of the British Isles. *Carex arenaria* L. *Journal of Ecology* **70**: 867–886.

NOBLE, J.C., BELL, A.D. & HARPER, J.L. 1979. The population biology of plants with clonal growth. I. The morphology and structural demography of *Carex arenaria*. *Journal of Ecology* **67**: 983–1008.

NORLINDH, T. 1972. Notes on the variation and taxonomy in the *Scirpus maritimus* complex. *Botaniska Notiser* **125**: 397–405.

O'MAHONY, T. 1983. *Carex divulsa* Stokes × *C. remota* L. (*C.* × *emmae* L. Gross) in Mid Cork, v.c. H14, new to Ireland. *Watsonia* **14**: 455.

O'MAHONY, T. 1989. *Carex divulsa* Stokes × *C. muricata* L. occurring as a spontaneous garden hybrid and wild plant in Cork, new to Ireland. *Irish Naturalists' Journal* **23**: 137–141.

O'MAHONY, T. 2004. *Carex divulsa* Stokes (Grey Sedge) × *C. muricata* L. (Prickly Sedge) in the Irish flora, and its implications for the taxonomy of the *C. muricata* group in Europe. *Irish Botanical News* No. 14: 5–14.

O'MAHONY, T. 2005. *Carex divulsa* Stokes subsp. *divulsa* (Grey Sedge) × *C. remota* L. (Remote Sedge) (= *C.* ×*emmae* L. Gross) (Cyperaceae) in the European flora. *Irish Botanical News* No. 15: 5–17.

OTENG-YEBOAH, A.A. 1977. Observations on *Blysmus* and *Blysmopsis*. *Notes from the Royal Botanic Garden, Edinburgh* **35**: 399–406.

PAGE, S.E. & RIELEY, J.O. 1985. The ecology and distribution of *Carex chordorrhiza* L. fil. *Watsonia* **15**: 253–259.

PANKHURST, R.J. & MULLIN, J.M. 1991. *Flora of the Outer Hebrides*. Natural History Museum Publications, London.

PEARMAN, D.A. & WALKER, K.J. 2004. An examination of J.W. Heslop Harrison's unconfirmed plant records from Rum. *Watsonia* **25**: 45–63.

PEARSALL, W.H. 1934. Some hybrid Carices. [*C. rostrata* × *vesicaria, C. paniculata* × *remota, C. remota* × *vulpina.*] *Report of the Botanical Society and Exchange Club of the British Isles* **10**: 682–685.

PERRING, F.H. & SELL, P.D. eds. 1968. *Critical Supplement to the Atlas of the British Flora*. Thomas Nelson, London.

PETCH, C.P. & SWANN, E.L. 1956. A hybrid sedge from West Norfolk. [*Carex pseudocyperus* × *C. rostrata.*] *Proceedings of the Botanical Society of the British Isles* **2**: 1–3 and plate.

PHILLIPS, M.E. 1953. Studies in the quantitative morphology and ecology of *Eriophorum angustifolium* Roth. I. The rhizome system. *Journal of Ecology* **41**: 295–318.

PHILLIPS, M.E. 1954a. Studies in the quantitative morphology and ecology of *Eriophorum angustifolium* Roth. III. The leafy shoot. *New Phytologist* **53**: 312–343.

PHILLIPS, M.E. 1954b. Biological Flora of the British Isles. *Eriophorum angustifolium* Roth. *Journal of Ecology* **42**: 612–622.

PHILP, E.G. 1988. *Scirpus triqueter* refound in Kent. *BSBI News* No. 49: 49.

PIGNOTTI, L. 2003. *Scirpus* L. and related genera (Cyperaceae) in Italy. *Webbia* **58**: 281–400.

PIGNOTTI, L. & MARIOTTI, L.M. 2004. Micromorphology of *Scirpus* (Cyperaceae) and related genera in south-west Europe. *Botanical Journal of the Linnean Society* **145**: 45–58.

PORLEY, R.D. 1999. Separation of *Carex vulpina* L. and *C. otrubae* Podp. (Cyperaceae) using transverse leaf sections. *Watsonia* **22**: 431–432.

PORTER, M.S. & FOLEY, M.J.Y. 2002. Cyperaceae [some taxa], in Preston, C.D., Pearman, D.A. & Dines, T.D. eds, *New Atlas of the British and Irish Flora*. Oxford University Press, Oxford.

PORTER, M.S. & ROBERTS, F.J. 1997. Bird's-foot Sedge (*Carex ornithopoda* Willd.) in Cumbria. *The Carlisle Naturalist* **5**: 18–23.

PRESTON, C.D. ed. 2004. John Raven's report on his visit to the Hebrides, 1948. *Watsonia* **25**: 17–44.

PRESTON, C.D. & CROFT, J.M. 1997. *Aquatic plants in Britain and Ireland*. Harley Books, Colchester.

PRESTON, C. D., PEARMAN, D.A. & DINES, T.D. eds. 2002. *New Atlas of the British and Irish Flora*. Oxford University Press, Oxford.

PROCTOR, M.C.F. 1991. Scanning electron micrographs of leaf surface characters in the *Carex nigra* group. *BSBI News* No. 57: 54–55.

PYKÄLÄ, J. & TOIVONEN, H. 1994. Taxonomy of the *Carex flava* complex (Cyperaceae) in Finland. *Nordic Journal of Botany* **14**: 173–191.

RATCLIFFE, D.A. 1964a. Mires and bogs, in Burnett, J.H. ed., *The Vegetation of Scotland*, Chapter 10. Oliver & Boyd, Edinburgh and London.

RATCLIFFE, D.A. 1964b. Montane mires and bogs, in Burnett, J.H. ed., *The Vegetation of Scotland*, Chapter 15. Oliver & Boyd, Edinburgh and London.

RATCLIFFE, D.A. 1968. An ecological account of Atlantic bryophytes in the British Isles. *New Phytologist* **67**: 365–439.

RATCLIFFE, D.A. ed. 1977. *A Nature Conservation Review*. 2 volumes. Cambridge University Press, Cambridge.

RAVEN, J.E. 1949. Alien plant introductions on the Isle of Rhum. *Nature* **163**: 104–105.

ŘEPKA, R. 2003. The *Carex muricata* aggregate in the Czech Republic: multivariate analysis of quantitative morphological characters. *Preslia, Praha* **75**: 233–248.

ŘEPKA, R. & DANIHELKA, J. 2005. Typification of the name *Carex muricata* var. *lamprocarpa* Wallr. and its nomenclatural consequences. *Preslia, Praha* **77**: 129–136.

RICH, T.C.G. 1994. The rediscovery of starved wood-sedge *Carex depauperata* Curtis ex With. at Godalming, Surrey after the Great Storm of 1987, in Kirby, K.J. & Buckley, G.P. eds, *Ecological responses to the 1987 Great Storm in the woods of south-east England*. English Nature Science no. 23. English Nature, Peterborough.

RICH, T.C.G. 1999. Conservation of Britain's biodiversity: *Cyperus fuscus* L. (Cyperaceae), Brown Galingale. *Watsonia* **22**: 397–403.

RICH, T.C.G. & BIRKINSHAW, C.R. 2001. Conservation of Britain's biodiversity: *Carex depauperata* With. (Cyperaceae), Starved Wood-Sedge. *Watsonia* **23**: 401–411.

RICH, T.C.G. & FITZGERALD, R. 2002. Life cycle, ecology and distribution of *Schoenoplectus triqueter* (L.) Palla (Cyperaceae), Triangular Club-rush, in Britain and Ireland. *Watsonia* **24**: 57–67.

RICH, T.C.G., JONES, R.A. & JEBB, M. 2000. Three new British sites for *Carex depauperata* With. (Cyperaceae) represented in the Irish National Herbarium, Glasnevin. *Watsonia* **23**: 340–341.

ROBERTS, F.J. 1977. Further adventive news: *Eleocharis austriaca* in N. Yorkshire. *BSBI News* No. 15: 16–17.

ROBERTS, R.H. & STIRLING, A. McG. 1974. *Eriophorum gracile* Roth. in Wales. *Nature in Wales* **14**: 19–21.

ROBERTSON, A. 1979. History of the classification of the genus *Carex*. *Taxon* **28**: 535–548.

ROBINSON, L. 2003. Observations on *Alopecurus borealis* at Green Fell in the northern Pennines, Cumbria, after foot and mouth. *BSBI News* No. 93: 11–12.

RODWELL, J.S. ed. 1991a. *British Plant Communities. Volume 1: Woodlands and scrub*. Cambridge University Press, Cambridge.

RODWELL, J.S. ed. 1991b. *British Plant Communities. Volume 2: Mires and heaths*. Cambridge University Press, Cambridge.

RODWELL, J.S. ed. 1992. *British Plant Communities. Volume 3: Grasslands and montane communities*. Cambridge University Press, Cambridge.

RODWELL, J.S. ed. 1995. *British Plant Communities. Volume 4: Aquatic communities, swamps and tall-herb fens*. Cambridge University Press, Cambridge.

RODWELL, J.S. ed. 2000. *British Plant Communities. Volume 5: Maritime communities and vegetation of open habitats.* Cambridge University Press, Cambridge.

ROSE, F. 1953. A survey of the ecology of British lowland bogs. *Proceedings of the Linnean Society of London* **164**: 186–211.

ROSE, F. 1989. *Colour Identification Guide to the Grasses, Sedges, Rushes and Ferns of the British Isles and North-western Europe.* Viking, London.

ROWELL, T.A. 1986. Sedge (*Cladium mariscus*) in Cambridgeshire: its use and production since the seventeenth century. *Agricultural History Review* **34**: 140–148.

SABBAGH, K. 1999. *A Rum affair.* Allen Lane, The Penguin Press, London.

SALMON, C.E. 1925. *Carex remota* × *divulsa. Journal of Botany* **63**: 140–141.

SAMUELSSON, G. 1922. Floristiska Fragment. IV. 2. *Carex nemorosa* Rebent. och *C. vulpina* L. *Svensk Botanisk Tidskrift* **16**: 207–220.

SAVILE, D.B.O. & CALDER, J.A. 1953. Phylogeny of *Carex* in the light of parasitism by the smut fungi. *Canadian Journal of Botany* **31**: 164–174.

SCHMID, B. 1980. *Carex flava* L. *s.l.* im Lichte der r-selektion. *Mitteilungen aus dem Botanischen Garten und Museum der Universität Zürich* **322**: 1–360.

SCHMID, B. 1983. Notes on the nomenclature and taxonomy of the *Carex flava* group in Europe. *Watsonia* **14**: 309–319.

SCHULTZE-MOTEL, W. 1967. In Hegi, G., *Illustrierte Flora von Mitteleuropa*, Edition 3, **2** (1): 61–64. Verlag Paul Parey, Berlin and Hamburg.

SELL, P.[D.] & MURRELL, [J.]G. 1996. *Flora of Great Britain and Ireland.* Volume 5. Cambridge University Press, Cambridge.

SERNANDER, R. 1906. Entwurf einer Monographie der europäischen Myrmecochora. *Kungliga Svenska Vetenskaps-Akademiens Handlingar* **41** (7): 1–410.

SHAVER, G.R., CHAPIN, F.S., III, & BILLINGS, W.D. 1979. Ecotypic differentiation in *Carex aquatilis* on ice-wedge polygons in the Alaskan coastal tundra. *Journal of Ecology* **67**: 1025–1046.

SHEPHERD, G.J. 1975. Experimental taxonomy in the genus *Carex* section *Vesicariae.* Unpublished Ph.D. thesis, University of Edinburgh.

SHEPHERD, G.J. 1976. The use of anatomical characters in the intrageneric classification of *Carex* (Cyperaceae). *Hoehnea* **6**: 33–54.

SHOWLER, A. 2004. *Carex muricata* ssp. *muricata* in Southern England. *BSBI News* No. 95: 32–33.

SIIRA, J. 1983. The distribution and ecology of *Blysmus rufus* (Cyperaceae) at Liminka and Oulunsalo on the NE coast of the Bothnian Bay. *Annales Botanici Fennici* **20**: 269–280.

SIMPSON, D.A. 1995. Relationships within Cyperales, in Rudall, P.J., Cribb, P.J., Cutler, D.F. & Humphries C.J. eds, *Monocotyledons: systematics and evolution* **2**: 497–509. Royal Botanic Gardens, Kew.

SIMPSON, D.A., FURNESS, C.A., HODKINSON, T.R., MUASYA, A.M. & CHASE, M.W. 2003. Phylogenetic relationships in Cyperaceae subfamily Mapanioideae inferred from pollen and plastid DNA sequence data. *American Journal of Botany* **90** (7): 1071–1086.

SIMPSON, D.A. & INGLIS, C.A. 2001. Cyperaceae of economic, ethnobotanical and horticultural importance: a checklist. *Kew Bulletin* **56**: 257–360.

SIMPSON, D.A., MUASYA, A.M., ALVES, M., BRUHL, J.J., DHOOGE, S., CHASE, M.W., FURNESS, C.A., GHAMKHAR, K., GOETGHEBEUR, P., HODKINSON, T.R., MARCHANT, A.D., REZNICEK, A.A., NIEUWBORG, R., ROALSON, E.A., SMETS, E., STARR, J.R., THOMAS, W.W., WILSON, K.L. & ZHANG, X. 2007. Phylogeny of Cyperaceae based on DNA sequence data – a new *rbcL* analysis. *Aliso* **23**: 72–83.

SIMPSON, D.A., MUASYA, A.M. & CAFFERTY, S. 2001. Typification of *Scirpus fluitans* and *Scirpus setaceus* (Cyperaceae). *Kew Bulletin* **56**: 1011–1012.

SIMPSON, N.D. 1960. *A Bibliographical Index of the British Flora*. Douglas Simpson, Bournemouth.

SINKER, C.A., PACKHAM, J.R., TRUEMAN, I.C., OSWALD, P.H., PERRING, F.H. & PRESTWOOD, W.V. 1985, 1991. *An Ecological Flora of the Shropshire Region*. Shropshire Trust for Nature Conservation (Shropshire Wildlife Trust in 1991), Shrewsbury.

SMITH, C. & ASHTON, P.A. 2006. Distinction between the sedges *Carex vulpina* L. and *Carex otrubae* Podp. and the potential for identification of hybrids. *Watsonia* **26**: 15–25.

SMITH, D.L. 1966. Development of the inflorescence in *Carex*. *Annals of Botany* **30**: 475–486.

SMITH, D.L. 1967. The experimental control of inflorescence development in *Carex*. *Annals of Botany* **31**: 19–30.

SMITH, D.L. 1969. The role of leaves and roots in the control of inflorescence development in *Carex*. *Annals of Botany* **33**: 505–514.

SMITH, D.L. & FAULKNER, J.S. 1976. The inflorescence of *Carex* and related genera. *The Botanical Review* **42**: 53–81.

SMITH, J. E. 1830. *The English Flora* **4**: 126. Edition 2. London.

SMITH, P.H. 2005. *Schoenoplectus pungens* on the Sefton coast. *BSBI News* No. 98: 30–33.

SMITH, S.G. & KUKKONEN, I. 1999. A new lectotype for *Scirpus maritimus (Cyperaceae)*. *Taxon* **48**: 355–357.

SPARLING, J.H. 1968. Biological Flora of the British Isles. *Schoenus nigricans* L. *Journal of Ecology* **56**: 883–899.

SPENCE, D.H.N. 1964. The macrophytic vegetation of freshwater lochs, swamps and associated fens, in Burnett, J.H. ed., *The Vegetation of Scotland*. Edinburgh.

STACE, C.A. 1975. *Schoenus* L., in Stace, C.A. ed., *Hybridization and the Flora of the British Isles*, 513. Academic Press, London.

STACE, C.A. 1991, 1997. *New Flora of the British Isles*. Cambridge University Press, Cambridge.

STACE, C.A. 2006. *List of Vascular Plants of the British Isles. Supplement 3.* Botanical Society of the British Isles, Leicester.

STANDLEY, L.A., 1990. Allozyme evidence for the hybrid origin of the maritime species *Carex salina* and *Carex recta* (Cyperaceae) in eastern North America. *Systematic Botany* **15**: 182–191.

STANDLEY, L.A., CAYOUETTE, J. & BRUEDERLE, L.P. 2002. *Carex* Linnaeus sect. *Phacocystis* Dumortier, in Flora of North America Editorial Committee eds, *Flora of North America North of Mexico* **23**: *Magnoliophyta: Commelinidae (in part): Cyperaceae*, 379–401. Oxford University Press, New York and Oxford.

STARR, J.R. & FORD, B.A. 2001. The taxonomic and phylogenetic utility and vegetative anatomy and fruit epidermal silica bodies in *Carex* (Sect. *Phyllostachys*) (Cyperaceae). *Canadian Journal of Botany* **79**: 362–379.

STEVENS, D.P. & BLACKSTOCK, T.H. 1993. Sexual dimorphism in *Eriophorum vaginatum* L. (Cyperaceae). *Watsonia* **19**: 190–192.

STEVENS, D.P. & BLACKSTOCK, T.H. 1997. Gynodioecy in British populations of *Eriophorum vaginatum* L. (Cyperaceae). *Watsonia* **21**: 247–257.

STEWART, A., PEARMAN, D.A. & PRESTON, C.D. eds. 1994. *Scarce plants in Britain*. Joint Nature Conservation Committee, Peterborough.

STOEVA, M.P. & ŠTĚPÁNKOVÁ, J. 1990. Variation patterns within the *Carex flava* agg. in Bulgaria and Czechoslovakia. *Preslia, Praha* **62**: 1–24.

STRANDHEDE, S.-O. 1966. Morphological variation and taxonomy in European *Eleocharis*, subser. Palustres. *Opera Botanica* **10**: 1–187.

SWAN, G.A. 1993. *Flora of Northumberland*, 351. Natural History Society of Northumbria, Newcastle upon Tyne.

SWAN, G.A. 1999. Identification, distribution and a new nothosubspecies of *Trichophorum cespitosum* (L.) Hartman (Cyperaceae) in the British Isles and N.W. Europe. *Watsonia* **22**: 209–233.

SWAN, G.A. 2003. New records for the subspecies of *Trichophorum cespitosum* (Deergrass) in Britain. *BSBI News* No. 93: 34–37.

SWAN, G.A. & RICHARDS, A.J. 2007. The *Eleocharis mamillata* H. Lindb. fil. aggregate (Cyperaceae) in the British Isles. *Watsonia* **26**: 317–325.

TAYLOR, F.J. 1956. Biological Flora of the British Isles. *Carex flacca* Schreb. *Journal of Ecology* **44**: 281–290.

TIMONEN, T. 1998. *Inflorescence structure in the sedge tribe Cariceae (Cyperaceae)*. Publications in botany from the University of Helsinki No. 26. Yliopistopaino, Helsinki.

TOIVONEN, H. 1974. Chromatographic comparison of the species of *Carex* section *Heleonastes* and some *Carex canescens* hybrids in Eastern Fennoscandia. *Annales Botanici Fennici* **11**: 225–230.

TOIVONEN, H. 1981a. Spontaneous *Carex* hybrids of *Heleonastes* and related sections in Fennoscandia. *Acta Botanica Fennica* **116**: 1–51.

TOIVONEN, H. 1981b. Notes on the nomenclature and taxonomy of *Carex canescens* (Cyperaceae). *Annales Botanici Fennici* **18**: 91–97.

TOIVONEN, H. & TIMONEN, T. 1976. Perigynium and achene epidermis in some species of *Carex*, subg. Vignea (Cyperaceae), studied by scanning electron microscopy. *Annales Botanici Fennici* **13**: 49–59.

THOMPSON, H.S. 1915. *Carex evoluta* Hartm. in Britain. *Journal of Botany* **53**: 309.

TUCKER, G.C. & MILLER, N.G. 1990. Achene microstructure in *Eriophorum* (Cyperaceae): taxonomic implications and paleobotanical applications. *Bulletin of the Torrey Botanical Club* **117**: 266–283.

540

TURLAND, N. 1997. (1277) Proposal to reject the name *Eriophorum polystachion (Cyperaceae)*. *Taxon* **46**: 115–116.

TYLER, T. 2002. Geographical distribution of allozyme variation in relation to post-glacial history in *Carex digitata*, a widespread European woodland sedge. *Biogeographica* **29**: 919–930.

TYLER, T. 2003. Allozyme variation in *Carex* sect. Digitatae – Evidence of introgression, genetic distinctiveness and evolution of taxa. *Plant Systematics and Evolution* **237**: 219–231.

U.K. BIODIVERSITY ACTION GROUP. 1998. *Action Plans, Volume 2. Vertebrates and vascular plants*. English Nature, Peterborough.

VAN DER MEIJDEN, R. & HOLVERDA, W.J. 2006. Revision of the HNH-herbarium material of *Carex lepidocarpa* Tausch and *Carex flava* L. in the Netherlands. *Gorteria* **31**: 129–136.

VAN WICHELEN, J., CAMELBEKE, K., CHAERLE, P., GOETGHEBEUR, P. & HUYSMANS, S. 1999. Comparison of different treatments for LM and SEM studies and systematic value of pollen grains in Cyperaceae. *Grana* **38**: 50–58.

WALKER, K.J. 2003. *Eriophorum gracile* formerly present in Northamptonshire (v.c. 32). *BSBI News* No. 92: 16–18.

WALLACE, E.C. 1975. *Carex* L., in Stace, C.A. ed., *Hybridization and the Flora of the British Isles*, 513–540. Academic Press, London.

WALLS, R.M. 1991. *Carex acutiformis*, *C. riparia* & *C. acuta*. *BSBI News* No. 57: 12–13.

WALTERS, S.M. 1949. Biological Flora of the British Isles. *Eleocharis* R. Br. *Eleocharis palustris* (L.) R. Br. em. R. & S. *Eleocharis uniglumis* (Link) Schult. *Journal of Ecology* **37**: 192–206.

WALTERS, S.M. 1953. *Eleocharis mamillata* Lindb. fil. and allied species. *Berichte der Schweizerischen Botanischen Gesellschaft* **63**: 271–286.

WALTERS, S.M. 1963. *Eleocharis austriaca* Hayek, a species new to the British Isles. *Watsonia* **5**: 329–335.

WALTERS, S.M. 1975. *Eleocharis* R. Br., in Stace, C.A. ed., *Hybridization and the Flora of the British Isles*, 512–513. Academic Press, London.

WALTERS, S.M. 1997. *Eleocharis quinqueflora* at Wicken Fen. *Nature in Cambridgeshire* No. 39: 53–54.

WEBB, D.A. & SCANNELL, M.S, 1983. *Flora of Connemara and the Burren*. Royal Dublin Society, Dublin, and Cambridge University Press, Cambridge.

WEIN, R.W. 1973. Biological Flora of the British Isles. *Eriophorum vaginatum* L. *Journal of Ecology* **61**: 601–615.

WELLS, T.C.E. 1975. The floristic composition of chalk grassland in Wiltshire, in Stearn L.F. ed., *Supplement to the Flora of Wiltshire*, 99–125. Wiltshire Archaeological & Natural History Society, Devizes.

WHEELER, B.D. 1978. The wetland plant communities of the River Ant valley, Norfolk. *Transactions of the Norfolk & Norwich Naturalists' Society* **24**: 153–187.

WHEELER, B.D. 1980a. Plant communities of rich-fen systems in England and Wales. I. Introduction. Tall sedge and reed communities. *Journal of Ecology* **68**: 365–395.

WHEELER, B.D. 1980b. Plant communities of rich-fen systems in England and Wales. II. Communities of calcareous mires. *Journal of Ecology* **68**: 405–420.

WHEELER, B.D. 1980c. Plant communities of rich-fen systems in England and Wales. III. Fen meadow, fen grassland and fen woodland communities, and contact communities. *Journal of Ecology* **68**: 761–788.

WHEELER, B.D., BROOKES, B.S. & SMITH, R.A.H. 1983. An ecological study of *Schoenus ferrugineus* L. in Scotland. *Watsonia* **14**: 249–256.

WHEELER, D. & MAYES, J. eds. 1997. *Regional climates of the British Isles.* Routledge, London.

WHILD, S.J. & LOCKTON, A.J. 2003. *Carex muricata* L subsp. *muricata* (Cyperaceae) in Shropshire. *Watsonia* **24**: 528–531.

WHITE, J. & DOYLE, G. 1982. The vegetation of Ireland: a catalogue raisonné. *Journal of Life Sciences, Royal Dublin Society* **3**: 289–368.

WIGGINTON, M.J. ed. 1999. *British Red Data Books: 1. Vascular plants.* Edition 3. Joint Nature Conservation Committee, Peterborough.

WIINSTEDT, K. 1945. Nr, 13. Cyperaceernes Udbredelse i Danmark. II. Caricoideae. *Botanisk Tidsskrift* **47**: 143–244 and 55 maps.

WILCOX, M. 2001. *Trichophorum cespitosum* nothosubsp. *foersteri* G.A. Swan nothosubsp. nov. *BSBI News* No. 87: 20.

WILLIS, J.C. 1985. *A Dictionary of the Flowering Plants and Ferns.* Cambridge University Press, Cambridge.

WILMOTT, A.J. 1938. *Carex spiculosa* var. *hebridensis* A. Benn. *Journal of Botany* **76**: 137–141.

WILSON, K.L. 1989. (931) Proposal to conserve 468 *Scirpus* L. (Cyperaceae) with *S. sylvaticus* L. as type. *Taxon* **38**: 316–320.

WRIGHT, F.R.E. 1948. Notes on growth form of tall rush-like plants in Braunton Burrows. *North-western Naturalist* **23**: 15–19.

YEO, R.R., FALK, R.H. & THURSTON, J.R. 1985. Morphology of slender spikerush seed (*Eleocharis acicularis* (L.) R. & S.). *Journal of Aquatic Plant Management* **23**: 83–87.

ZHANG, S.R. 2001. A preliminary revision of the supraspecific classification of *Kobresia* Willd. (Cyperaceae). *Botanical Journal of the Linnean Society* **135**: 289–294.

ZUKOWSKI, W. & KLIMKO, M. 1979. Variability of fruits of species of *Eleocharis* genus, subseries *Palustres* in Poland. *Bulletin de la Société des Amis des Sciences et Lettres, Poznan* **D19**: 83–90.

INDEX TO ENGLISH NAMES

Bold text indicates species numbers. *Italics* indicate synonyms.
Names with 'Sedge' as the second element are indexed only under the first element.

INDEX TO LATIN NAMES

Names accepted in this book are printed here in a non-italic typeface and referred to the species number (in **bold** face). *Synonyms* (including those not mentioned in the text but used by other authors covering the British Isles) are in *italics* and are equated to a taxon by reference to its number. Those taxa otherwise mentioned in the text are referred to a page number in light face. Generic names are in **bold** face and specific and subspecific epithets in light face. For a full synonymy see Sell & Murrell (1996).

Carex *flava* subsp. *jemtlandica*
(Palmgr.) P.D. Sell   =78a var.
subsp. *oedocarpa*
(Andersson) P.D. Sell   =78b
subsp. *oederi* Syme p.p.   =78c
subsp. *pulchella* (Lönnr.)
P.D. Sell   =78c var.
subsp. *scotica* (E.W. Davies)
P.D. Sell   =78a var.
subsp. *serotina* (Mérat)
P.D. Sell   =78c
flavella V.I. Krecz.   =77
frigida auct., non All.   =72
× fulva Gooden.   76 ×78
fulva Thuill., non Gooden.   =36
fulva auct.   =76
fusca All.   =100
fusca auct., non All.   =93
× gaudiniana Guthnick   50 × 51
× *germanica* K. Richt.   =37 × 35
gibsonii Bab.   =100
glacialis Mackenzie   515
glauca Scop.   =67
goodenowii J. Gay
nom. illegit.   =100
var. *stolonifera*
(Hoppe) Asch.   455
var. *strictiformis*
(L.H. Bailey) Kük.   455
var. *subcaespitosa* Kük.   455
var. *tornata* (Fr.) Kük.   455
gracilis Curtis   =98
× grahamii Boott   61 × 62
× grantii A. Benn.   95 × 97
× grossii Fiek   55 × 61
grypos Schkuhr   =50
halleri auct.   =94
hartmanii Cajander   450
× haussknechtii Senay   39 × 40
helodes Link   =71

× helvola Blytt ex Fr.   54 × 53
× hibernica A. Benn.   97 × 100
hirta L.   55
hordeiformis Wahlenb.   515
hordeistichos Vill.   515
hornschuchiana Hoppe   =76
hostiana DC.   76
hubbardii Nelmes   516
hudsonii A. Benn.   =101
humilis Leyss.   82
hyperborea Drejer   =102
incurva Lightf.   =47
inflata auct.   =60
inflata Huds.   =61
inflata var. *involuta* (Bab.) Druce
=60 × 61
intermedia Gooden.,
non Retz.   =44
inversa R. Br.   516, 517
× involuta (Bab.) Syme   60 × 61
irrigua (Wahlenb.)
Sm. ex Hoppe   =91
jemtlandica (Palmgr.) Palmgr.
=78a var.
juncella (Fr.) Th. Fr.   7, 455
juncella auct.   =100
× justi-schmidtii Junge   59 × 60
× *kneuckeriana* Zahn   =39 × 48
lachenalii Schkuhr   53
laevigata Sm.   71
laevigata × pallescens 59, 356, 408
laevigata × viridula
subsp. oedocarpa   59
lagopina Wahlenb.   =53
lamprocarpa auct.,
non (Wallr.) Čelak.   =41b
lasiocarpa Ehrh.   56
leersii F.W. Schultz,
non Willd.   =42b

548

Carex *teretiuscula* Gooden. =**37**
× *tetrastachya* Traunst. ex Saut.,
   non Scheele =**54** × **50**
tomentosa auct. =**56**
tomentosa L. =**84**
× tornabenii Chiov. **73** × **75**
tricostata Fr. =**98**
trinervis Degl. **99**, 515
tumidicarpa Andersson =**78b**
× turfosa Fr. **101** × **100**
uliginosa L. =**27**
undulata Kuntze =**79**
ustulata Wahlenb.
   nom. illegit. =**88**
vacillans Drejer 458
vaginata Tausch **69**
vahlii Schkuhr =**94**
ventricosa Curtis =**70**
verna Chaix, non Lam. =**83**
vesicaria L. **61**
   subsp. *grahamii* (Boott)
   Hook. f. =**61** × **62**
   subsp. *saxatilis* (L.)
   Hook. f. =**62**
   var. *involuta* Bab. =**60** × **61**
vesicaria sensu Huds. =**60**
villosa Stokes nom. illegit. =**55**
virens Lam. =**42a**
virgata Sol. ex Boott 516
viridula Michx.
   subsp. brachyrrhyncha (Čelak.)
   B. Schmid **78a**
   var. jemtlandica (Palmgr.)
   Blackstock & P.A. Ashton
      387, 396
   var. scotica (E.W. Davies)
   B. Schmid 387, 393, 396
   subsp. brachyrrhyncha ×
   saxatilis **78a** × **62**

   subsp. oedocarpa (Andersson)
   B. Schmid **78b**
   subsp. oedocarpa × laevigata
      388
   subsp. viridula **78c**
   var. bergrothii (Palmgr.)
   B. Schmid 387, 406
   var. pulchella (Lönnr.)
   B. Schmid 387, 406
vitilis auct. =**54**
vulgaris Fr. nom. illegit. =**100**
vulpina L. **38**
vulpina auct. =**39**
vulpina × otrubae **38** × **39**
vulpinoidea Michx. 516, 518
× winkelmannii
   Asch. & Graebn. 58
witheringii Gray =**43**
xanthocarpa Degl. =**76** × **78**
Chaetocyperus *acicularis* (L.)
   Nees =**17**
pygmaeus (Torr.) Walp. =**19**
Chaetospora *compressa* (L.)
   Gray =**27**
nigricans (L.) Kunth =**29**
rufa (Huds.) Gray =**28**
Cladium mariscus (L.) Pohl **31**
Clavula *acicularis* (L.) Dumort.
   =**17**
   baeothryon (L. f.) Dumort. =**18**
   comosa Dumort. =**17**
Cyperus *acicularis* (L.) With.
   =**17**
   eragrostis Lam. **26**
   fuscus L. **25**
   haworthii Gray =**25**
   horizontalis Salisb. =**27**
   longus L. **24**
   nigricans (L.) With. =**29**

Kobresia *bipartita* auct.　　=**34**
caricina Willd.　　=**34**
simpliciuscula (Wahlenb.)
　　Mack.　　**34**
Leucoglochin *pauciflora*
　　(Lightf.) Heuff.　　=**104**
Limnochloa *baeothryon*
　　(L. f.) Rchb.　　=**18**
parvula (Roem. & Schult.) Rchb.
　　=**19**
Mariscus *acicularis* (L.) Moench
　　=**17**
Rhynchospora alba (L.) Vahl　**32**
fusca (L.) W.T. Aiton　　**33**
Schoenoplectus *americanus* auct.,
　　non (Pers.) Volkart　=**12**
× carinatus (Sm.) Palla　**11 × 9**
nothosubsp. *kuekenthalianus*
　　(Junge) P.D. Sell　=**11 × 10**
× kuekenthalianus (Junge)
　　D.H. Kent　　**11 × 10**
lacustris (L.) Palla　　**9**
subsp. *tabernaemontani*
　　(C.C. Gmel.) Å. & D. Löve
　　=**10**
maritimus (L.) Lye　=**8**
pungens (Vahl) Palla　**12**
tabernaemontani (C.C. Gmel.)
　　Palla　　**10**
triqueter (L.) Palla　　**11**
Schoenus *albus* L.　=**32**
compressus L.　=**27**
ferrugineus L.　　**30**
fuscus L　=**33**
mariscus L.　=**31**
monoicus Sm.　=**34**
nigricans L.　　**29**
rufus Huds.　=**28**
Scirpidium *aciculare* (L.)
　　Nees　　=**17**

Scirpoides holoschoenus (L.)
　　Soják　　**20**
Scirpus *acicularis* L.　=**17**
americanus auct., non Pers.　=**12**
arunensis Druce　=**11 × 10**
baeothryon L. f.　=**18**
campestris Roth　=**18**
carinatus Sm.　=**11 × 9**
cernuus Vahl　=**22**
cespitosus L.　=**6**
subsp. *germanicus* (Palla)
　　Brodd.　=**5**
chaeta Schult.　=**17**
compressus (L.) Pers.,
　　non Moench　=**27**
duvalii Hoppe　=**11 × 9**
filiformis Savi, non Burm. f.　=**22**
fluitans L.　=**23**
germanicus (Palla) Lindm.　=**6**
glaucus Sm., non Lam.　=**9**
halleri Vill.　=**18**
holoschoenus L.　=**20**
hudsonianus (Michx.)
　　Fernald　=**6a**
kuekenthalianus Junge　=**11 × 10**
lacustris L.　=**9**
subsp. *tabernaemontani*
　　(C.C. Gmel.) Syme　=**10**
subsp. *carinatus* (Sm.) Syme
　　=**11 × 9**
maritimus L.　=**8**
multicaulis Sm.　=**16**
mucronatus auct.　=**11, 12**
nanus Spreng., non Poir.　=**19**
palustris L.　=**13**
subsp. *uniglumis* (Link) Syme
　　=**15**
pauciflorus Lightf.　=**18**
parvulus Roem. & Schult.　=**19**
pusillus Vahl　=**19**

Scirpus *pygmaeus* (Vahl) A. Gray,
non Lam. =**22**
quinqueflorus Hartmann =**18**
romanus L. =**20**
rufus (Huds.) Schrad. =**28**
savii Sebast. & Mauri =**22**
scheuchzeri Brügger =**11** × **10**
sepium Honck. =**18**
setaceus L. =**21**
sylvaticus L. **7**
tabernaemontani C.C. Gmel =**10**
tetragonus Walker,
non Poir. =**15**
triqueter L. =**11**
uniglumis Link =**15**
Scleria bracteata Cav. 517
Trichophorum alpinum (L.)
Pers. **6a**, 515
austriacum Palla =**6**
cespitosum (L.) Hartm. **6**
subsp. *austriacum*
(Palla) Hegi =**6**
subsp. *germanicum*
(Palla) Hegi =**5**

× foersteri (G.A. Swan)
D.A. Simpson **6** × **5**
germanicum Palla **5**
Vignea *arenaria* (L.) Rchb. =**43**
axillaris Rchb. =**39** × **48**
chordorrhiza (L. f.) Rchb. =**45**
dioica (L.) Rchb. =**51**
disticha (Huds.) Peterm. =**44**
divisa (Huds.) Rchb. =**46**
divulsa (Stokes) Rchb. =**42a**
elongata (L.) Rchb. =**52**
incurva (Lightf.) Rchb. =**47**
intermedia Rchb.
nom. illegit. =**44**
lagopina (Wahlenb.) Rchb. =**53**
muricata (L.) Rchb. =**41**
paniculata (L.) Rchb. =**35**
paradoxa Rchb. =**36**
paniculata (L.) Rchb. =**35**
remota (L.) Rchb. =**48**
stellulata (Gooden.) Rchb. =**50**
stricta Rchb. =**101**
teretiuscula (Gooden.) Rchb. =**37**
vulpina (L.) Rchb. =**38**

The Botanical Society of the British Isles

The BSBI is for everyone who is interested in the flora of Britain and Ireland. It traces its origins back to 1836, when it was founded as the Botanical Society of London. From its earliest days it has welcomed both professional and amateur members, and it remains the biggest and most active organisation devoted to the study of botany in the British Isles.

Information on the status and distribution of British and Irish flowering plants, ferns and charophytes is gathered through a network of vice-county recorders; this is the basis for plant atlases, county Floras and publications on rare and scarce species and is vital for botanical conservation. The BSBI was a major partner in the production of *New Atlas of the British and Irish Flora* and a related CD-ROM published by Oxford University Press in September 2002.

The BSBI organises plant distribution surveys, publishes handbooks on difficult groups of plants and has national referees available to members to name problematic specimens. Conferences and field meetings are held throughout Britain and Ireland and sometimes abroad. The society also publishes a scientific journal, *Watsonia*, and conference reports. Members are kept informed by a newsletter three times a year.

An education programme supported by the BSBI aims to bring high-quality botanical training within the reach of all, from A Level students to professional development and postgraduate courses.

Details of membership and other information about the BSBI may be obtained from The Hon. General Secretary, Botanical Society of the British Isles, c/o Department of Botany, The Natural History Museum, Cromwell Road, London SW7 5BD.

The society's website is <http://www.bsbi.org.uk/index.html>.

The following books are available from the official agents for BSBI publications, Summerfield Books, 3 Phoenix Park, Skelton, Penrith, Cumbria, CA11 9SD (Telephone 01768 484909; Fax 01768 484910; E-mail <info@summerfieldbooks.com>). Full details are available on this website: <http://www.summerfieldbooks.com/bsbi-publications.asp>.

BSBI handbooks

Each handbook deals in depth with one or more difficult groups of British and Irish plants.

No. 1 *Sedges of the British Isles* – A. C. Jermy, D. A. Simpson, M. J. Y. Foley & M. S. Porter. Third edition, 2007, incorporating full accounts of 35 species of Cyperaceae and 47 hybrids in addition to the 76 species and subspecies of *Carex*. 568 pp., with descriptions, line drawings and distribution maps. A5 paperback. [Previous editions 1968 and 1982.]

No. 2   *Umbellifers of the British Isles* – T. G. Tutin. 1980, reprinted 2006. 200 pp., with descriptions of 73 species facing line drawings by Ann Farrer. Small paperback.

No. 3   *Docks and knotweeds of the British Isles* – J. E. Lousley & D. H. Kent. 1981. Out of print.

No. 4   *Willows and poplars of Great Britain and Ireland* – R. D. Meikle. 1984, reprinted 2006. 200 pp., with descriptions of 65 species, subspecies, varieties and hybrids of *Salix* and *Populus*, illustrated with line drawings by Victoria Gordon. Small paperback.

No. 5   *Charophytes of Great Britain and Ireland* – Jenny A. Moore. 1986, reprinted 2005 with a new preface and corrections by C. D. Preston. 144 pp., with descriptions of 39 species and varieties of Characeae (stoneworts), line drawings by Margaret Tebbs and 17 distribution maps. Small paperback.

No. 6   *Crucifers of Great Britain and Ireland* – T C. G. Rich. 1991, reprinted 2006. 344 pp., with descriptions of 148 taxa of Brassicaceae (Cruciferae), 129 of them with line drawings by various artists, and 60 distribution maps. Small paperback.

No. 7   *Roses of Great Britain and Ireland* – G. G. Graham & A. L. Primavesi. 1993, reprinted with corrections 2005. 208 pp., with descriptions, facing line drawings by Margaret Gold, of 13 native and nine introduced taxa of *Rosa*, briefer descriptions of 76 hybrids, and 33 maps. A5 paperback.

No. 8   *Pondweeds of Great Britain and Ireland* – C. D. Preston. 1995, reprinted 2003. 352 pp., with descriptions and line drawings of all 50 species and hybrids of *Potamogeton*, *Groenlandia* and *Ruppia*, most with distribution maps; detailed introductory material and bibliography. A5 paperback.

No. 9   *Dandelions of Great Britain and Ireland* – A. A. Dudman & A. J. Richards. 1997, reprinted with minor alterations 2000. 344 pp., with descriptions of 235 species of *Taraxacum*, most of them illustrated by silhouettes of herbarium specimens; drawings of bud involucres of 139 species by Olga Stewart and 178 distribution maps. A5 paperback.

No. 10   *Sea beans and nickar nuts* – E. Charles Nelson. 2000, reprinted 2003. 156 pp., with descriptions of nearly 60 exotic seeds and fruits found stranded on beaches in north-western Europe (many illustrated by Wendy Walsh) and of the mature plants (some with drawings by Alma Hathway), accounts of their history and folklore, growing instructions, etc. A5 paperback.

Other publications

Alien plants of the British Isles – E. J. Clement & M. C. Foster. 1994. 616 pp. Lists 3,586 recorded non-native species (of which 885 are established), with English names, frequency, status, origin, references to descriptions and illustrations, and selected synonyms. Paperback.

Alien grasses of the British Isles – T. B. Ryves, E. J. Clement & M. C. Foster. 1996. 234 pp. A companion volume to the last, listing over 700 non-native grasses; includes keys to bamboos and eight of the larger and more difficult genera and 29 pp. of drawings by G. M. S. Easy. Paperback.

Illustrations of alien plants of the British Isles – E. J. Clement, D. P. J. Smith & I. R. Thirlwell. 2005. 480 pp., including 444 full-page line drawings of introduced, naturalised and casually occurring alien plants in Britain and Ireland. The drawings are largely from a collection put together by the late David McClintock, originally for publication in his planned Volume 3 of *A New Illustrated British Flora*. A5 paperback.

Plant crib – T. C. G. Rich & A. C. Jermy. 1998, reprinted 2006. 400 pp. An expertly written identification guide for some 325 difficult taxonomic groups, with explanations, keys and illustrations of plant details. A4 paperback.

List of vascular plants of the British Isles – D. H. Kent. 1992. 400 pp. Nomenclature and sequence as in Clive Stace's *New Flora of the British Isles* (1991, 1997), with selected synonyms. Paperback. Supplied with five errata lists. Three supplements (published 1996, 2000 and 2006) are also available.

Vice-county census catalogue of vascular plants of Great Britain, the Isle of Man and the Channel Islands – C. A. Stace, R. G. Ellis, D. H. Kent & D. J. McCosh (eds). 2003. 432 pp. A full listing by species of the vice-counties from which vascular plants have been recorded. A5 paperback.

Change in the British Flora 1987–2004 (A report on the BSBI Local Change survey) – M. E. Braithwaite, R. W. Ellis & C. D. Preston. 2006. 390 pp., with colour photographs, distribution maps, tables and graphs. A comparison of the results of two surveys of selected 2 km × 2 km squares. Large paperback.

Atlas of British and Irish brambles – A. Newton & R. D. Randall. 2004. 98 pp., with 330 hectad distribution maps of *Rubus* species, summaries of distribution and notes on changes. A5 paperback.

British alpine hawkweeds – David Tennant & Tim Rich. 2007. A monograph of British *Hieracium* section *Alpina*. Approximately 245 pp., with over 170 drawings and colour photographs and five paintings by Ramond C. Booth. A4 hardback and paperback.

Botanical Links in the Atlantic Arc – S. J. Leach, C. N. Page, Y. Peytoureau & M. N. Sandford (eds). 2006. 336 pp., with colour photograph section, black-and-white photographs, maps and figures. A wide-ranging series of papers on the flora of the atlantic coastal regions of Europe. Proceedings of an international conference held at Camborne, Cornwall, in 2003, published as BSBI Conference Report No. 24, dedicated to the memory of Dr Franklyn H. Perring. Hardback.

Current taxonomic research on the British and European Flora – J. P. Bailey & R. G. Ellis (eds). 2006. 156 pp., with colour photographs and text illustrations. Proceedings of a conference held at the University of Leicester in 2003 to mark the retirement of Prof. Clive Stace, published as BSBI Conference Report No. 25. Paperback.

Other publishers' books

Aquatic plants in Britain and Ireland – C. D. Preston & J. M. Croft. 1997. 365 pp. Accounts and distribution maps of 200 aquatic plants in 72 genera, with 72 line drawings by G. M. S. Easy. Large paperback reprint, published 2001 by Harley Books.

New Atlas of the British and Irish Flora – C. D. Preston, D. A. Pearman & T. D. Dines (eds). 2002. 921 pp. Distribution maps and accompanying text for 2,412 plants, with introductory chapters. Very large hardback with CD-ROM, published by Oxford University Press.